# LASERS

VOLUME 4

# LASERS

*A Series of Advances*

Edited by ALBERT K. LEVINE

DIVISION OF PURE AND APPLIED SCIENCES
THE CITY UNIVERSITY OF NEW YORK
RICHMOND COLLEGE
STATEN ISLAND, NEW YORK

and

ANTHONY J. DeMARIA

ELECTROMAGNETICS AND PHYSICS LABORATORIES
UNITED TECHNOLOGIES RESEARCH CENTER
UNITED TECHNOLOGIES CORPORATION
EAST HARTFORD, CONNECTICUT

## VOLUME 4

MARCEL DEKKER, Inc., New York and Basel

TK
7872
L3A1
L2
v.4
PHYS

08 2/24/70

# CONTENTS

Chapter 3    **Helium-Neon Lasers and the Positive Column**

Raymond Arrathoon

Chapter 4    **Optical Parametric Oscillators**

R. G. Smith

# CONTRIBUTORS TO VOLUME 4

RAYMOND ARRATHOON,* Bell Laboratories, Incorporated, Murray Hill, New Jersey

H. G. DANIELMEYER,† Max Planck Institut für Festkörperforschung, Stuttgart, Federal Republic of Germany

PETER W. SMITH, Bell Laboratories, Incorporated, Holmdel, New Jersey

R. G. SMITH, Bell Laboratories, Incorporated, Murray Hill, New Jersey


*Present address: Solarex Ltd., Troy, Idaho.
†Present address: Institut für Angewandte Physik, Universität Hamburg, Federal Republic of Germany.

# CONTENTS OF OTHER VOLUMES

# PREFACE

The sixteenth anniversary of the first demonstration of pulsed coherent emission from single-crystalline ruby occurs in 1976. Few developments have excited the imagination of scientists and engineers and have had such a profound influence on science and technology as has that achievement. At first the inherent attraction of characterizing, exploring, and broadening a new physical phenomenon drew many researchers into this area, who quickly showed that laser action could be attained over a wide spectral range in crystalline systems different from ruby and in other optically transparent media such as gases, glasses, and liquids. During this early period operating characteristics of lasers were continually pushed to higher values and exploitation of the phenomenon for scientific and technological purposes grew concomitantly. Today laser performance in selected embodiments has reached spectacular values: pulsed output of less than a picosecond duration with peak power exceeding a terawatt; cw output with average power exceeding 60 kilowatts; frequency stability on the order of 1 part in $10^{14}$; operating wavelengths ranging from the ultraviolet to the submillimeter; efficiency exceeding 60 percent. The availability of such extraordinary coherent sources has made possible new areas of experimental research involving, for example, optical harmonic generation, optically generated plasmas, stimulated scattering, photon echoes, self-induced transparency, optical adiabatic inversion, optical shocks, optical parametric amplification, optical radar and ranging, isotope separation and enrichment by optical techniques, extremely high resolution spectroscopy, and holography.

The laser device field today is multidisciplinary and contributes to and draws upon such fields as solid state, molecular and atomic physics, spectroscopy, acoustics, electronics, plasma physics, semiconductor technology, organic and inorganic chemistry, crystallography, thin film technology, fluid dynamics, aerodynamics, and combustion physics. The impressive advances in laser state-of-the-art has led to notable technological advances and has fostered significant and rapidly growing commercial applications. Laser devices and systems already have important uses in industrial, medical, communications, and consumer areas, and many additional devices and systems are in development. Meanwhile, the earlier scientific and military applications are still expanding.

*Lasers* is a series of critical reviews that evaluate the progress made in the field of lasers. The contributing authors are scientists who are intimately involved in expanding the research frontiers in their specialties and, therefore, write with the authority that comes from personal contribution.

The series provides the background, principles, and working information needed by physical and biological scientists who seek to use lasers as a tool in their research and by engineers who wish to develop the laser phenomenon for commercial and military applications. Moreover, these critical reviews are sufficiently intensive that they can be used by a specialist in one portion of the laser field to bring himself up to date authoritatively in other areas of the field.

# LASERS

VOLUME 4

*Chapter 1*

# Progress in Nd:YAG Lasers

*H. G. Danielmeyer* *

Max Planck Institut für Festkörperforschung
Stuttgart, Federal Republic of Germany

*Present address*: Institut für Angewandte Physik, Universität Hamburg, Federal
Republic of Germany

1

# I. Introduction

Neodymium-doped yttrium aluminum garnet, $YAlG:Nd^{3+}$, alias Nd:YAG, has become one of the most successful laser materials. Basically, this is due to the unique properties of the $Nd^{3+}$ ion that have been known [1] long before $Nd^{3+}$ was lased in a crystalline [2] and a glass host [3]. There is practically no competition for the $Nd^{3+}$ ion as far as cw and pulsed sources of reasonable power in the spectral region around 1 $\mu$m are concerned.

However, there was a lot of competition [4] in seeking efficient hosts for $Nd^{3+}$ before the Nd:YAG laser was developed [5]. There are, of course, many hosts into which $Nd^{3+}$ fits reasonably well with or without energy transfer, charge compensation, and size compensation. There are also hosts that have good heat conductivity (at least before they are activated, that is, doped with an impurity) and that do not solarize at higher pump levels. These hosts may simultaneously be stable, hard, polishable, and easy to grow. The most important factor for a good host is, however, the crystal field at the $Nd^{3+}$ site. The transitions of $Nd^{3+}$ are electric dipole parity forbidden. Transition probabilities of the order of $10^4$ per second are obtained only if the site is acentric [6]. This allows transitions of the forced electric dipole type through mixing of states of opposite parity. The local crystal field must further provide a suitable distribution of branching ratios for the 52 possible fluorescence lines of $Nd^{3+}$ as well as Stark level splittings such that concentration quenching by cross relaxation [8, 9] between neighboring $Nd^{3+}$ ions is negligible. Finally, the absorption bands should be broad and intense enough for efficient optical pumping, and the quantum yield should be high.

It is difficult to see how this set of requirements could be fulfilled by one optimal host. In fact, there are two types. Glasses have nonequivalent sites, which leads to inhomogeneous broadening, large linewidths, and relatively high threshold, so that Nd:glass lasers are suited for high-peak-power-pulsed operation. (See the chapter by Snitzer and Young in Volume 2.) Crystals can have nearly identical sites with homogeneous phonon broadening, narrow linewidth, and low threshold for the four-level system of $Nd^{3+}$, so that Nd:crystal lasers are suited for cw and medium-power-pulsed operation.

So far, YAG has proven to be the best choice for continuous $Nd^{3+}$ lasers. However, as the title of this chapter implies, the Nd:YAG laser has had its problems.

Between 1968 and 1972 strong research and development efforts were necessary to understand, improve, and adapt the Nd:YAG laser for machining [10], ranging [11], communications [12-14], and laboratory use. Judging from the publishing rate shown in Fig. 1 for some representative journals, this phase is coming to an end. Most of the problems are indeed understood. Some of them, specifically those related to the stability of mode-locked, Q-switching, and single-frequency operation, have been solved. Others, specifically those related to overall pump efficiency, higher fundamental mode output power, and miniaturization, could not be solved because of inherent limitations of the material itself, such as narrow absorption bands, limited doping level, low gain, and thermal birefringence.

It is not surprising, then, that the search for new hosts for $Nd^{3+}$ has been resumed after the Nd:YAG boom. Promising new alternatives are, for instance, fluoro-oxyapatites [15], oxysulfides [16], aluminum oxides [17-20], multicomponent garnets [21], and ultraphosphates [22]. It can be claimed that the chances of at least some of these materials are very good if one considers their handicap against the development effort that has gone into the Nd:YAG laser.

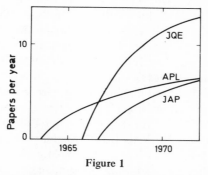

**Figure 1**

Annual publication rate of papers on Nd:YAG in *Applied Physics Letters, Journal of Applied Physics,* and *IEEE Journal of Quantum Electronics.*

## II. The Material

$Nd_x Y_{3-x} Al_5 O_{12}$, Nd:YAG, can be grown by the Verneuil method, from the flux, and with better success by the Czochralski method [23]. Growth direction and laser rod axis are usually [111]. Because of the low distribution coefficient of neodymium ($\sim 0.2$), it is difficult to obtain a homogeneous doping level [24]. It is also difficult to determine the true doping level to better than 10%. The optimum value for cw operation corresponds to about 1% replacement of Y by Nd. At higher doping levels, the efficiency of the laser material decreases because of concentration quenching, inhomogeneities, and reduced heat conductivity. The gain of Nd:YAG is therefore relatively small.

Attempts to increase the gain by codoping have not been very successful, mainly because the crystal quality deteriorates with any additional impurity. Two different avenues can be pursued: codoping with energy-transferring ions ($U^{3+}$, $Cr^{3+}$) to increase the absorption; and codoping with volume-compensating ions ($Sc^{3+}$, $Ga^{3+}$, $Lu^{3+}$) to increase the distribution coefficient of neodymium. Trivalent codopants are necessary to avoid charge compensation problems. One exemplary attempt of each alternative will be discussed because they have met with partial success.

Codoping with lutetium increases the distribution coefficient of neodymium by 50% [24]. This allows for somewhat higher doping levels that may yield 10-30% more output power for the same pumping [19]. The threshold of Nd,Lu:YAG is, however, 20-50% higher than the threshold of Nd:YAG [19]. Whereas the absorption spectrum is only very little changed [25], the two strongest fluorescence lines at 1.061 and 1.064 $\mu$m split into two components [26] with a separation of 3 cm$^{-1}$. This can be seen at 2 K, where the stronger component of each line is 2.5 cm$^{-1}$ wide. In Nd:YAG, these lines are less than 1 cm$^{-1}$ wide [27]. At room temperature, where the main laser transition at 1.064 is 5 cm$^{-1}$ wide for 1% Nd:YAG [27], the linewidth is 8.8 cm$^{-1}$ and 9.6 cm$^{-1}$ for 0.7% Nd, Lu:YAG and 1.3% Nd,Lu:YAG, respectively. The splitting into two components implies the existence of two dominant types of sites with different crystal fields for $Nd^{3+}$, probably clusters [26] of YAG and LuAG. The broadening implies either a distribution of sites around the dominant types (inhomogeneous broadening) or increased phonon interaction (homogeneous broadening).

Codoping with chromium sensitizes Nd:YAG through energy transfer from the upper ruby laser level 2E of $Cr^{3+}$ to the lowest pump band of $Nd^{3+}$. Nd,Cr:YAG was lased [28] shortly after Nd:YAG [5]. Chromium has also been used as sensitizer for Tm:YAG [29], Nd:YAlO$_3$ [19], and Nd:glass [30], where the transfer efficiency is 50% for a concentration corresponding to a mean distance of 18 Å between $Cr^{3+}$ and $Nd^{3+}$. Note that 18 Å is also the mean distance between $Nd^{3+}$ in about 1% doped Nd:YAG; and much higher concentrations are not possible. The transfer time between Cr and Nd is 6.2 msec in Nd:YAG [28]. Since the fluorescent lifetime of $Nd^{3+}$ is shorter, energy transfer from $Cr^{3+}$ is a bottleneck. Finally, efficient pumping of the two $Cr^{3+}$ absorption bands requires a source with wavelengths shorter than 6,000 Å, where YAG is subject to solarization probably caused by creation of color centers. (See the section on pumping.) Tungsten halogen lamps cannot be used at all since tungsten would melt before the black-body temperature for pumping $Cr^{3+}$ is reached. Thus, Nd,Cr:YAG is so far not a competitive cw laser material.

Because of the existence of three stable compounds between $Y_2O_3$ and $Al_2O_3$ (the monoclinic $2Y_2O_3 \cdot Al_2O_3$, the perovskite $Y_2O_3 \cdot Al_2O_3$, and the garnet $3Y_2O_3 \cdot 5Al_2O_3$), one observes occasionally inclusions of other phases, namely of Nd:YAlO$_3$, in Nd:YAG [163].

## A. Physical Properties of Nd:YAG

### 1. The Host

$Y_3Al_5O_{12}$ is cubic with space group Ia3d. The $Al^{3+}$ sites are fourfold- and six-fold-coordinated. The latter site can be occupied by $Cr^{3+}$, as in the case of ruby [32]. Although a complete structure analysis does not exist for YAG, one can infer from the analysis of YIG, yttrium iron garnet, that the nearest neighbors of Y are eight oxygen ions. They form an orthorhombically distorted cube that gives $D_2$ symmetry [33]. However, some $Nd^{3+}$ Stark level splittings can be explained satisfactorily by a crystal field of $D_{2d}$ symmetry, so that the rare-earth site in YAG is nearly tetragonal [7]. This is the highest possible symmetry that still removes the parity restriction of the selection rule and all degeneracy except for Kramer's degeneracy [1]. If the site symmetry is higher than tetragonal, $Nd^{3+}$ probably does not lase. $Nd:LiNbO_3$ lases only when strained [34], for instance.

The physical properties are summarized in Table 1. Most of the quantities were determined only for the pure host. In most cases, the changes effected by a 1% doping level are negligible. The heat conductivity values depend very much on the sample and its doping. The scatter of this value can be estimated from Ref. 34, where the heat conductivity was 0.11 W/cmK and 0.15 W/cmK for $Nd^{3+}$ concentrations of $4 \times 10^{19}$ /cm$^3$ and $1.4 \times 10^{20}$ /cm$^3$, respectively—a change in the wrong direction. The refractive index [39] is shown in Fig. 2. The linear and second-order terms have been calculated from the refractive index data.

### 2. The Nd$^{3+}$ Ion

The electron configuration of $Nd^{3+}$ is $(Kr)4d^{10}4f^3 5s^2 5p^6 = (Xe)4f^3$. The three 4f electrons are shielded from the crystal field by two outer electron shells, so that the crystal-field interaction is much smaller than the spin-orbit coupling. Consequently, the energies of the $J= |S + L|$ manifolds vary very little for different hosts. Only Stark level splittings between the $J + \frac{1}{2}$ components of each manifold are energetically comparable to the crystal-field interaction, and depend on the host. The wave functions have been calculated [42]. Only few high-energy levels depart significantly from Russell-Saunders coupling [43]. The level designation follows therefore the gas spectroscopy scheme $^{2S+1}X_J$, where X is S, P, D, F, G, H, I, K, or L, respectively. The spins of the three 4f electrons can add to $S = \frac{1}{2}$ or $S = \frac{3}{2}$. The ground state is $^4I_{9/2}$.

Table 1

Physical Properties of $Y_3Al_5O_{12}$

| Property | Magnitude | Units, remarks | Ref. |
|---|---|---|---|
| Density | 4.56 | g cm$^{-3}$, 100 K | 35 |
| | 4.55 | g cm$^{-3}$, 300 K | 35, 40 |
| Lattice constant | 12.003 | Å, 300 K | 40 |
| Mean Y density | $1.385 \times 10^{22}$ | cm$^{-3}$, 24Y$^{3+}$ per unit cell | |
| Poisson's ratio | 0.25 | 298 K | |
| Elastic constants | $c_{11} = 33.32 \times 10^{11}$ | dyn cm$^{-2}$, 298 K | 38 |
| | $c_{12} = 11.07 \times 10^{11}$ | dyn cm$^{-2}$, 298 K | 38 |
| | $c_{44} = 11.50 \times 10^{11}$ | dyn cm$^{-2}$, 298 K | 38 |
| Longitudinal | $8.5630 \times 10^5$ | [001] cm/sec | 38 |
| sound velocity | $8.6016 \times 10^5$ | [110] cm/sec | 38 |
| Transverse | $5.0293 \times 10^5$ | [001] cm/sec | 38 |
| sound velocity | $5.0274 \times 10^5$ | [110], [00$\bar{1}$] | 38 |
| | $4.9438 \times 10^5$ | [110], [1$\bar{1}$0] | 38 |
| Elastooptic | $p_{11} = -0.0290$ | 300 K | 37 |
| constants | $p_{12} = +0.0091$ | 300 K | 37 |
| | $p_{44} = -0.0615$ | 300 K | 37 |
| Lin. expansion | $\alpha = 6.9 \times 10^{-6}$ | K$^{-1}$, 300 K | 36 |
| Temp. coefficient | $dn/dT = +7.3 \times 10^{-6}$ | K$^{-1}$, 1.06 $\mu$m, 300 K | 36 |
| Therm. coefficient | $\alpha + dn/ndT = 1.1 \times 10^{-5}$ | K$^{-1}$, 1.06 $\mu$m, 300 K | 41 |
| Heat conductivity | 0.58 (1% Nd) | W cm$^{-1}$, 100 K | 35, 24 |
| | 0.13 (1% Nd) | W cm$^{-1}$, 300 K | 35, 24 |
| Specific heat | 19.4 | cal mol$^{-1}$ K$^{-1}$, 100 K | 35 |
| | 88.8 | cal mol$^{-1}$ K$^{-1}$, 300 K | 35 |
| Refractive index | n = 1.818 | air, 1.06 $\mu$m, 300 K | 39 |
| Lin. dispersion | $dn/d\lambda = -270$ | cm$^{-1}$, 1.06 $\mu$m, 300 K | Fig. 2 |
| Second-order | $d^2n/d\lambda^2 = +7 \times 10^6$ | cm$^{-2}$, 1.06 $\mu$m, 300 K | Fig. 2 |

## B. Absorption

### 1. Absorption from the Ground State

Figure 3 shows the absorption, the level designations, the main wavelengths, the integrated absorption coefficients $\int k(\lambda) \, d\lambda$ for each group, and the line strengths [33] for the absorption of Nd:YAG from the ground state manifold at 300 K. The absorption was measured for a sample with 1% doping, and the line strengths for sample with 0.75% doping, i.e., concentrations of $1.4 \times 10^{20}$ and $1.06 \times 10^{20}$ $Nd^{3+}/cm^3$, respectively. It can be seen that the absorption is relatively small. The average 1/e absorption length is of the order of centimeters for the strongest pump bands. The absorption lengths for the absorption peaks are still several millimeters. The peak cross sections into the $^4I_{3/2}$ level are given in Table 2.

## 2. Absorption from Other States

Except for the ground state, the upper laser levels $^4F_{3/2}$ are the only states with a significant population when the system is pumped. Ions in these states can absorb, for instance, the pump light or the laser light. The relevant transitions [33] are listed in Table 3. The only significant absorption is that to the $^2G1_{9/2}$ level, which competes with the main laser transition at 1.06 $\mu$m because its line strength is comparable to the line strength of the 1.06-$\mu$m fluorescence from the $^4F_{3/2}$ level. This competition should be quite independent of the host, and reduces the laser efficiency. The competitions utilizing the second harmonic of the laser light (0.53 $\mu$m), or pump light at 0.8 $\mu$m (luminescent diodes), are negligible.

At 300 K, the population of the lowest-frequency tail (0.83 $\mu$m) of the lowest pump band is about an order of magnitude smaller than the population of the upper laser level $^4F_{3/2}$. Competition due to absorption from the lowest pump

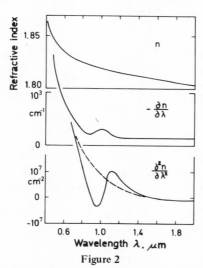

Figure 2

Dispersion in YAG at 300 K. The linear and quadratic terms have been calculated from the refractive index.

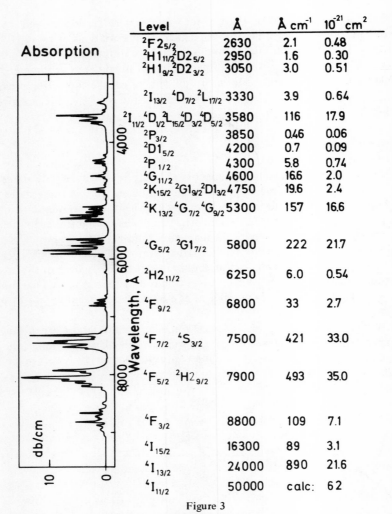

| Level | Å | Å cm$^{-1}$ | $10^{-21}$ cm$^2$ |
|---|---|---|---|
| $^2F2_{5/2}$ | 2630 | 2.1 | 0.48 |
| $^2H1_{11/2}{}^2D2_{5/2}$ | 2950 | 1.6 | 0.30 |
| $^2H1_{9/2}{}^2D2_{3/2}$ | 3050 | 3.0 | 0.51 |
| $^2I_{13/2}{}^4D_{7/2}{}^2L_{17/2}$ | 3330 | 3.9 | 0.64 |
| $^2I_{11/2}{}^4D_{1/2}{}^2L_{15/2}{}^4D_{3/2}{}^4D_{5/2}$ | 3580 | 116 | 17.9 |
| $^2P_{3/2}$ | 3850 | 0.46 | 0.06 |
| $^2D1_{5/2}$ | 4200 | 0.7 | 0.09 |
| $^2P_{1/2}$ | 4300 | 5.8 | 0.74 |
| $^4G_{11/2}$ | 4600 | 16.6 | 2.0 |
| $^2K_{15/2}{}^2G1_{9/2}{}^2D1_{3/2}$ | 4750 | 19.6 | 2.4 |
| $^2K_{13/2}{}^4G_{7/2}{}^4G_{9/2}$ | 5300 | 157 | 16.6 |
| $^4G_{5/2}{}^2G1_{7/2}$ | 5800 | 222 | 21.7 |
| $^2H2_{11/2}$ | 6250 | 6.0 | 0.54 |
| $^4F_{9/2}$ | 6800 | 33 | 2.7 |
| $^4F_{7/2}{}^4S_{3/2}$ | 7500 | 421 | 33.0 |
| $^4F_{5/2}{}^2H2_{9/2}$ | 7900 | 493 | 35.0 |
| $^4F_{3/2}$ | 8800 | 109 | 7.1 |
| $^4I_{15/2}$ | 16300 | 89 | 3.1 |
| $^4I_{13/2}$ | 24000 | 890 | 21.6 |
| $^4I_{11/2}$ | 50000 | calc: | 62 |

Figure 3

The absorption of Nd:YAG at 300 K from the ground state $^4I_{9/2}$. The Nd$^{3+}$ concentrations are $1.4 \times 10^{-20}$ /cm$^3$ for the absorption, and $1.06 \times 10^{20}$/cm$^3$ for the integrated absorption coefficient in Å/cm and the line strength in cm$^2$, respectively.

band into $^2P_{1/2}$ and $^2K_{15/2}$ utilizing pump radiation at 0.81 $\mu$m, or the laser radiation at 1.06 $\mu$m, is probably small, but it does exist.

### C. Fluorescence and Laser Lines

The fluorescence levels of Nd$^{3+}$ are illustrated in Fig. 4. Their energies are

Table 2

Radiative Lifetimes, Cross Sections, and Linewidths for Some
Transitions from the $^4F_{3/2}$ Levels in Nd:YAG at 300 K

| Manifold | Transition $4F \rightarrow 4I$ | Rad. lifetime $(10^{-3}$ sec$)$ | Cross section $(10^{-20}$ cm$^2)$ | Linewidth $(cm^{-1})$ | Ref. |
|---|---|---|---|---|---|
| $^4I_{9/2}$ | $2 \rightarrow 1$ | 3.3 | 4.1 | 12.5 | 27 |
| | $1 \rightarrow 1$ | 14 | 1.1 | 12.5 | 27 |
| | $2 \rightarrow 2$ | 10 | 2 | 10 | 140 |
| | $2 \rightarrow 3$ | 2 | 8 | 10 | 140 |
| | $1 \rightarrow 2$ | 5 | 4 | 10 | 140 |
| | $1 \rightarrow 3$ | 7 | 3 | 10 | 140 |
| | $2 \rightarrow 4$ | 3 | 6 | 10 | 140 |
| | $1 \rightarrow 4$ | 5 | 2 | 20 | 140 |
| | $2 \rightarrow 5$ | 2 | 10 | 10 | 140 |
| | $1 \rightarrow 5$ | 2 | 8 | 10 | 140 |
| $^4I_{11/2}$ | $1 \rightarrow 1$ | 0.5 | 44 | 3 | 74 |
| | $1 \rightarrow 2$ | 0.7 | 80 | 5.2 | 53 |
| | $2 \rightarrow 3$ | 4 | 17 | 4.2 | 53 |
| | Laser | 0.55 | 87 | 5.4 | 177 |
| | Laser | 0.6 | 70 | 5.4 | 172 |

given in cm$^{-1}$ for 77 K [47] and 300 K [140]. The $^4F_{3/2}$ level is the only one
that is not relaxed predominantly by multiphonon processes in any host. Its
separation from the next lower $^4I_{15/2}$ manifold is in YAG 4600 cm$^{-1}$. The
phonon spectrum [45] extends up to 800 cm$^{-1}$. However, from an experiment-
al fit of the $^4F_{3/2}$ (1) $\rightarrow$ $^4I_{11/2}$ (1) line shift vs temperature [27], the effective
Debye temperature is only 430 cm$^{-1}$. This means that at least eleven phonons
would be required to bridge the gap between $^4F_{3/2}$ and $^4I_{15/2}$ levels. A relaxation
process of that order would be less likely than migration of the excitation energy
to an impurity (impurity quenching) at about $10^{14}$ impurities per cm$^3$. (See Section II, D, 3.) This could explain why the radiative quantum efficiency of the
$^4F_{3/2}$ level may be very high in pure, weakly doped Nd materials. For Nd:YAG,
early measurements [46] gave 0.995 for the quantum efficiency. However, ab-

Table 3

Absorption from the $^4F_{3/2}$ Levels

| Terminal state | Wavelength ($\mu$m) | Line strength (cm$^2$) |
|---|---|---|
| $^4G_{7/2}$ | 1.35 | $1.9 \times 10^{-21}$ |
| $^2G_{19/2}$ | 1.06 | $2.19 \times 10^{-20}$ |
| $^2P_{1/2}$ | 0.88 | $3 \times 10^{-23}$ |
| $^2D_{15/2}$ | 0.80 | $4 \times 10^{-23}$ |
| $^4D_{7/2}$ | 0.532 | $2.7 \times 10^{-21}$ |

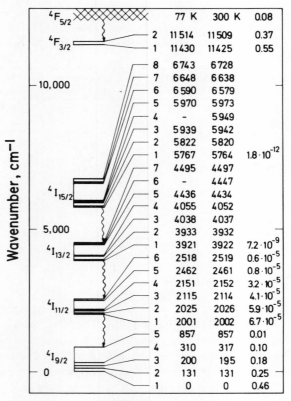

**Figure 4**

Fluorescence levels in Nd:YAG. Shown are from left to right the level designations, the phonon relaxations into thermal equilibrium (wavy lines), level numbers, the level energies in wavenumbers at 77 K [47] and 300 K [140], and the thermal equilibrium populations, separate from the upper and lower laser level systems. The $^4I_{11/2}$ level populations should be multiplied by 0.46.

solute cross-section measurements are so difficult for $Nd^{3+}$ that error limits below 50% should be examined critically. More recent measurements give a smaller value for the radiative quantum efficiency (0.65) [141]. The truth lies probably in between [172, 180].

All the other levels relax within $10^{-6}$ sec or less to thermal equilibrium. The pump levels are in thermal equilibrium with the $^4F_{3/2}$ level, and the $^4I$ levels are in thermal equilibrium with the lattice. The pump system relaxes with the flourescent-lifetime of the $^4F_{3/2}$ level ($2.3 \times 10^{-4}$ sec). The relative population of the levels (thermal occupation),

$$p(\nu) = \frac{\exp(-h\nu/kT)}{\Sigma\exp(-h\nu/kT)} \qquad (1)$$

is given in the last column of Fig. 4 for 300 K.

The fluorescence into the $^4I_{3/2}$ and $^4I_{5/2}$ manifolds is weaker than the fluorescence into $^4I_{11/2}$ and $^4I_{9/2}$ manifolds, but by no means negligible. Figures 5 through 8 give the fluorescence spectra at 300 K.

## 1. Branching Ratios, Lifetimes, and Cross Sections

The branching ratios have been measured for all transitions except for some into the $^4I_{15/2}$ manifold that are too weak. Table 4 shows the transitions and the branching ratios

$$\beta = \frac{\int I_\lambda d\lambda}{\Sigma\int I_\lambda d\lambda} \qquad (2)$$

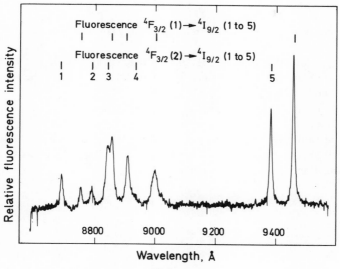

**Figure 5**

Room temperature fluorescence into the ground state manifold of Nd:YAG at 300 K [140].

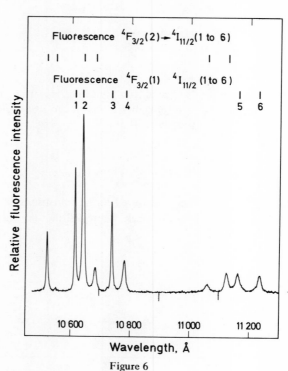

Figure 6

Room temperature fluorescence into the $^4I_{11/2}$ manifold of Nd:YAG at 300 K [140].

where $I_\lambda$ is the radiation intensity per unit wavelength for 300 K and 77 K. All transitions are identified with the level numbers shown in Fig. 4. The transitions that have been lased are given in Table 6.

The lifetimes and cross sections that have been determined so far are listed in Table 2. For a Lorentzian line shape, which results from homogeneous broadening, the transition probability for an ion A, the radiative lifetime $\tau_r$, the full linewidth at half-maximum $\delta\nu$, the line wavelength $\lambda$, the refractive index n, and the peak cross section $\sigma_0$ are related by [53]

$$A = \frac{1}{\tau_r} = \frac{4\pi^2 n^2 \sigma_0 \, \Delta\nu}{\lambda^2} \tag{3}$$

Table 4

Branching Ratios [48] for the Transitions from the $^4F_{3/2}$ Level

| Manifold | Wavelength ($\mu$m, 300 K) | Transition | Branching ratio 300 K | 77 K |
|---|---|---|---|---|
| $^4I_{9/2}$ | 0.8689 | 2 → 1 | 0.015 | — |
| | 0.8753 | 1 → 1 | 0.0096 | 0.012 |
| | 0.8791 | 2 → 2 | 0.014 | — |
| | 0.8844 | 2 → 3 | 0.023 | — |
| | 0.8854 | 1 → 2 | 0.043 | 0.090 |
| | 0.8905 | 1 → 3 | 0.029 | 0.058 |
| | 0.8934 | 2 → 4 | 0.0064 | — |
| | 0.9003 | 1 → 4 | 0.026 | 0.039 |
| | 0.9386 | 2 → 5 | 0.033 | — |
| | 0.9462 | 1 → 5 | 0.039 | 0.061 |
| | | | 0.24 | 0.28 |
| $^4I_{11/2}$ | 1.0520 | 2 → 1 | 0.048 | 0.015 |
| | 1.0551 | 2 → 2 | 0.0033 | — |
| | 1.0616 | 1 → 1 | 0.086 | 0.11 |
| | 1.0639 ⎱ | 1 → 2 ⎱ | 0.14 | 0.047 |
| | 1.0643 ⎰ | 2 → 3 ⎰ | 0.045 | 0.080 |
| | 1.0684 | 2 → 4 | 0.047 | 0.020 |
| | 1.0739 | 1 → 3 | 0.070 | 0.10 |
| | 1.0782 | 1 → 4 | 0.055 | 0.085 |
| | 1.1056 | 2 → 5 | 0.016 | 0.0084 |
| | 1.1123 | 2 → 6 | 0.040 | 0.022 |
| | 1.1160 | 1 → 5 | 0.050 | 0.066 |
| | 1.1226 | 1 → 6 | 0.032 | 0.042 |
| | | | 0.63 | 0.60 |
| $^4I_{13/2}$ | 1.3182 | (2 → 1) | 0.018 | 0.0098 |
| | 1.3193 | (2 → 2) | 0.0057 | 0.0020 |
| | 1.3328 | 1 → 1 | 0.0071 | 0.010 |
| | 1.3346 | 1 → 2 | 0.013 | 0.020 |
| | 1.3380 | 2 → 3 | 0.020 | 0.0097 |
| | 1.3409 | 2 → 4 | 0.0076 | 0.0030 |
| | 1.3534 | 1 → 3 | 0.0036 | 0.0043 |
| | 1.3563 | 1 → 4 | 0.016 | 0.031 |
| | 1.4134 | 2 → 5 | 0.010 | 0.0032 |
| | 1.4304 | 1 → 5 | 0.0064 | 0.012 |
| | 1.4434 | 1 → 7 | 0.0093 | 0.016 |
| | | | 0.12 | 0.12 |
| $^4I_{15/2}$ | 1.833 | 1 → 5 | 0.003 | — |

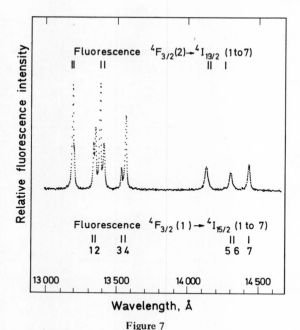

**Figure 7**

Room temperature flourescence into the $^4I_{13/2}$ manifold of Nd:YAG at 300 K [140].

The cross section is a convenient parameter since it permits calculation of the unsaturated gain of the material of length z simply from

$$G = \exp[\sigma(\nu) N z]$$ (4)

where $N$ is the inversion density along the laser axis, that is, the population difference between the upper and lower level per unit volume, and $\sigma(\nu)$ is the cross section at the signal frequency. Equation (4) is written for the simplest case, where $N$ is constant along the laser axis in the active medium of length z, and constant across the laser beam. As a function of frequency, the cross section is given by

$$\sigma(\nu) = \frac{\sigma_0}{1 + [(\nu - \nu_0)/(\Delta\nu/2)]^2}$$ (5)

for a Lorentzian line, where $\nu_0$ is the center frequency of the line. Only a few lines are not Lorentzian in Nd:YAG, notably the 0.9003-μm transition [27].

Since the radiative quantum efficiency of the $^4F_{3/2}$ levels is smaller than 1, the total radiative lifetime of Nd:YAG is larger than the fluorescent lifetime $\tau = 2.3 \times 10^{-4}$ sec. For doping levels above 1.5 atomic percent Nd, the fluorescent

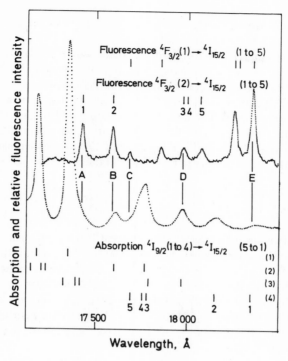

**Figure 8**

Room temperature fluorescence and absorption into the $^4I_{15/2}$ manifold of Nd:YAG showing that portion of the spectrum where overlapping occurs [140]. The overlappings A through E cause fluorescence quenching at higher doping levels through cross relaxation.

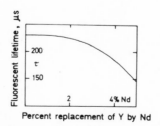

**Figure 9**

Shortening of the fluorescent lifetime of the $^4I_{3/2}$ state in Nd:YAG, in agreement with cross-relaxation theory [140]. The experimental data [54, 55] have been corrected for reabsorption.

lifetime decreases with increasing doping level [54] according to Fig. 9 (See Section D).

The main laser transition at 1.064 $\mu$m is actually a double transition because the 1.0639-$\mu$m and 1.0643-$\mu$m lines overlap at room temperature [53]. The cross section of the laser line differs, therefore, from an earlier measurement [44], which gives $\sigma_0 = 5.5 \times 10^{-19}$ if proper corrections are made for the linewidth, refractive index, and radiative linewidth. A new determination [141] of the cross section gives for the total cross section of the laser line within experimental error the same value, that is, $\sigma_0 = 5 \times 10^{-19}$ cm$^2$. At about 170 K, the main laser line changes to 1.0616 $\mu$m according to the change in the branching ratios (Table 4).

## 2. Line Shifts and Linewidths

All levels have constant energies between 0 and 100 K, and change by less than 15 cm$^{-1}$ between 100 and 300 K (Fig. 4). Most of the line shifts are governed by the energy shifts of the initial $^4F_{3/2}$ levels. Their energies decrease with temperature according to Fig. 10 within experimental error by the same amount [27]. It should be mentioned that there is one discrepancy for the line shift of the 0.9462-$\mu$m line $^4F_{3/2}$ (1) $\rightarrow$ $^4I_{3/2}$ (5) between the value of Fig. 4 ($-5$ cm$^{-1}$) and the value of Ref. 27 ($+2$ cm$^{-1}$). All level shifts follow qualitatively the change shown in Fig. 10.

The linewidths are governed by homogeneous phonon broadening [27]. Figure 11 shows the widths of three lines as a function of temperature [27, 54]. Deviations from Lorentzian line shape for several lines at low temperatures indicate inhomogeneous strain broadening. Some weak satellite lines occurring in the spectrum may be due to Nd pairs, different sites for Nd$^{3+}$, and phonon sidebands in the case of Cr$^{3+}$ impurity [27].

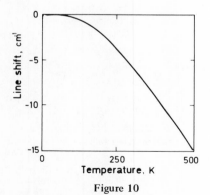

**Figure 10**

Energy shift of both $^4I_{3/2}$ levels with temperature in Nd:YAG [27].

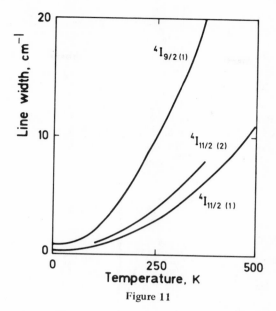

**Figure 11**

Linewidths versus temperature of three transitions between the lower $^4I_{3/2}$ level and the ground state [27], the lowest $^4I_{11/2}$ level [27] and the second $^4I_{11/2}$ level [55].

## 3. Laser Oscillations

Only a third of all possible transitions have been lased so far. Table 5 summarizes the work for the major laser transition at 1.064 μm. Sections IV and V will deal exclusively with this work.

The other laser transitions are summarized in Table 6. If the 1.064-μm laser transition is suppressed by antireflection coatings on the rod and high cavity losses at 1.064 μm, most of the 12 transitions into the $^4I_{11/2}$ manifold can be lased. It should be mentioned here that the 1.0616-μm transition is strong enough to lase together with the 1.064-μm transition. Laser action of the transitions into the $^4I_{9/2}$ manifolds requires strong pumping or cooling of the rod or both, since the thermal population of the highest level is still 1% at room temperature. This is 200 times the thermal population of the final states of the 1.064-μm transition. Laser oscillation to the two upper $^4I$ manifolds is relatively inefficient because of the small branching ratios.

### D. Energy Transfer

The optical properties of Nd materials are characterized by several transfer

Table 5

Survey of the Work on the Main Laser Doublet at 1.0640 μm

| Topic | References |
|---|---|
| Spectroscopy | 7, 33, 43, 45, 56, 140, 141 |
| Energy transfer | 28, 31, 55, 57-59, 167 |
| Nd:YAG degradation | 33, 45, 60 |
| Ion and tungsten lamps | 61-70, 85, 168, 169, 177 |
| Luminescent diodes | 71-75, 148 |
| Cooling | 76, 77 |
| Thermal effects | 78-84 |
| CW oscillation | 5, 41, 49, 58, 61, 65, 66, 72, 74, 75, 78, 85-87, 177 |
| Pump-pulsed | 88-92 |
| Q-switching | 10, 12, 13, 88, 91-101, 177 |
| Mode locking | 88, 102-123, 174 |
| Spiking and relaxation oscillations | 69, 104, 126-130 |
| Frequency stabilization | 41, 58, 87, 96, 98, 120, 131-135, 170, 173 |
| Output control | 10, 58, 87, 91, 104, 107, 136-138, 175 |
| Harmonic generation | 14, 88, 99, 100, 118, 119, 124, 125 |

processes [140, 165]. Two processes have fundamental importance for the efficiency and operation of Nd:YAG lasers: migration of the excitation energy between the Nd ions, and cross relaxation between the Nd ions. Both processes involve energy transfer from an excited Nd ion to an adjacent Nd ion. They are illustrated in Fig. 12.

Energy migration is the full exchange of the excitation energy between two Nd ions. This process conserves the excitation energy so that the fluorescent lifetime is not much affected. However, this process may be effective in reducing spatial hole burning, that is the $\sin^2 kz$ spatial modulation of the inversion along the laser axis that results from the $\cos^2 kz$ stimulating intensity of a standing wave in the resonator [59]. Energy migration between adjacent Nd ions leads macroscopically to energy diffusion. The mean spacing between the ions is 18 Å in 1% Nd:YAG (Table 1). A quarter wavelength in Nd:YAG is 1460 Å at 1.06 μm. Therefore, about eight unidirectional migration steps are required for the diffusion of the excitation energy from a location of maximum inversion to the adjacent location of minimum inversion along the laser axis. This mobility of the excitation energy can partially smooth out spatial hole burning. It was shown that this happens in Nd:YAG [59]. The efficiency of single-frequency operation increases if energy migration is present, since the excitation energy can be used more uniformly for stimulated emission.

Cross relaxation is a partial energy exchange between adjacent Nd ions. Inspection of the fluorescence levels on Fig. 4 shows that such a process is only possible if the initial states of the emitter and absorber are $^4F_{3/2}$ and $^4I_{9/2}$, respectively, and the final states are $^4I_{15/2}$ (see Fig. 12).

Each cross relaxation destroys one $^4F_{3/2}$ excitation, and leaves two ions in the $^4I_{15/2}$ state. This state is short-lived because of phonon relaxation (see Section II, C), so that the process is quite irreversible. Therefore the fluorescence is quenched if the cross relaxation rate becomes comparable to the radiative decay rate; i.e., the flourescent lifetime of the $^4F_{3/2}$ level shortens. This is one of the worst limitations of Nd:YAG, and happens obviously for concentrations beyond 1.5% (Fig. 9). Transfer and quenching mechanisms are discussed in more detail in Ref. 179.

### Table 6

#### Observed Laser Transitions in Nd:YAG

| Wavelength ($\mu$m) | Operating characterisitcs | Ref. |
|---|---|---|
| 0.8905 | Littrow prism, high mirror | |
| 0.9003 | Transmission at 1.06 $\mu$m, longitudinal | 51 |
| 0.9386 | Xe-laser pump pulse 420 W, 290 $\mu$sec | |
| 0.9462 | Q-switch output 2 kW, 180 nsec, SHG | 52[a] |
| | Q-switch output 8 kW, 200 nsec, SHG 3 kW | |
| 1.0520 | 1.4 mW cw threshold 594 W tungsten lamp | 49[a] |
| | Q-switch output $>$0.3 mJ, SHG $>$0.2 mJ | |
| 1.0616 | 7.0 mW cw threshold 350 W tungsten lamp | 49[a] |
| | Q-switch output $>$0.3 mJ, SHG $>$0.2 mJ | |
| 1.0639 | 11.9 mW cw threshold 286 W tungsten lamp | 49[a] |
| 1.0643 | Q-switch output 5 kW, 100 nsec, SHG 3 kW | |
| 1.0739 | 6.3 mW cw threshold 348 W tungsten lamp | 49[a] |
| | Q-switch output $>$0.3 mJ, SHG $>$0.2 mJ | |
| 1.1123 | 4.2 mW cw threshold 623 W tungsten lamp | 49[a] |
| | Q-switch output $>$0.3 mJ, SHG $>$0.2 mJ | |
| 1.1160 | 1.4 mW cw threshold 646 W tungsten lamp | 49[a] |
| | Q-switch output $>$0.3 mJ, SHG $>$0.2 mJ | |
| 1.1226 | 2.1 mW cw threshold 676 W tungsten lamp | 49[a] |
| | Q-switch output 6 kW, 220 nsec, SHG 3 kW | |
| 1.319 | 30 W cw threshold 457 W tungsten lamp | 49[a] |
| | Q-switch output, 5 kW, 100 nsec, SHG 4 kW | |
| 1.335 | Q-switch output $>$0.3 mJ, SHG $>$0.2 mJ | a |
| 1.338 | Q-switch output $>$0.3 mJ, SHG $>$0.2 mJ | a |
| 1.358 | Q-switch output $>$0.3 mJ, SHG $>$0.3 mJ | a |
| 1.833 | 2 Prisms, antireflection coating for 1.0 $\mu$m, 10 kW pump | 50 |

[a]Chromatix Model 1000 Nd:YAG Laser System. Quantronix Model 114 Systems, operating at 1.06 $\mu$m, provide up to 16 W cw ($TEM_{00}$), 100 W cw (multimode), 32 kW ($TEM_{00}$) Q-switch, and 200 kW (multimode) Q-switch. These data were quoted for 1973.

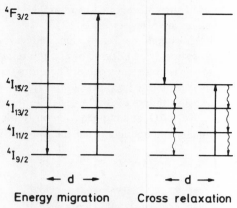

**Figure 12**

Models for energy migration and cross relaxation between neighboring $Nd^{3+}$ ions separated by a distance d. The wavy transitions indicate fast phonon relaxation processes, the solid transitions indicate near-field electric dipole resonance transfers.

## 1. Resonance Transfer

Energy migration and cross relaxation involve resonance transfer of the excitation energy between Nd ions. In a lattice where the ion mobility is very small, there are basically three mechanisms that can lead to resonance transfer [139]. Exchange interaction due to overlap of the 4f wave functions can be excluded since it is only effective over a few Å units. Quadrupole or magnetic dipole interactions can be excluded since they are 7 or 8 orders of magnitude less effective than electric dipole interactions. The existence of forced electric dipole transitions between the levels of the Nd ion has been discussed in the introduction and in Section II, A, 1. Resonance transfer by electric dipole interaction between adjacent Nd ions in the lattice is therefore the most likely process responsible for energy migration and cross relaxation in Nd:YAG, and this has been verified for tungstate hosts [167]. Quantitatively one obtains for the transition probability [140]

$$W_{12} = \frac{2\pi}{3} N^2 \frac{\sigma_{oa}}{\tau_r k_i^4} \frac{1}{1 + [\nu_r - \nu_a)/\Delta\bar{\nu}]^2} \tag{6}$$

where N is the concentration of Nd ions, $\overline{\Delta\nu}$ the mean of the two linewidths, $\nu_r - \nu_a$ the frequency difference of the two transitions, $k_i$ the mean internal wave vector of the two transitions, $\sigma_{oa}$ the peak cross section of the absorbing transition, and $\tau_r$ the radiative lifetime of the fluorescing transition.

## 2. Cross Relaxation

Figure 8 discloses five overlappings between fluorescence and absorption lines in Nd:YAG, which are identified by the letters A through E in Fig. 13. Process A is threefold and process D twofold. Each process contributes to the cross relaxation rate according to Eq. (6) with its own weight, which is the probability of the neighbor ion's being in the Stark level required for reabsorption, i.e., the thermal equilibrium population p from Fig. 4. The absorption cross sections can be obtained from Fig. 8 with

$$\sigma_{oa} = \frac{\alpha}{pN_0} \tag{7}$$

where $N_0 = 0.7 \times 10^{20}$ is the (small) doping level of the sample used for Fig. 8; p is the thermal equilibrium population of the absorbing level; and $\alpha$ is the peak absorption from Fig. 8 (5% per cm for the strongest line at 1.74 $\mu$m). The radia-

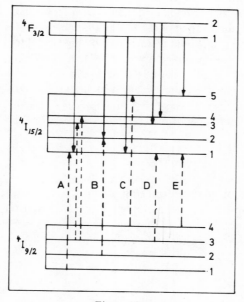

**Figure 13**

Detail of the overlappings A through E from Fig. 8. Process A consists of three different exchanges and process D of two, for a total of eight resonance transfers between Nd ions. Each transfer leaves both interacting ions in the $^4I_{15/2}$ state, which decays radiationless into the ground state.

tive lifetime of the fluorescent lines can be obtained from the branching ratios $\beta$ given in Table 4. Since there are in the $r^{-6}$ average about ten nearest neighbors, and the range of the $k_i$'s is small, one obtains from Eq. (6) for the cross-relaxation rate

$$W_x = \frac{20\pi}{3} \frac{N^2}{\tau N_0 k_i^4} \sum \frac{\alpha\beta}{1 + [(\nu_r - \nu_a)/\overline{\Delta\nu}]^2} \tag{8}$$

where $\tau$ is the total flourescent lifetime, at small concentration, of the $^4F_{3/2}$ states. The sum over the eight processes is $5.5 \times 10^{-5}$ cm$^{-1}$, so that $W_x = 10^{-42}$ [cm$^6$] N$^2/\tau$. From this one obtains for the flourescent lifetime.

$$\tau(N) = \frac{\tau}{1 + 10^{-42}[cm^6]N^2} \tag{9}$$

which fits the experimental results within 10% (Fig. 9). Fluorescence quenching in Nd:YAG can therefore be explained indeed with cross relaxation via the $^4I_{15/2}$ manifold. If its position were only 3% shifted to higher energies, overlappings would not occur, the gain would be increased by higher doping, and Nd:YAG would be interesting for integrated optics too. Thus, Nd:YAG is a very unfortunate material. It may be the only one out of a great many possible laser materials that shows such an unfavorable Stark level splitting. The temperature dependence of the levels is so small that flourescence quenching in Nd:YAG should not depend on temperature very much between 77 K and 300 K.

## 3. Energy Migration

Since the excitation energy is transferred in full to one of the neighbor ions, all fluorescence transitions can contribute to resonance transfer. This is simultaneously very effective since the overlappings are perfect ($\nu_r = \nu_a$ for all $k_i$). With Eq. (3), one obtains for transfer probability

$$W_J = \frac{20\pi}{3} \frac{N^2}{\tau^2} \sum \frac{\beta^2}{\Delta\nu k_i^6} \tag{10}$$

For 1% doped Nd:YAG, one obtains from this equation [140] a transfer time of $1/W_J = 3 \times 10^{-7}$ sec, which is much shorter than the lifetime of the $^4F_{3/2}$ state.

Consequently, one cannot think of the upper laser state as an excitation being bound to any single Nd ion in Nd:YAG. The excitation is rather distributed over $W_J\tau \approx 750$ Nd ions, and the diffusion distance $d\sqrt{W_J\tau}$ is 500 Å, where $d = 18$ Å is the mean separation between Nd ions. Since this is shorter than a quarter-wavelength, spatial hole burning is reduced but not eliminated by energy migration in Nd:YAG. From the experimental value [59] of the diffusion constant $D = W_J d^2 \approx 5 \times 10^{-7}$ cm$^2$/sec, one obtains a diffusion length of $\sqrt{D\tau} \approx 10^3$ Å for the $^4F_{3/2}$ states.

## III. Pumping

### A. Optical Pumping and Degradation

Nd:YAG must be pumped optically. This means that the pump source must be optically imaged onto the material. The optimum pump geometry depends therefore on the geometry of the active material and the source. The lowest pump bands that can be used if the four-level features of the Nd ion are to be utilized are the $^4F_{5/2}$ and $^2H29_{/2}$ bands around 8,000 Å (Fig. 3). These bands are the only ones accessible to black-body radiation. Gas discharge lamps can pump the higher pump bands centered around 7,500 Å, 5,800 Å, and 5,300 Å. The latter and also all others below 5,300-Å wavelength are however not ideally suited for pumping because Nd:YAG degrades with irradiation shorter than 6,000 Å.

This degradation consists of the generation of a broad background absorption between 3,000 Å and 6,000 Å, which reduces the laser efficiency considerably [60] with increasing pump frequency, intensity, and time. Heating to about 400°C may eliminate the background absorption [21]. It has been observed, however, that annealed material degrades nearly immediately to its former level with much smaller irradiation than before [70]. The physical nature of the degradation is still poorly understood. Probably it is due to photoreduction [45] of Nd$^{3+}$ to Nd$^{2+}$ [179], or to formation of some unspecified color centers [70]. It is clearly evident that the centers are connected with the Nd doping since degradation is neither observed in very pure YAG nor in A,B,C:YAG, where A, B, C = Pr, Ho, Er, Tm, or Yb. These ions fit much better into YAG than Nd [33].

## B. Gain, Threshold, and Slope Efficiency

### 1. Gain Saturation

This section describes the most frequent case, the gain of the main laser line at 1.064 $\mu$m illustrated in Fig. 14. The formulation can be readily applied to any other transition.

If a TEM$_{00}$ beam of optical power $P_L$ passes through the laser rod, the stimulating intensity at a distance r from the laser axis is

$$I(r) = \frac{2P_L}{\pi w^2} \exp\left(-\frac{2r^2}{w^2}\right) \qquad \int_0^\infty I(r)\, \pi d r^2 = P_L \qquad (11)$$

where w is the beam radius, defined as $(1/e)^2$ of the power drop. Since the populations are in detailed thermal equilibrium,

$$\frac{N_3}{N_4} = \exp\left[\frac{h(\nu_4 - \nu_3)}{kT}\right] \qquad (12)$$

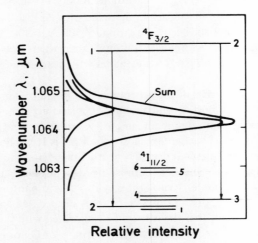

**Relative intensity**

Figure 14

Detail of the laser doublet 1.064 $\mu$m at room temperature [46]. The transition $1 \rightarrow 2$ corresponds to the stronger line at 1.0641 $\mu$m, and the transition $2 \rightarrow 3$ corresponds to the line at 1.0645 $\mu$m.

$$\frac{N_1}{N_2} = \exp\left[\frac{h(\nu_2 - \nu_1)}{kT}\right] \tag{13}$$

If the pump rate $R(r)$ (number of $^4F_{3/2}$ states pumped per unit volume per unit time) is in equilibrium with the total decay rates $A_3 N_3$ and $A_4 N_4$ of the upper laser levels and with the stimulated decay rates, then

$$R(r) - A_3 N_3 - A_4 N_4 - \frac{I(r)}{h\nu}\left[\sigma_I(N_3 - N_1) + \sigma_{II}(N_4 - N_2)\right] = 0 \tag{14}$$

where $\nu$ is the laser frequency and $\sigma_I$, $\sigma_{II}$ are the cross sections for the transitions I and II. Participation of $^2H_{29/2}$ and higher pump bands has been neglected for this rate equation. These equations can be solved for the effective gain coefficient

$$\sigma N = \sigma_I(N_3 - N_1) + \sigma_{II}(N_4 - N_2) \tag{15}$$

(compare Eq. (4)). The result is

$$\sigma N = \frac{R(r)\dfrac{(b_3\sigma_I + b_4\sigma_{II})}{(b_3 A_3 + b_4 A_4)} - (\sigma_I N_1 + \sigma_{II} N_2)}{1 + \dfrac{I(r)}{h\nu}\dfrac{(b_3\sigma_I + b_4\sigma_{II})}{(b_3 A_3 + b_4 A_4)}} \tag{16}$$

where

$$b_3 = \frac{N_3}{N_3 + N_4} \quad \text{and} \quad b_4 = \frac{N_4}{N_3 + N_4} \tag{17}$$

It may be worth noting that (14) describes the detailed balance of pump, spontaneous emission, and stimulated emission that must exist at any point of the laser medium, provided that the gain is small so that I is a function only of the mode profile and not of the distance of propagation. The effective gain coefficient is therefore a constant of the mode and is independent of r. Since the lower levels are in thermal equilibrium with the ground state, $N_1$ and $N_2$ are also independent of r if the inversion is not saturated. Equation (16) can be written

$$\sigma N = \frac{\sigma N(I = 0)}{1 + I(r)/I_s} \tag{18}$$

where $\sigma N(I = 0)$ is the unsaturated gain coefficient, and

$$I_s = \frac{h\nu}{\sigma_E \tau} \tag{19}$$

is the saturation parameter. The effective lifetime

$$\tau = (b_3 A_3 + b_4 A_4)^{-1} \tag{20}$$

is identical to the fluorescent lifetime of the upper laser state, which is $2.3 \times 10^{-4}$ sec at room temperature (Fig. 9). Using the room temperature values [53], one finds $\sigma_I = 4.6 \times 10^{-20}$ cm$^2$, $\sigma_{II} = 8.0 \times 10^{-19}$ cm$^2$; and (from Fig. 4) $b_3 = 0.60$, $b_4 = 0.40$, the effective cross section here defined by

$$\sigma_E = b_3 \sigma_I + b_4 \sigma_{II} \tag{21}$$

is $3.4 \times 10^{-19}$ cm$^2$. With these values, one gets for the saturation parameter at room temperature for the main 1.064-$\mu$m laser transition

$$I_s = 2.3 \quad kW/cm^2 \tag{22}$$

This is a meaningful quantity: if $I(r) = I_s$, the effective gain is reduced to half its small-signal value for the same pump rate; the stimulated lifetime

$$\tau_s = \frac{I_s}{I(r)} \tau \tag{23}$$

equals the fluorescent lifetime; and half of the total fluorescence power is stimulated emission near the laser axis.

Neglect of the pump band participation and, in particular, uncertainties in the cross sections limit the accuracy of the theoretical value for $I_s$. Various laser properties, for instance the relaxation oscillation frequency [90, 179], can be predicted with the saturation parameter (22). The saturation parameter depends on the temperature and on the doping level beyond 1.5% doping.

## 2. Threshold Pump Power for TEM$_{00}$ Operation

Since the pump efficiencies of all the absorption bands are nearly unity, each absorbed quantum will yield one excited laser state (Auger recombinations at high pump rates [140] are neglected). For a free running TEM$_{00}$ laser, where several axial modes oscillate simultaneously, the threshold pump density at frequency $\nu_p$ is therefore

$$H_T = h\nu_p R \ (I = 0) \tag{24}$$

The value R (I = 0) can be calculated from (16) and the round-trip gain condition

$$\exp(2\sigma N\ell) \exp(-L)(1-T) = 1 \tag{25}$$

where $\ell$ is the uniformly pumped length of the active material, and L is the total cavity loss except for the output power transmission T. Since L, T $\ll$ 1 in most cases, one can simplify (25) to

$$\sigma N = \frac{(L+T)}{2\ell} \tag{26}$$

This can be equated to (16). Note that in a laser cavity, however, I(r) has to be replaced by 2I(r) since the beam passes twice through the rod for one round trip. This case is again different from the single-frequency case where spatial hole burning develops, which makes I(r) a function of z, the coordinate along the laser axis. (See section V.)

From Eqs. (16), (20), (21), (24), and (26), one obtains for the threshold pump density

$$H_T = \frac{h\nu_p}{\sigma_E \tau} \left( \sigma_I N_1 + \sigma_{II} N_2 + \frac{L+T}{2\ell} \right) \tag{27}$$

The first two terms are due to the reabsorption loss from the lower laser levels.

At room temperature and 1% doping, $\sigma_I N_1 + \sigma_{II} N_2 = 4.9 \times 10^{-3}/\text{cm}$. The third term is due to the resonator loss. Assuming an output transmission factor of $T = 2 \times 10^{-2}$, a cavity loss of $L = 10^{-2}$ (which means antireflection-coated rod surfaces and includes absorption at the rod ends), and a pumped length of $\ell = 3$ cm, $(L + T)/2\ell = 5 \times 10^{-3}$. In this example, the reabsorption and cavity losses are nearly equal and the threshold pump density (27) is

$$H_T = \frac{30 \text{ W}}{\text{cm}^3} \tag{28}$$

for the 8,000-Å pump band. This power is absorbed before any laser action takes place. It is advantageous, therefore, to make the rod volume not much larger than the mode volume

$$V_{TEM_{00}} = \pi w^2 \ell \tag{29}$$

Note that a rod radius $r_0 = \sqrt{2}w$ would allow only 98% of the intensity to pass through the rod corresponding to $L = 4 \times 10^{-2}$ (integrate Eq. (11)). Since the rod edges are not sharp, one needs often a minimum rod radius of $r_0 = 2w$ to keep $L < 10^{-2}$. This means that the total absorbed power at threshold

$$W_T = \pi r_0^2 \ell H \tau \tag{30}$$

is at least 2.8 W for $r_0 = 0.1$ cm (w = 0.05 cm), $\ell = 3$ cm, $L + T = 3 \times 10^{-2}$, and 8,000-Å pump.

## 3. Slope Efficiency for TEM$_{00}$ Operation

In the case of laser oscillation, $I \neq 0$, the gain of a mode depends on the desired mode profile $I(r)$ and the actual pump profile $R(r)$. This can be seen from Eq. (16). Highest efficiency is obtained if these profiles are matched. Otherwise the inversion or other transverse modes must balance the mismatch, which means excess spontaneous emission, or multimode operation, respectively. If the pump profile has the TEM$_{00}$ distribution, one gets for the pump power from (16), (26), and integration of (11)

$$W = \epsilon W_T + \epsilon \frac{\nu_p}{\nu} \left(1 + \frac{L}{T}\right) P_0 \tag{31}$$

$$P_0 = TP_L \tag{32}$$

is the $TEM_{00}$ output power of the laser, and $\epsilon$ is a factor $< 1$ that measures the pump efficiency, defined as the number of $^4F_{3/2}$ states generated per unit time divided by the number of photons emitted by the pump source per unit time. Thus, $\epsilon$ includes lamp characteristics as well as imaging quality. The factor of $P_0$ in (31) is the inverse of the slope efficiency.

If $\epsilon$ includes the source conversion efficiency, i.e., the ratio of optical output power to electrical input power, the ratio $P_0/W$ is the overall efficiency.

If the pump profile has a uniform distribution, the pump power density must be large enough to provide balance for within the mode volume. From (16) it follows that the pump power can be written approximately

$$W' = \epsilon W_T + 8\epsilon \, \frac{\nu_p}{\nu} \left(1 + \frac{L}{T}\right) P_0 \tag{33}$$

for a rod of radius 2w. A nearly uniform distribution is usually encountered in side pumping with tungsten or ion-discharge lamps when the rod diameter is equal to or smaller than the source diameter. Compared with the matched case (31), which can be achieved by longitudinal pumping with a laser beam [142], the slope efficiency is reduced by a factor of eight.

For large diameter rods, absorption of the pump light becomes significant for side pumping. Then the pump profile has a dip in the center of the rod. Without restraints, such a laser will preferentially oscillate in high-order transverse modes simply because the highest field intensities of a mode occur further from the axis as the order of the mode is higher. Rods of more than a few millimeters diameter are therefore not practical for fundamental mode operation with side pumping. The slope efficiency will be substantially less than in the case of the uniform pump profile, which is already bad enough. An exact calculation for Gaussian beams including the effects of inversion profile, reabsorption, and pump profile is given in Ref. 179.

## C. Pump Lamps and Geometries

### 1. Lamps

The most frequently used pumping arrangement is side pumping by tungsten lamps, and gas discharge lamps filled with krypton or xenon. Tungsten lamps are cheaper, and have a useful life of several hundred hours compared with a lifetime of less than 100 hours of cw gas discharge lamps. Note that closed pumping chambers decrease the lifetime specifically for tungsten lamps if the input power is not reduced to compensate for backreflection. Lifetimes quoted by manufacturers may therefore be unrealistic. On the other hand, the power load of gas discharge lamps can be four times higher than the power load of tungsten lamps, which are limited to 0.5 kW/cm for 0.5-cm diameter filaments by the melting point of tungsten [61]. The lifetime of tungsten lamps has been increased somewhat by adding iodine or bromine; these substances transport evaporated tungsten back to the filament provided that the lamp is not cooled. Thus, the housing radiates a good portion of the lamp power in the infrared. The filament has a tendency to sag and vibrate, which disturbs the output. The lifetime of the discharge lamps is limited by inside deposits on the quartz jacket, which makes the lamps look brown after about 50 hours of operation.

Matching lamp emmisions to the absorption of $Nd^{3+}$ is nearly hopeless in practice [68]. In theory [168], there could be a large saving because of the poor Nd absorption (Fig. 3). The black-body radiation of tungsten lamps at 3,000 K gives $\epsilon \sim 33$. At best only 3% of electrical input power can actually be absorbed [66] by $Nd^{3+}$. For fundamental mode operation, Eq. (33) yields an overall slope efficiency of less than 1%. The multimode overall efficiency may reach 1%. Krypton lamps emit a larger fraction of their power in the Nd absorption bands, and $\epsilon \sim 20$. For a 100-W cw laser, overall efficiencies of 2.9% and 1.8% have been reported for single-ellipse and double-ellipse pump chambers, respectively [65, 85]. Argon lamps would give the best match for the $Nd^{3+}$ absorption; however, their radiative efficiency is too low [64]. Xenon lamps are inferior to krypton lamps for cw operation but not necessarily for pulsed operation, for which different results [62, 63, 67] contradict each other, probably because of variations in experimental conditions. For pump flashes of 20 to 40 joules, the optimum fill pressures are 700 Torr for Kr lamps and 1,000 Torr for Xe lamps; the threshold with Kr was 58% of that with Xe [67]. For high current densities, in the range of 2.4 $kA/cm^2$ to 2.7 $kA/cm^2$, the line emission of Kr decreases relative to the continuum emission, so that Xe lamps become superior [67]. More complex lamps have also been constructed. For instance, an Ar-K-Hg lamp gave an overall efficiency three times higher than that of tungsten lamps [66]. However, the lamp can only be operated ac and manufacturing cost is not competitive with Kr lamps.

## 2. Pump Chambers

Some of the pump geometries [169] are sketched in Fig. 15. Helical pump lamps cannot be imaged efficiently and are used only for flash excitation. Close-coupled chambers are very economical, but still inefficient for $TEM_{00}$ operation. Ellipsoids [143, 144] are seldom used because they must be large compared with the sum of the rod and source lengths for good imaging; this leads either to ineffi-

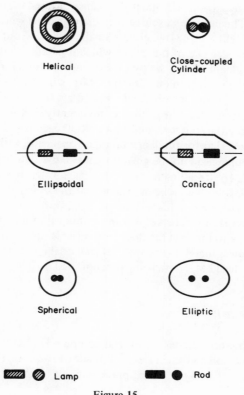

**Figure 15**

Schematic pump configurations

cient or to big, heavy, and expensive designs. Conical chambers, which give excellent imaging [68], are very easy to fabricate. Both designs have the disadvantage that one laser end is not accessible; this is in contrast to all other pump chambers. Spherical enclosures [69] are also big, heavy, and expensive. They reach an imaging efficiency of 75% if rod and source are placed some distance apart—necessary for cooling and mounting purposes [145].

This distance comes naturally with the commonly used elliptic cylinder chamber [146] as the distance between the two focal axes, $\sqrt{(a^2 - b^2)}$, where a/2 is the major and b/2 is the minor axis of the ellipse. The imaging efficiency [147] reaches 70%. Silver coatings on the polished surfaces would be the best for reflectivity (98%). Because of corrosion, gold (96%) is most frequently used. Aluminum (97%) forms a protective oxide layer, which is, however, not safe in case the ellipse is flooded with coolant liquids like water or alcohol. On the other hand, if cooling is achieved with glass jackets around the source and the laser rod, the source image becomes asymmetric because of ray deviations and screening by the jackets. The image of a source with circular cross section becomes, to first approximation, elliptic [68] where the smaller axis is about equal to the source radius. The longer axis of the image, which is parallel to the short axis of the elliptical pump chamber, may be twice the source radius (Fig. 16). The image is also longer than the source. In one example [68], where a/2 = 4.45 cm, b/2 = 4.22 cm, s = 2.00 cm (source length), and c = 3.20 cm (length of pump chamber), the image was 30% larger than the source. Consequently, in this configuration, for optimal efficiency the source should be about 30% shorter than the rod. It should be emphasized that for fundamental mode operation with side pumping the radius of the source need not be greater than $\sim 0.6w$. This is clearly shown by the result of Fig. 16. Recalling from Section III,B,3 that the optimum rod diameter is approximately $4w$, we can assume that the source diameter need not be greater than 15% of the rod diameter. For larger source diameter, the $TEM_{00}$ pump efficiency decreases whereas higher-order modes are pumped more effectively. It does not pay to increase the diameter of the lamp. To the contrary, the additional pump power increases the thermal load of the rod, and this causes a significant drop in the $TEM_{00}$ efficiency (Section III,D).

## 3. Luminescent Diode Pump

The use of luminescent diodes for optical pumping [71] is attractive because of narrow band emission and small size. If P is added to GaAs, the diode emission can be shifted [72, 73] into the lowest pump band of Nd:YAG. Room-tempera-

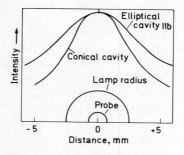

**Figure 16**

Pump power profile for sidepumping in conical and elliptical pump chambers [68]. Because of water shields and the acentric shape, the profile measured parallel to the short axis of the ellipse is considerably wider than the profile measured parallel to the long axis, where it is identical with the ideal case of the conical cavity. The cross sections of the pump lamp's filament and of the probe used for measuring the profile are given as reference.

ture operation [74, 75] of a diode-pumped Nd:YAG laser was obtained with a semielliptic cylinder pump chamber. Ulitmately 64 $GaAs_{0.85}P_{0.15}$ diodes were used. They emitted 0.2 to 0.9 W of optical power at 7,290 to 8,020 Å in a 200- to 260-Å band for an electrical input power of 7 to 30 W. The laser output power was a few milliwatts, giving an overall efficiency of less than $10^{-4}$. Recently a high-reflection-coated Nd:YAG rod 0.5 cm long and 0.045 cm in diameter reached threshold when pumped longitudinally with a luminscent diode of 19 mW optical output power. The pump light was confined by a reflecting tube [148].

It might also be possible to pump Nd: YAG directly into the $^4F_{3/2}$ level with GaAs diodes. This is less desirable since the system then becomes three-level.

### D. Thermal Effects

The power absorbed in Nd:YAG per unit volume is given by

$$H = \frac{W}{\pi r_0^2 \ell \epsilon} = H_T + \frac{W - \epsilon W_T}{\pi r_0^2 \ell \epsilon} \qquad (34)$$

It was assumed that $\epsilon \gg 1$, i.e., $P_0 \ll W$. Taking $\ell = 10$ cm, $r_0 = 0.3$ cm, and L/T $= 0.5$, one obtains from (27) $H_T = 4.5$ cal/sec $cm^3$ at room temperature. For cw krypton lamps, $\epsilon \sim 20$, which yields a threshold input power of $\epsilon W_T = 1.1$ kW from (30). With these data, Eq. (34) is plotted in Fig. 17. The experimental points [79] are very close to the theoretical curve. The slope is not exactly unity since the useful optical output power is usually not proportional to the input power. This is quite evident for tungsten lamps: the black body temperature increases with the input power, and the frequency of the peak emission shifts towards shorter wavelengths, thus improving the match between the lamp emission and the absorption band.

It is clear from Eq. (34) and Fig. 17 that the rod must be cooled for continuous operation. Since the heat conductivity is finite, a radial temperature gradient results. For uniform heating, the temperature profile is parabolic. Since the index of refraction depends on the temperature, a parabolic index profile results.

The first consequence is thermal lensing, which can be described by an effective focal length [79]

$$f = \kappa \left[ \ell H \left( \frac{1}{2} \frac{dn}{dT} + \alpha C n^3 \right) \right]^{-1} \qquad (35)$$

where $\kappa$ is the heat conductivity; $\ell$, the length of the rod; H, the absorbed power; dn/dT, the temperature coefficient of the refractive index; $\alpha$, the thermal expansion coefficient; C, the elastooptic coefficient; and n, the index of refraction (values are given in Table 1). The effective focal length is of the order of 1 m or less [83].

Thermal lensing can be compensated for by grinding a negative lens [149] on the rod with radius

$$R = -2(n-1)f \tag{36}$$

This can increase the $TEM_{00}$ output power by a factor of 5 [78] to about an order of magnitude [82].

The second consequence is multifocusing, which can be calculated from the photoelastic constants and the thermal strains set up by the temperature gradient. If the rod axis is (111), the radial and tangential changes of the refractive index are given [79] by

$$\Delta n_{r,\phi} = -S_{r,\phi} \frac{n^3 \alpha H}{2\kappa} r^2 \tag{37}$$

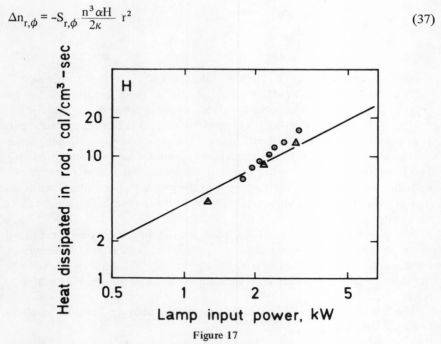

**Figure 17**

Energy dissipation in a Nd:YAG rod versus krypton pump lamp input power [79]. Circles are from thermal focusing and triangles from thermal birefringence, and the solid line is calculated from Eq. (34) without any adjustment of parameters.

where

$$S_r = \frac{(17\nu - 7)p_{11} + (31\nu - 17)p_{12} + 8(\nu + 1)p_{44}}{48(\nu - 1)} \tag{38}$$

and

$$S_\phi = \frac{(5\nu - 3)p_{11} + (11\nu - 5)p_{12}}{16(\nu - 1)} \tag{39}$$

The p's are elastooptic constants, and $\nu$ is Poisson's ratio (Table 1). Different polarizations see different indices of refraction and different focal lengths.

The last consequence is birefringence. One obtains from Eq. (37)

$$n_\phi - n_r = \frac{n^3}{48} \frac{1 + \nu}{1 - \nu} \frac{\alpha H}{\kappa} (p_{12} - p_{11} - 4p_{44})r^2 \tag{40}$$

Since the elastic constant combination in (40) is nonzero (unfortunately YAG is photoelastically highly anisotropic), Nd:YAG is biaxial [80] with different axes at any point in the r, $\phi$ plane (Fig. 18) when pumped.

The phase delay from (40) may be as high as a quarter-wavelength, which explains the significant decrease of the output power of Nd:YAG lasers if a polarizer is inserted into the cavity. Besides concentration quenching, this is the worst deficiency of Nd:YAG. It can only be removed if the cylindrical symmetry is changed in favor of rectangular symmetry, or if the host is changed in favor of one already strongly birefringent. Changing the YAG orientation is not effective, although for low-power operation [001] is slightly preferable [81]. Efforts to compensate for birefringence have had limited success. For instance, one can split the YAG rod and put a 90° rotator in between to exchange the polarizations [84].

## IV. Dynamics

### A. General Remarks

The Nd:YAG laser, like other lasers, shows a number of instabilities; these are illustrated qualitatively in the spectrum of Fig. 19. Spiking is a tipper oscillation, in which the inversion builds up to threshold to the point at which the photon avalanche dumps the inversion to restart the cycle. The characteristic time of this highly nonlinear process is the buildup time of the inversion, which is, under certain conditions, close to the fluorescent lifetime $\tau$ of the upper laser level.

The so-called relaxation oscillation is an exchange of energy between the system of excited atoms (inversion) and photons (cavity radiation). In contrast to the spiking case, the characteristic time of relaxation oscillations can be calculated from the linearized rate equations; it turns out to be the geometric mean

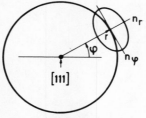

Figure 18

Thermal birefringence in Nd:YAG due to a parabolic radial temperature gradient.

between the lifetimes of the two participating systems: the stimulated lifetime $\tau_s$ of the excited atoms, and the cold cavity lifetime of the photons

$$\tau_Q = \frac{2\mathcal{L}}{c(T + L)} \qquad (41)$$

where $\mathcal{L}$ is the optical length of the cavity and c the light velocity in vacuum. Since $\tau_s$ depends on the laser power according to Eq. (23), relaxation oscillations can be recognized by their power dependence.

Axial mode locking is the coupling of axial modes with constant-phase relation, which forms a wave packet traveling forth and back within the cavity. The characteristic time is therefore the signal round-trip time of the cavity

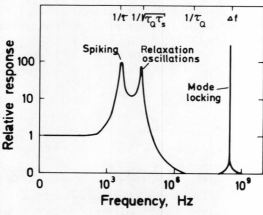

Figure 19

Schematic diagram of instabilities in Nd:YAG lasers. Shown is the output modulation (peak intensity over average intensity) versus frequency of cavity loss modulation. In the case of spiking and relaxation oscillation pulsing, pump modulation will produce a similar response [68]. All instabilities can be generated by feedback loops, and stabilized by means of the phase relation between output pulses and modulation.

$$\tau_c \approx \frac{2\,\ell}{c} \tag{42}$$

Whereas spiking and relaxation oscillations are relatively weakly damped in Nd:YAG, mode locking is relatively strongly damped by the nonlinear dispersion of the host. This will be shown. The practical consequences are that self mode locking is, in contrast to the He-Ne laser, not detectable [129] in Nd:YAG, while spiking and relaxation oscillations are easily excited by perturbations of the pump power, and cavity loss, and the cavity frequency.

Unwanted fluctuations of the cavity loss are caused by mechanical vibrations of the mirrors or the rod. Mechanical stability requirements are illustrated by the fact that velocity components of $10^{-3}$ cm/sec along the laser axis cause spiking [129]. Since the rod surfaces are not perfectly antireflecting, one should in general not align the rod parallel to the wavefronts. Slight longitudinal vibrations will otherwise cause output fluctuations. This is because the rod surfaces form subcavities, which determine which longitudinal modes will oscillate; if the subcavity spacings change, different longitudinal modes are preferred. The resulting mode hopping causes instability of the output. The rod surfaces seem to behave worse than should be expected from the quality of antireflection coatings. This suggests that a strong absorption occurs within the surface layer, which is, from energy diffusion (Section II,D,3), about 500 Å thick. This can be used to quiet down the fluctuations and reduce the number of oscillating modes to less than five by adjusting the rod's position and the cavity length in such a way that all optical lengths have integer ratios [170].

A second source of cavity loss fluctuations is local temperature fluctuations induced by the coolant flow around the rod. These fluctuations can be damped with sleeves around the rod. Crystal quartz has, for this purpose, an optimum combination of specific heat and heat conductivity [77]. It has also been found that turbulent flow of the coolant with Reynolds numbers above 10,000 yields better output stability than laminar flow [76]. This may in most cases eliminate any need for sleeves, which unfortunately introduce a long-term thermal and optical contact problem between the rod and the sleeve. A third source of cavity-loss perturbations is angular vibration of the mirrors, which should not exceed 1 min of arc [129].

Unwanted fluctuations of the pump power can be reduced by stabilized power supplies. It has been shown [129] that cw operation with a stability of $10^{-2}$ of the output power requires that the pump intensity is at least stable to $10^{-4}$, where the kHz spectral region is critical.

Where high peak powers are desired, the Nd:YAG instabilities can be advantageous. In these cases, they are driven by modulation of the cavity loss, the pump power, the cavity frequency at the spiking frequency, the relaxation oscillation frequency, and the mode locking frequency. Progress has been made towards stable operation in these modes.

## B. Relaxation Oscillations

For a laser with output power $P_L T$, the number of photons in the cavity is given by

$$P = \frac{P_L \tau_c}{h\nu} \qquad (43)$$

If the intensity is simply averaged over the mode cross section $\pi w^2$, one obtains for the stimulating intensity

$$I = \frac{2P_L}{\pi w^2} \qquad (44)$$

provided that spatial hole burning is prevented either by moving the rod through the standing wave pattern [129] or by allowing for axial multimode oscillation.

From Eqs. (19), (23), (43), and (44), the stimulated lifetime can be obtained:

$$\tau_s = \frac{\pi w^2}{2\sigma} \frac{\tau_c}{P} \qquad (45)$$

The effective cross-section subscript has been dropped. Since the inversion n increases with the pump rate $\zeta$ and decreases through spontaneous $(\tau)$ and stimulated $(\tau_s)$ emissions, the rate equation of the population inversion is

$$\dot{n} = \zeta - \frac{n}{\tau} - \frac{2\sigma}{\pi w^2} \frac{pn}{\tau_c} \qquad (46a)$$

Compared with Eq. (14), the pump rate R is modified to become $\zeta$, which now includes a fraction of the spontaneous decay rate; the transition is simplified to one line; and the equilibrium is generalized by allowing for a change of n with time.

The photon population p increases through spontaneous emission $\tau_s$ and decreases through cavity losses $\tau_Q$. The rate equation is therefore

$$\dot{p} = \frac{2\sigma}{\pi w^2} \frac{pn}{\tau_c} - \frac{p}{\tau_Q} \qquad (46b)$$

This is perhaps the most easily interpreted form of the rate equations. It shows explicitly that stimulation is proportional to the ratio of transition cross section (the microscopic area that can be stimulated) to mode cross section (the macroscopic area that stimulates); the round-trip frequency $1/\tau_c$ of stimulation; and the number of photons and inverted states. Because of Eq. (43), p can be replaced by $P_L$, which can be measured directly.

Equation (46) has two singular points in the n-p plane. Relaxation oscillations occur around the stable equilibrium point

$$n_0 = (T + L) \frac{\pi w^2}{2\sigma} \tag{47a}$$

$$p_0 = \zeta \tau_Q - \frac{\pi w^2}{2\sigma} \frac{\tau_c}{\tau} \tag{47b}$$

Except for multiplication with the active mode volume (29), Eq. (47a) is identical with (26).

If at time t = 0 the photon population is perturbed by $\delta p$, it will return to equilibrium according to

$$p = p_0 + \delta p \exp(-at) \exp[i(\omega_0^2 - a^2)^{1/2} t] \tag{48}$$

where a is defined below. This follows from a solution of the rate equations (46a, b) if they are linearized, i.e., for small perturbations. The circular frequency of the relaxation oscillation

$$\omega_0 = (\tau_Q \tau_s)^{-1/2} \tag{49}$$

is the geometric mean of the cavity decay rate and the stimulated decay rate; and the damping constant

$$a = \frac{1}{2} \left( \frac{1}{\tau} + \frac{1}{\tau_s} \right) \tag{50}$$

is the arithmetic mean of the spontaneous decay rate and the stimulated decay rate [129]. Since $\tau$ is large for Nd:YAG, the damping constant is quite small, so that Nd:YAG lasers are generally very sensitive to small perturbations. The higher the laser is operated above threshold (the higher the stimulated decay rate), the greater the damping and the better the stability. Relaxation oscillation frequency and damping constant have recently been calculated for the case of Gaussian beams including the effects of inversion profile and reabsorption, and this exact result differs from the simplified case considered here (see Ref. 179).

## 1. Loss Modulation

If the loss of the cavity is modulated sinusoidally with a modulation index

$$\xi = \frac{\delta(T + L)}{T + L} \qquad (51)$$

which modulates $\tau_Q$, the response of the system is given by

$$p = p_0 + \delta p \ \exp[i(\phi + \omega t)] \qquad (52)$$

where

$$\delta p = \xi \frac{p_0}{\tau_Q} \left[ \frac{\omega^2 + 4a^2}{(\omega^2 - \omega_0^2)^2 + 4a^2 \omega^2} \right]^{1/2} \qquad (53)$$

and

$$\phi = \pi - \arctan \frac{\omega(\omega^2 - \omega_0^2 + 4a^2)}{2a\omega_0^2} \qquad (54)$$

These relations have been verified for pure loss modulation and simultaneous elimination of spatial hole burning [129]. A residual reflectivity of $10^{-3}$ of the antireflection-coated rod surfaces is sufficient cause for relaxation oscillations. If perfectly aligned, the rod surfaces form subcavities with the laser mirrors. If the rod moves by just a fraction of the optical wavelength relative to the mirrors, the subcavity spacings change and thus produce slightly different cavity losses for the oscillating modes. This change will be amplified or attenuated by the laser system depending on the frequency of the loss modulation. The amplification factor is, according to Eq. (53),

$$\frac{\delta p}{p_0 \xi} = 1 + \frac{\tau_s}{\tau} \qquad \text{for } \omega \ll \omega_0 \qquad (55a)$$

$$\frac{\delta p}{p_0 \xi} = \frac{\tau}{\tau_Q(1 + \tau/\tau_s)} \qquad \text{for } \omega \approx \omega_0 \tag{55b}$$

$$\frac{\delta p}{p_0 \xi} = \frac{1}{\omega \tau_Q} \qquad \text{for } \omega \gg \omega_0 \tag{55c}$$

Near the peak of the response the amplification (55b) can be very large; a factor of 300 has been demonstrated [129]. This makes it possible to obtain repetitive pulses of high peak power with a very small modulator drive (controlled relaxation oscillation pulsing).

### 2. Frequency Change

The Nd: YAG laser is also very sensitive to small changes of the cavity frequency. If one cavity mirror is moved at $10^{-3}$ cm/sec along the axis, the output becomes unstable (the corresponding Doppler shift of the frequency is only 10 Hz). For velocities between $10^{-2}$ cm/sec and 80 cm/sec, the output consists of a regular train of pulses at the relaxation oscillation frequency. Spectrally the output consists of a number of axial modes that are continuously swept across the gain curve. Their amplitudes form a stable envelope [129] that is shifted in frequency by

$$\Delta f = \left[ \frac{3 v \nu_0 (\Delta \nu)^2 \ln(p_0/p_n)}{8c(T + L)} \right]^{1/3} \tag{56}$$

away from the center of the gain curve at $\nu_0$. In Eq. (56), v is the mirror velocity, and $p_n$ is the noise population of the cavity modes from which each axial mode builds up as it enters the gain curve.

### 3. Pump Modulation

If the pump power of the laser is modulated sinusoidally with a modulation index

$$\eta = \frac{\delta \zeta}{\zeta} \tag{57}$$

the response of the system is given by Eq. (52), where

$$\delta p = \eta \frac{p_0}{\tau_Q} 2a [(\omega^2 - \omega_0^2)^2 + 4a^2 \omega^2]^{-1/2} \tag{58}$$

and

$$\varphi = - \arctan \frac{2a\omega}{\omega_0^2 - \omega^2} \tag{59}$$

These expressions have been verified with a luminescent diode-pumped Nd:YAG laser [90]. Figure 20 shows the output modulation, and Fig. 21 the output phase. The amplification factor is

$$\frac{\delta p}{p_0 \eta} = 1 + \frac{\tau_s}{\tau} \qquad \qquad \text{for } \omega \ll \omega_0 \tag{60a}$$

$$\frac{\delta p}{p_0 \eta} = \left( \frac{\tau_s}{\tau_Q} \right)^{1/2} \qquad \qquad \text{for } \omega \approx \omega_0 \tag{60b}$$

$$\frac{\delta p}{p_0 \eta} = \frac{1}{\tau_Q \omega^2} \left( \frac{1}{\tau} + \frac{1}{\tau_s} \right) \qquad \text{for } \omega \gg \omega_0 \tag{60c}$$

Near the peak of the response, the amplification (60b) can be very large; a factor 100 has been demonstrated [90]. Pump-power modulation is a very convenient way of obtaining repetitive pulses of high peak power with a very small modulation. These pulses can be stabilized with a feedback circuit that drives the pump modulation from the output pulses by means of a phase shifter and an amplifier [90]. The average laser power is conserved in that process.

## C. Spiking

Equation (46) has a second singular point in the n-p plane. Spiking occurs around the instable saddle point

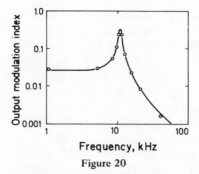

Figure 20

Relaxation oscillations. Output modulation index versus frequency of pump modulation [90] for a pump modulation index of $4 \times 8\cdot10^{-3}$. Circles experimental, solid line calculated from Eq. (58) (no adjustable parameter).

$$n_0 = \zeta\tau \qquad\qquad\qquad\qquad (61a)$$

$$p > p_0 = 0 \qquad\qquad\qquad\qquad (61b)$$

In contrast to the case of relaxation oscillations, the spiking mode cannot be calculated from the linearized rate equations. It is a highly nonlinear process, in which the photon spike dumps the inversion like a giant pulse. The period between spikes is therefore governed by the recovery time of the inversion, which is always close to the fluorescent decay time $\tau$. After recovery, the second spike develops. The exact period can be calculated only with computers; a closed form solution cannot be found. Computer treatments of the coupled rate equations date back to 1960 and have fascinated workers continuously. Recently the identical problem was rediscovered for plasma oscillations [150].

Spiking can be controlled with amplitude/phase modulation [128] and with pump modulation [90]. It can be self-excited [90] and suppressed [137] with feedback loops. Figure 22 shows that a very regular train of spikes can be obtained with feedback between the output and the pump. Since the average output power is conserved, one can obtain high peak powers. The frequency of the spikes is always in the low-kHz range, and the width of the spikes is fixed by the

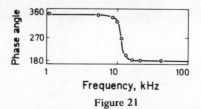

Figure 21

Relaxation oscillations. Phase of the output pulses versus pump modulation. Circles experimental [90], solid line calculated from Eq. (59) (no adjustable parameter).

np coupling, so that the peak powers obtainable are generally 100 times larger than the average power. The amplitudes of the pulses are very uniform, and so is the phase relative to the drive (Fig. 22). Such pulses may prove to be very suitable for micromachining and SHG (second harmonic generation).

Since spiking and relaxation oscillations are responses of the system of coupled rate equations to the same perturbations, their physical nature is identical. Mathematically as well as phenomenologically the difference is quantitative: small perturbations and the possibility of linearization characterize the case of relaxation oscillations, and large perturbations with high nonlinearity characterize the case of spiking. This could be demonstrated with pump modulation experiments [90]: for small modulations, only the relaxation oscillation mode could be obtained; for large modulations (modulation index > 1), only the spiking mode could be obtained. For intermediate modulations (modulation index ≈ 1), one can pull the laser response quite continuously from one regime to the other by adjusting the modulation frequency. A sharp phase relation between output and modulation exists, however, only in the vicinity of the two regimes. A third regime is obtained for high modulation index at very low frequency (below the spiking frequency), where the output consists of a train of damped relaxation oscillations [90]. This can typically be observed also with rectangular pump pulses [151].

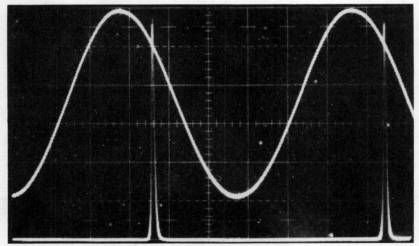

**Figure 22**

Resonance excitation of spiking with a luminescent diode pumped Nd:YAG laser [90]. The oscilloscope trace shows the sinusoidally modulated diod current (100 mA/division) and the output spikes (15 mW/division). Average laser output was 1 mW for the same dc diode level. Time scale is 50 $\mu$ sec/division. These spikes can be self-generated with a broadband feedback loop between output and diode pump. Relaxation oscillations can only be self-generated if the feedback loop contains a narrow-band filter tuned to the relaxation oscillation frequency.

## D. Q-switching and Dumping

Because of the small damping constant (Eq. (50)) and low relaxation oscillation and spiking frequencies, the Q-switching rate of Nd:YAG lasers is limited to
the low-kHz range. In addition, low threshold for laser oscillation (four-level system) limits the energy storage capabilities. In spite of this, improvements on
the first Q-switching result [93], obtained with rotating mirror at 100 Hz resulting in 250-W peak power pulses with 200-nsec width, were (see Table 6) spectacular. The main efforts were directed to generate pulses with better amplitude
stability and constant mode pattern, either for machining applications or for
SHG. Second harmonic generation requires high fundamental power and is very
sensitive to the mode pattern in the fundamental beam. Machining applications
for cutting and drilling require reproducible peak power and angular beam stability.

Beam divergence and mode volume are insensitive to variation in the average
focal length (Eq. (35)) produced by thermal lensing if the point

$$\left(1 - \frac{\mathcal{L}}{R_1} - \frac{d_1}{f}\right)\left(1 - \frac{\mathcal{L}}{R_2} - \frac{d_2}{f}\right) = \frac{1}{2} \tag{62}$$

is selected [10] in the cavity stability diagram [171], where d is the distance between rod and mirror, f is given by Eq. (35), R is the mirror radius, and $\mathcal{L}$ is the
optical cavity length. Simultaneously, this optimization yields an order-of-magni-
tude improvement of the laser efficiency. Without this, the $TEM_{00}$ peak power
is more than an order of magnitude smaller than the multimode peak power [101].

Rotating mirrors [95] and prisms [94] are generally less reliable than electrooptic [88] and acoustooptic [91] Q-switches. The electronic devices allow control of the cavity loss with better timing and amplitude precision. For a low-
power laser of a few mW output, it is possible, for instance, to tune a single frequency over 180 GHz with a $LiNbO_3$ Q-switching crystal (the single frequency
jumped, however, over a range of 15 GHz for each setting) [96]. Acoustooptic
Bragg scattering switches deflect the beam. This can be used to provide feedback
during the pump pulse and to dump the radiation after its buildup time. If, for
instance, the fraction $\alpha$ of the light is deflected to a cavity mirror, the fraction
$1 - \alpha$ is dumped, $\alpha^2$ is fed back, and $\alpha(1 - \alpha)$ is lost [92]. Three mirror cavities
permit recovery of the lost fraction, and focusing of the beam into the sound
field, which is important since the sound propagation time across the beam limits
the switching speed just as the rise time of the sound field does. A rise time of
5 nsec has been obtained with a ZnO transducer driven at 450 MHz; 200-W peak
power pulses were dumped at a 175-kHz rate from a continuously pumped Nd:
YAG laser having 2-W average output power [12]. Continuously pumped lasers

offer also the possibility of using the internal timing provided by the coupled
rate equations (see Sections IV, B and C) for stabilization. This is very convenient with diode-pumped Nd:YAG [90]. In Nd:YAlO$_3$, some mode stabilization
was achieved by opening the Q-switch after the first spike had just developed
and after the inversion had recovered from the last spike [91]. It is known that
injection of a small Nd:YAG signal can control, for a limited length of time,
even the mode pattern of parametric oscillators driven by giant ruby laser pulses [152] and Nd:glass laser radiation [176]. Another way of stabilizing the
mode pattern for lasers of very high power is to use resonant multisurface reflectors instead of dielectric mirrors. By temperature-tuning the laser wavelength
to the reflector peak, a single-mode Nd:YAG laser was made that had a coherence length equal to the pulse length [98]. Lamp lifetime and repetition rate
can be increased simultaneously by simmering the lamp between pulses [89].

Internal second harmonic generation and Q-switching have been achieved with
separate elements in two- [99] and three-mirror [100] cavities. Unfortunately,
Nd:YAG absorbs its second harmonic so that 100% conversion is an optimistic
extrapolation. The damage threshold [100] of LiIO$_3$ is below 2 MW/cm$^2$, and
the damage threshold of Ba$_2$NaNb$_5$O$_{15}$ ("bananas"), because of surface pitting,
below 0.5 MW/cm$^2$. LiNbO$_3$ damages still more easily at 0.53 $\mu$m.

### E. Mode Locking

#### 1. General Remarks

Reference 155 gives a qualitative survey of the general topic of mode locking.
The amplitudes contained in

$$V_0 = E_0 \sum_{m = -\infty}^{+\infty} \exp\left[-2(\ln 2)\left(\frac{\delta\nu}{\overline{\Delta\nu}}\right)^2 m^2\right] \exp[2\pi i(\nu + m\delta\nu)t + i\phi m] \qquad (63)$$

resemble a mode-locked train of pulses with the repetition rate $\delta\nu$ and the locking range $\overline{\Delta\nu}$ if the phases $\phi_m$ are constant. Replacing the sum by an integral
($\delta\nu \ll \overline{\Delta\nu}$), one obtains for the case $\phi_m = 0$, using a Fourier cosine transform
[159],

$$V_{AM} = \left(\frac{\pi}{2\ln 2}\right)^{1/2} \frac{\overline{\Delta\nu}}{\delta\nu} E_0 \exp\left[-\frac{\pi^2 \overline{\Delta\nu}^2}{2\ln 2} t^2\right] \exp(2\pi i\nu t) \qquad (64)$$

This is one pulse of an AM mode-locked pulse train. Amplitude modulation (AM) mode locking can be produced:

1. By amplitude modulation with Pockels cells [88] and acoustooptic modulators [102], which gives

$$A(t) = \exp[-2\epsilon \sin^2(\pi\delta\nu t)] \approx \exp[-2\epsilon(\pi\delta\nu)^2 t^2] \tag{65}$$

where $\epsilon$ is the modulation index.

2. By phase modulation with $LiNbO_3$ [103, 104, 115], KDP [120], or $Ba_2NaNb_5O_{15}$ for simultaneous SHG [118, 119], which gives

$$A(t) = \exp[-i2\epsilon \cos(2\pi\delta\nu t)] \approx \exp(\mp i2\epsilon)\, \exp[\pm i4\epsilon(\pi\delta\nu)^2 t^2] \tag{66}$$

3. By passive mode locking with saturable dyes such as Kodak 9860 in dichloroethane [109], flowing at 10 cm/sec for better stability [112]. The approximations in (65) and (66) are possible since the pulses must pass through the modulator at times of minimum loss or minimum phase change. Los modulation proceeds with half the pulse repetition rate (65). Phase modulation allows for a positive and a negative mode where the phases of the pulses differ by $\pi$ (66). This ambiguity leads to instabilities where the laser jumps between the modes. The jumping [117] takes of the order of $10^{-4}$ sec, which suggests that the spiking and relaxation oscillation instabilities support it. Stable operation in one mode can be achieved by providing an additional loss for one phase only. An elegant scheme, which combines phase and loss modulation in a Brewster prism phase modulator that simultaneously deviates the beam for one phase, is described in Ref. 122.

For constant phases other than all $\phi_m = 0$, one obtains other mode-locked pulses. Frequency modulation mode locking is obtained if

$$\phi_{-2m} = \phi_{2m} = 0, \pi \quad \text{and} \quad -\phi_{-(2m+1)} = \phi_{2m+1} = 0, \pi$$

which leads to pulses of the form [114]

$$V_{FM} = E_0' \exp\left[-\frac{\pi^2 \overline{\Delta\nu}^2}{2 \ln 2} t^2\right] \exp\left[2\pi i \left(\nu \pm \frac{\pi \overline{\Delta\nu}^2}{4 \ln 2} t\right) t\right]. \tag{67}$$

The carrier frequency has a linear shift during the pulse; it chirps across the locking range. The bandwidth is therefore larger [114] than with AM mode locking.

Frequency modulation mode locking can be produced with phase modulation. It is important to place the phase modulator close to one cavity mirror, for the effective single-pass phase retardation is given by [156]

$$\epsilon = \epsilon_0 \frac{2\mathcal{L}}{\pi a} \sin \frac{\pi a}{2\mathcal{L}} \cos \frac{\pi b}{\mathcal{L}} \approx \epsilon_0 \cos \frac{\pi b}{\mathcal{L}} \tag{68}$$

where a is the optical length of the modulator, b its distance to one mirror, and $\mathcal{L}$ the optical length of the cavity.

The case of FM mode locking must not be confused with FM laser oscillation [156], where a single frequency sweeps forth and back within the gain curve at the mode locking frequency so that the output is continuous. This mode of operation can be achieved by detuning the phase modulation frequency $\delta\nu$ by 0.2 to 7 MHz. The smaller the detuning, the larger the sweep—which can be as large as 120 GHz for Nd:YAG [113]. It has been suggested that a single stable frequency at the second harmonic can be obtained by splitting the output of an FM laser into two beams, delaying one beam by $1/(2\delta\nu)$, and combining the beams in a second-harmonic generator where the sweeps cancel to zero [160]. Stable single frequency may, however, be obtained more effectively by other means (Section V). For smaller detuning (200 kHz), FM mode locking results [114].

For still smaller detuning, in the range 10 – 30 kHz, the mode-locked pulse trains become modulated at the relaxation oscillation [103, 104, 115] and the spiking [120] frequencies. This is again due to the small damping constant (Eq. (50)). In the schematic instability spectrum of Fig. 19, the mode-locking peak has actually four sidebands spaced at the relaxation oscillation and spiking frequencies, respectively. Probably they cover a range since the low-frequency instabilities can be pulled [90]. Carrier sweep similar to the case of a continuous change of the cavity frequency [129] has also been observed for mode-locked pulses [123].

So far only the mode-locking peak itself has been treated theoretically [114, 157, 174]. It is an exacting task to solve the problems of nonlinear mode interactions (mode locking) and nonlinear rate equations (e.g., spiking) simultaneously; hence a satisfactory understanding of all experimental results cannot be expected at present. Practically, however, mode-locking spiking can be quite important since peak powers can be obtained that are two orders of magnitude higher than the peak powers in steady mode-locked pulse trains.

## 2. AM Loss Locking with Host Dispersion

Some gas lasers have been reported to self-lock. In contrast to one report

[106], self mode locking could not be observed for Nd:YAG [105, 154]. That it cannot be expected, at least not for small pumping levels typical of continuous operation, can be shown by analyzing AM loss locking with host dispersion, for instance. Frequency modulation phase locking can be calculated in exactly the same way (for the case of FM phase locking without host dispersion see Ref. 114).

When the signal (63) passes twice through the rod of length $\ell$, each spectral component experiences the gain

$$g = \exp\left\{\frac{\sigma_0 N\ell}{1 + i\dfrac{m\delta\nu}{\Delta\nu/2}}\right\} \tag{69}$$

where $-\infty < m < +\infty$ is the mode index, and the phase delay [153]

$$\Phi = -2\pi\frac{\ell}{\lambda_0}\left[2n + 2n_g\frac{\delta\nu}{\nu_0}m + \lambda^2\frac{d^2n}{d\lambda^2}\left(\frac{\delta\nu}{\nu_0}\right)^2 m^2\right] \tag{70}$$

There exists an exact analytical solution for the pulse leaving the rod,

$$V_{2\ell} = gV_0\exp(i\Phi) \tag{71}$$

if the gain is small, depending on the ratio $\overline{\Delta\nu}/\Delta\nu$ (locking range/gain width), by means of the error fuction for complex argument [158]. Since it is an experimental fact for Nd:YAG lasers that $\overline{\Delta\nu}/\Delta\nu \approx 0.2$, however, one can as well expand (69) to third order in m and obtain a solution with a Fourier cosine transform:

$$V_{2\ell} = \frac{\sqrt{\dfrac{\pi}{2\ln 2}\dfrac{\overline{\Delta\nu}}{\delta\nu}}\exp(\sigma N\ell)}{\sqrt[4]{\beta^2 + (4\gamma\ell/\ln 2)^2}}\exp\left[2\pi i\nu\left(t - \frac{2n\ell}{c}\right)\right]\exp\left[-\frac{i}{2}\arctan\frac{4\gamma\ell}{\beta}\right]$$

$$\times\exp\left[-\frac{\pi^2\overline{\Delta\nu^2}}{2\ln 2}\left(t - \frac{2n_g\ell}{c} - \frac{\sigma N K\ell}{\pi\Delta\nu}\right)^2\frac{\beta - i4\gamma\ell/\ln 2}{\beta^2 + (4\gamma\ell/\ln 2)^2}\right] \tag{72}$$

where

$$\beta = 1 + 2 \frac{\sigma N \ell}{\ln 2} \left( \frac{\overline{\Delta \nu}}{\Delta \nu} \right)^2 \tag{73}$$

$$K = 1 + \left\langle 4m^2 \left( \frac{\delta \nu}{\Delta \nu} \right)^2 \right\rangle_{av} \approx 1 + \frac{1}{2} \left( \frac{\overline{\Delta \nu}}{\Delta \nu} \right)^2 \tag{74}$$

and [153]

$$\gamma = \frac{\pi}{4} \lambda \frac{d^2 n}{d\lambda^2} \left( \frac{\Delta \nu}{\nu} \right)^2 \tag{75}$$

The pulse (72) travels now twice through the loss modulator (65), which is assumed, for simplicity, to have negligible length. The cavity length consists only of rod and modulator lengths, an assumption that does not remove any generality. One mirror has a power transmission factor T; other resonator losses L are included by adding them to T. The amplitude reflection factor of the mirror is consequently

$$r = \sqrt{[1 - (T + L)]} \tag{76}$$

After having passed twice through the rod and twice through the modulator, and having been reflected once, the pulse becomes

$$V_c = rA \left( t - \frac{2n_g \ell}{c} - \frac{\sigma N K \ell}{\pi \Delta \nu} \right) V_{2\ell} \tag{77}$$

Self-consistency requires that the round-trip pulse equal the original pulse (64) delayed by the round-trip time $1/\delta \nu$:

$$V_c = V_{AM} \left( t - \frac{1}{\delta \nu} \right) \tag{78}$$

Equations (64), (65), (72), (76), and (78) lead to another equation that is not given here since it is too lengthy to be surveyed readily. This equation allows isolating three quantities (time, phase, amplitude) and comparing right- and left-hand expressions resulting from Eq. (78) as follows:

(a) Time comparison yields

$$\frac{1}{\delta\nu} = \frac{2n_g\ell}{c} + \frac{\sigma NK\ell}{\pi\Delta\nu} \tag{79}$$

The second term on the right, owing to gain dispersion, is negligible for cw pumped Nd:YAG. It follows that the pulse rate $1/\delta\nu$ is given by the group delay through the cavity, and the axial mode spacing (= modulation frequency) $\delta\nu$ by the effective group index of refraction of the cavity,

$$n_g = n - \lambda \frac{dn}{d\lambda} \tag{80}$$

In Nd:YAG, at 1.064 $\mu$m, $n_g$ is 2.7% larger than n (Table 1). Linear gain dispersion in Nd:YAG is small compared with linear host dispersion, since the linear terms in m of the phases from (69) and (70) are

$$\frac{\sigma N}{\Delta\nu/2} \ell m \delta\nu \ll \frac{4\pi n_g}{c} \ell m \delta\nu \tag{81}$$

Only the host contributes to second-order dispersion; the gain has no second-order dispersion term.

(b) Comparison of the time constants yields for the real parts

$$\overline{\Delta\nu^2} \left(1 - \frac{\beta}{\beta^2 + (4\gamma\ell/\ln 2)^2}\right) = 4\epsilon \ln 2 (\delta\nu)^2 \tag{82}$$

If the nonlinear host dispersion is neglected ($\gamma\ell = 0$) and the gain is small ($\beta \approx 1$), Eq. (82) gives for the locking range

$$\overline{\Delta\nu} = \left(\frac{\ln 2}{\Delta\nu\,\delta\nu}\right)^{1/2} \left(\frac{2\epsilon}{\sigma N\ell}\right)^{1/4} \tag{83}$$

which is identical with the results for AM and FM mode locking without host dispersion [114]. Equation (82) shows that even if the gains are very small ($\beta \to 1$), however, the modulation index $\epsilon$ that produces a given locking range does not go to zero because of the nonlinear host dispersion term $(4\gamma\ell/\ln 2)^2$. Unfortunately, efforts to compensate for this term by inserting another material having the opposite sign of second-order dispersion are hindered by the fact that around 1 $\mu$m all practical materials have the same sign of second-order dispersion [153]. Self-locking can therefore not be expected. This may be different for high-gain pump-pulsed operation [111].

Equation (83) discloses that it is easier to obtain a larger locking range (shorter pulses) by increasing the axial mode spacing (shortening the cavity) than by increasing the modulator amplitude.

(c) Comparison of the amplitudes yields, when they are squared,

$$\exp(2\sigma N\ell) = \frac{\sqrt{\beta^2 + (4\gamma\ell/\ln 2)^2}}{1 - (T + L)} \tag{84}$$

Gain saturation is responsible for the first term of the root, and host broadening for the second term. For $\gamma\ell \ll \beta \approx 1$ and $T + L \ll 1$, one gets for the round-trip power gain

$$2\sigma N\ell = \frac{T + L}{1 - [(\overline{\Delta\nu}/\Delta\nu)^2/\ln 2]} \tag{85}$$

which explains why the average mode-locked output power is smaller than the free-running output power for equal cavity losses and equal pumping. It also shows that a larger locking range, $\overline{\Delta\nu} \to \Delta\nu$, or shorter pulses, can be obtained only with a sacrifice in average output power.

*3. Detuning*

If the modulation frequency is tuned away from $\delta\nu$ by $\delta f$, the round-trip time and pulse period change by

$$d\tau = -\frac{df}{(\delta\nu)^2} \tag{86}$$

and the laser can respond by changing the carrier frequency by

$$d\nu = 2\,\frac{\ell n_g{}^2\,df}{\lambda^3 d^2 n/d\lambda^2} \tag{87}$$

This follows from equating (86) to

$$d\tau = \frac{d}{d\nu}\left(\frac{c}{2\ell n_g}\right) df = \frac{2\ell}{\nu^2}\,\lambda\,\frac{d^2 n}{d\lambda^2}\,df \tag{88}$$

which shows that the laser can compensate for the detuning by shifting the signal frequency to hit a different point along the host dispersion curve. (It is clear that for laser cavities filled not entirely with Nd:YAG, the effective group velocity has to be used instead of the velocity of Nd:YAG.)

The factor of df in Eq. (87) is of the order of $10^7$, so that a kHz change in the modulation frequency would already suffice to shift the carrier frequency out of the gain curve. In contrast to pure loss modulation, phase modulation creates a Doppler shift of the pulse if it passes through the modulator not at the extremes of the phase excursion. This Doppler shift can cancel the active medium shift (87) so that detuning is less critical with phase modulators. The analysis gets somewhat more complicated due to off-center line saturation, but partial agreement with experiment has been obtained [114, 115, 121]. The resulting characteristic of detuning versus phase delay between pulses and modulation (Fig. 23) can be used to stabilize mode locking either by locking the modulation frequency to the cavity's inverse round-trip time (79) or by locking the cavity length to the length required for a given locking frequency [104, 107]. The procedures are identical with stabilizing relaxation oscillations [90]. Also identical are the problems with mode-selecting elements in the cavity. For stable longitudinal mode locking, it is advisable to have all intracavity surfaces at the Brewster angle [115].

## V. Stabilization

Stabilization of spiking, relaxation oscillation pulsing, and mode locking have been discussed in previous sections. This section focuses on single-frequency operation and frequency stabilization.

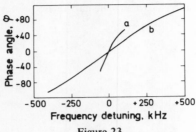

Figure 23

Phase of mode locked output pulses versus detuning of the phase modulation frequency from the axial mode spacing, which was 264 MHz for the curve a [115] and 388 MHz for curve b [103].

In practically all cases in which single-frequency operation is required, fundamental transverse mode is required also. The latter is usually achieved with a suitable aperture. For "high" power operation (above $\sim 0.2$ W), the rod itself will not suffice as aperture because of thermal effects (Section III,D) and badly matched pump profiles (Section III,B). Stable single-frequency operation requires, in addition, pump sources stable to more than $10^{-4}$ of the pump power, cavity losses stable to more than $10^{-4}$ of the total loss, mechanical stability so that axial velocity components of vibrations are below $10^{-4}$ cm/sec, angular stability of the mirrors to more than 1 min of arc (Section IV), and other provisions [176].

The reason for multimode operation of Nd:YAG lasers is spatial hole burning [59]. Consequently, there are two approaches possible: to eliminate spatial hole burning, or to use axial mode selectors.

### A. Elimination of Spatial Hole Burning

In the standing wave field of one axial laser mode, the stimulated lifetime defined by Eqs. (23) or (45) will be a function of the position along the laser axis z, according to

$$\tau_s(z) = \frac{\pi w^2}{2\sigma} \frac{\tau_c}{p \sin^2 kz} = \frac{\tau_s}{\sin^2 kz} \tag{89}$$

Where $kz = 2\pi n z/\lambda$ is near a multiple of $\pi$, the material is not stimulated effectively, the local stimulated lifetime becomes very large compared with the spontaneous lifetime, and the local inversion density develops a peak to the benefit of parasitic axial modes.

In a ring laser, it is possible to eliminate spatial hole burning by suppressing one direction of travel; this is usually achieved with a Faraday rotator. A single-frequency output power of 0.75 W has been achieved [172], and it has been demonstrated that the Nd:YAG rod itself can be used to provide the Faraday rotation.

For low-power operation where thermal birefringence is not a problem, Nd: YAG is optically isotropic. This makes it possible to eliminate spatial hole burning also in a standard laser cavity by placing the rod between two quarter-wave plates. If their fast axes are perpendicular to each other and oriented at 45° relative to polarizers placed between the quarter-wave plates and the cavity mirrors, one can show that in the laser medium each mode splits into two perpendicularly polarized components with equal intensity that are shifted relative to each other by a quarter wavelength. Since $\sin^2 kz + \cos^2 kz = 1$, the stimulated lifetime is independent of z, i.e., spatial hole burning is absent. (The two perpendicularly polarized waves can also be viewed as a circularly polarized wave.) Since the line is homogeneously broadened, any wave having a frequency within the gain curve can now withdraw all the power from the inverted system. Therefore, elimination of spatial hole burning results in a single-frequency output that contains the maximum possible laser power for a given loss and pump condition. Another advantage of the method is that it requires only passive elements. The laser will oscillate stably in the mode experiencing the highest gain, i.e., close to the center of the gain curve. An output power of 0.2 W has been achieved with this technique [135]. Without the quarter-wave plates and polarizers, the laser exhibited a multitransverse output power of 1.6 W. The disadvantages of the method are the large number of additional surfaces introduced into the cavity, and the requirement that the laser material be absolutely isotropic—not a trivial requirement.

A method that can be used for anisotropic materials and arbitrarily high power levels is the drift method. It uses the slow response of the inversion to a change of the stimulating field. The inversion can relax to a new equilibrium at best at the rate of $^4F_{3/2}$ lifetime, which is usually of the order of $10^{-4}$ sec. If the standing wave pattern is by some means made to drift by a quarter wavelength within that relaxation time of $10^{-4}$ sec, the inversion sees effectively only the time average of the sinusoidal distribution (89), and spatial hole burning cannot develop. The required drift velocity $v = \lambda/4\tau_s$ is of the order of 0.2 cm/sec.

If one moves the rod back and forth between the cavity mirrors with such a small velocity, the laser output condenses spontaneously into a single frequency that contains the full multimode output power [87]. It was realized that in such experiments the required velocities were somewhat smaller than the calculated values. Some inherent quality of Nd:YAG must therefore aid in smoothing out spatial hole burning; this quality is the energy migration, discussed in Section II,D,3.

Phenomenologically, energy migration can be included in the rate equation (46a) by adding a diffusion term proportional to the diffusion constant defined in Section II,D,3. If drift is allowed as well, the stimulated lifetime becomes

$$\tau_s(z, t) = \frac{\tau_s}{\sin^2 k(z + vt)} \tag{90}$$

and the rate equation (46a) can be written

$$\mathring{n}(z, t) = \zeta - \frac{n(z, t)}{\tau} - \frac{n(z, t)}{\tau_s} \sin^2 k(z + vt) + D \frac{d^2 n(z, t)}{dz^2} \tag{91}$$

This equation must be solved subject to the boundary condition

$$\exp\left[ \int_0^{2\ell} \sigma(k) 2 \sin^2(kz) n(z, t) \, dz \right] = 1 + L + T \tag{92}$$

for the gain that expresses the conservation of stimulated energy. (The cross section has been written as a function of k instead of as a function of $v$, to conform with Eq. (91).) For small gains there exists a solution in form of a trigonometric series expansion for n(z, t) with recursion formulas for the coefficients [158]. Exact to first order, the result is (59)

$$n(z, t) = \frac{L + T}{\sigma(k)\ell} \left[ 1 + \wp \frac{(C/2) + C \cos 2k(z + vt) + B \sin 2k(z + vt)}{B^2 + C^2 - \wp(C/2)} \right] \tag{93}$$

where the drift parameter is defined as

$$B = \frac{2kv\tau}{n} \tag{94}$$

and the hole parameter as

$$C = 1 + \wp + 4k^2 D\tau \tag{95}$$

The excitation parameter

$$\mathcal{P} = \frac{P}{\pi w^2 I_s T} \tag{96}$$

is the internal laser power $P/T$ divided by the saturation power $\pi w^2 I_s$. For Nd:
YAG at 1.06 $\mu$m, $4k^2 D\tau \approx 5$ [158].

The exact soluation for the case of zero drift and diffusion of Eq. (91) is, for
comparison,

$$n(z) = \frac{L + T}{\sigma(k)\ell} \frac{\mathcal{P}}{1 - (1 + 2\mathcal{P})^{-1/2}} \frac{1}{1 + 2\mathcal{P}\sin^2(kz)} \tag{97}$$

if one mode with wave vector k saturates the inversion. It can be seen that spatial
holes may be quite deep if $\mathcal{P}$ is large, and that the depth is reduced considerably
if the diffusion constant D for excited states is large (Eqs. (93) and (95)). For
Nd:YAG, the minimum drift velocity required for spontaneous single-frequency
operation [59]

$$v_{min} = \frac{\lambda}{4\pi\tau} \left[ \frac{C}{2} \left( \frac{\ell \Delta\nu}{2} \right)^2 \mathcal{P} - C^2 \right]^{1/2} \tag{98}$$

is also considerably reduced by energy migration.

The drift need not be uniform. In fact, it can be shown that if the rod is
placed between two phase modulators, and the amplitude of the phase modulation is adjusted so that

$$J_0(2\epsilon) = 0 \tag{99}$$

where $J_0$ is the zero-order Bessel function, every axial point in the rod sees exactly the same average stimulating field [58]. This can be understood immediately
because any wave phase modulated according to Eq. (99) will have no component in its original frequency after passage through the modulator, so that a standing wave is not possible. The minimum frequency $\delta f$ of the phase modulation required for spontaneous single-frequency operation can be found from (98) with

$$\delta f = \frac{v_{min}}{(\lambda/2)N} \tag{100}$$

where $N = 1, 2, \ldots$ indicates the order of the solution to Eq. (99), which is actually used for modulation. The required modulation frequency is of the order of a few hundred kHz for cw Nd:YAG lasers; this is a convenient range for electrooptic phase modulation. With $LiNbO_3$ modulators, spontaneous single-frequency operation was achieved and simultaneously doubled [98].

## B. Mode Selection

### 1. General Remarks

Elimination of spatial hole burning removes the cause of multimoding at some cost, for the elements that have to be inserted into the cavity are lossy. Usually it is faster and cheaper to live with spatial hole burning, and to provide selective loss to prevent oscillation of other modes that sponge on the inversion peaks left by the desired mode. The depth of the holes in Nd:YAG requires considerable selectivity, however. In contrast to spectral hole burning, where the immediate axial neighbors of an oscillating mode are in a power-broadened zone of smallest parasitic gain, the case of spatial hole burning is characterized by the fact that the nearest axial neighbors of an oscillating mode have the highest parasitic gain. This can be shown by calculating the unsaturated gain of a parasitic mode with wavevector $k'$,

$$\exp[g(k')] = \exp\left[\int_0^{2\ell} \sigma(k')\, 2\sin^2 k(z + vt)\, n(z, t)\, dz\right] \tag{101}$$

from (93). The result is

$$g(k') = (L + T)\frac{\sigma(k')}{\sigma(k)}\left[1 - \frac{\wp C/2}{B^2 + C^2 - \wp(C/2)}\right.$$

$$\left. + \frac{(\frac{1}{2})p\sin(\pi M\ell/\mathcal{L})}{(\pi M\ell/\mathcal{L})(B^2 + C^2 - \wp(C/2))}\,(B\sin\psi - C\cos\psi)\right] \tag{102}$$

where

$$\psi = \frac{2\pi M d}{\mathcal{L}} \tag{103}$$

and $M$ is an axial mode integer for $k'$, counted from $M = 0$ for the allowed mode with wave vector $k$. It is interesting to see from Eq. (102) that a drift introduces an asymmetry of the gain profile when the rod is not centered in the cavity, i.e., when $d \neq \mathcal{L}/2$, so that $\sin\psi \neq 0$.

Usually the characteristics of subcavities in the laser resonator are superimposed on the gain. Specifically, the Nd:YAG rod will have residual mode-selecting properties resulting from sources discussed in Section IV, A. This leads in a free-running laser to a preference of modes for which $M \approx \mathcal{L}/\ell, 2\mathcal{L}/\ell, \ldots$ . These modes see, according to Eq. (102), the unsaturated gain

$$g(k') = (L + T) \frac{\sigma(k')}{\sigma(k)} \left[ 1 + \frac{\mathcal{P}C/2}{B^2 + C^2 - (\frac{1}{2})\mathcal{P}C} \right] \qquad (104)$$

The laser output will therefore consist of those modes for which $\mathcal{L}/\ell$ is close to an integer with considerable jumping between these modes since their unsaturated gain may, as Eq. (104) shows for large $\mathcal{P}$, be actually twice as large as the saturated gain of the mode that oscillates momentarily and builds the hole. The more the modes that oscillate simultaneously, the smaller the unsaturated gain for new parasites: the stability of the laser power in time generally improves with the number of oscillating modes.

Single-frequency operation requires a mode selector that provides a loss equal to $g(k') - (T + L)$ for all $k' \neq k$, ideally without being lossy at $k$. Since the gain curve is usually wide compared with the axial mode spacing, $\sigma(k') \approx \sigma(k)$. The mode-selector loss required is now only a function of the excitation, drift, and diffusion parameters. Figure 24 shows the loss required as a fraction of the total

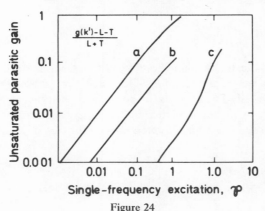

Figure 24

Axial mode selection. The ratio of the unsaturated net gain of parasitic modes to the saturated gain of oscillating mode is shown as a function of the excitation parameter of the oscillating mode [compare Eq. (96)]. Curve a is from Eq. (105) ($k' \approx k$) for spatially immobile excited states; curve b is from Eq. (104) for diffusing states with $4k^2D\tau = 5$ (Nd: YAG); curve c is from Eq. (104) for drifting states with $2kv\tau = 25$ (argon ion laser). Mode selectors must provide an additional loss equal to this unsaturated net gain for all unwanted modes.

cavity loss. It also illustrates the reduction of selectivity resulting from energy diffusion in Nd:YAG relative to the case of zero drift and zero diffusion that gives, from Eq. (97),

$$g(k') = (L + T) \frac{\sigma(k')}{\sigma(k)} (1 + 2\wp)^{1/2} \tag{105}$$

Simultaneously, Fig. 24 gives the depth of spatial holes, i.e., the difference between inversion peaks and valleys relative to the inversion required to overcome the cavity losses.

A mode selector must have, besides sufficient selectivity, a free spectral range large enough so that no second mode can oscillate within the gain curve. If the saturating mode oscillates near line center, one obtains from Eq. (5), on using the transformation $k' = 2\pi(\nu_0 + F)/c$ for the range where $g(k') \leq L + T$ in Eq. (104), a minimum free spectral range of

$$F = \frac{\Delta\nu}{2} \left[ \frac{\wp C/2}{B^2 + C^2 - \wp C/2} \right]^{1/2} \tag{106}$$

From Eq. (105), one obtains for the case of zero drift and diffusion

$$F = \frac{\Delta\nu}{2} \left[ (1 + 2\wp)^{1/2} - 1 \right]^{1/2} \tag{107}$$

Figure 25 shows the double minimum relative free spectral range $2F/\Delta\nu$ required for axial mode selectors as a function of the excitation parameter of the desired mode. Simultaneously Fig. 25 gives the potential oscillating bandwidth of laser oscillation. (If many modes oscillate simultaneously, the bandwidth is reduced due to multiple saturation; Fig. 25 refers only to the case of single-mode saturation.)

### 2. Verifications

There are many mode-selection schemes that potentially fulfill the spectral range and selectivity requirements for Nd:YAG lasers. The simplest of all is the metal film mode selector [161] that provides loss for all modes not having a standing wave null at the position of the film. It works beautifully for gas lasers where selectivity requirements are low. However, it was not possible to find a film for Nd:YAG that simultaneously provides sufficient loss for all the undesired modes and is thin enough to have a small loss for the desired mode [86].

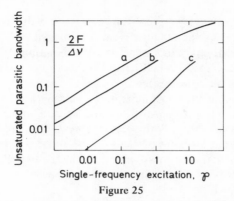

**Figure 25**

Axial mode selection. The ratio of the maximum oscillation bandwidth to the linewidth of the laser transition is shown as a function of the excitation parameter [Eq. (96)] of the oscillating mode. Curve a is from Eq. (107) ($k' \approx k$) for spatially immobile excited states; curve b is from Eq. (106) for diffusing states with $4k^2 D\tau = 5$ (Nd:YAG); curve c is from Eq. (106) for drifting states with $2kv\tau = 25$ (argon ion laser). Mode selectors must have at least the free spectral range F to achieve single-frequency operation.

Best results were obtained with a 50-Å thick NiCr film evaporated on a fused silica flat of 0.25-cm thickness. The second surface of the flat served with a high-reflectivity coating as laser mirror. The single-frequency output power was 60 mW, compared with a multimode $TEM_{00}$ output power of 130 mW (linearly polarized).

A single-frequency output power of 150 mW was obtained with an optimally designed crystal quartz Fabry-Perot etalon, which must be tilted to be lossy for unwanted modes. The design parameters such as etalon material, surface reflectivity, tilt angle, thickness, and insertion loss are given in Ref. 41. If a certain single-mode output power P is desired (see Eq. (96)), the required reflectivity R of the etalon surfaces is given by

$$\frac{R}{(1-R)^2} = (L+T) \frac{\wp C/2}{B^2 + C^2 - \wp C/2} \left( \frac{\mathcal{L}}{2\pi na} \right)^2 \tag{108}$$

where Eq. (104) with $\sigma(k') \approx \sigma(k)$ has been used, and where n and a are the refractive index and the thickness of the etalon, respectively. From Eq. (106), it follows that

$$a \leqslant \frac{c}{n\,\Delta\nu} \left[ \frac{B^2 + C^2 - \wp C/2}{\wp C/2} \right]^{1/2} \tag{109}$$

where the equals sign gives lowest insertion loss. It is worth mentioning that the walkoff loss generated by the tilt angle is small compared with coating losses, so that the inherent disadvantage of the method does not limit its usefulness.

Mode selection in Nd:YAG is inefficient because of thermal birefringence when multimode output powers reach the order of watts, and because of the high selectivity requirement, which more or less automatically means high insertion losses of the mode selectors. At the cost of increased complexity, it is possible to obtain better selectivity with combinations of film and etalon mode selectors [134]. Even at low power levels ($<$ 1 W), mode selection is inefficient because of excess spontaneous emission near the inversion peaks. Without energy diffusion, only two-thirds of the multimode power can be obtained in a single frequency [59].

## C. Frequency Stabilization

Since thermal changes of the cavity are not correlated with the frequency-determining characteristics of any technique used for generating a single-frequency output, the laser frequency will usually drift and occasionally jump by $c/2\mathcal{L}$. This can only be prevented if the cavity length is stabilized relative to a standard that stabilizes the frequency.

The absence of a Lamb dip and the large linewidth of the 1.064-$\mu$m transition call for an external standard. A 25-m folded Michelson interferometer with the temperature kept constant within $10^{-3}$ degrees has so far been the most elaborate standard [133]. The long-term stability was measured to be $\delta\nu/\nu = 10^{-9}$ relative to the standard. The absolute stability must have been much lower since the interferometer was not shielded from fluctuations of the room's atmosphere. Atmospheric pressure fluctuations alone cause long-term changes in the air's refractive index of the order of $10^{-7}$, which limits directly the absolute stability. The short-term stability was due to mechanical vibrations of the laser cavity and was measured to be $3 \times 10^{-9}$. A beating experiment between two lasers showed that the instantaneous linewidth was smaller than 300 Hz.

Nd:YAG lasers with internal mode selectors can be stabilized relative to the mode selector's frequency discriminant. This is economical since it does not require a second standard. Usually one modulates the cavity length so that the laser frequency is modulated by some fraction of the axial mode spacing. The loss-versus-frequency curve of the mode selector discriminates so that the output power becomes modulated. Phase-sensitive detection of the output modulation with respect to the cavity length modulation generates an error signal that is amplified and used to keep the effective cavity length locked. Safe locking for a 150-mW output requires, however, an FM amplitude of $\delta f = 8$ MHz, which actually contradicts the goal. This problem can be eliminated by using a birefringent etalon that provides for two simultaneously oscillating modes cor-

responding to the ordinary and extraordinary waves. For a judicious choice of
the etalon temperature, one low-level mode can be positioned at one wing of
the etalon's transmission maximum while the high-level mode coincides with
the other transmission maximum. The problem reduces to keeping the amplitude of the low-level mode constant. This does not require lock-in techniques
or frequency modulation. For a temperature stability of $10^{-2}$ degrees, an
absolute frequency stability of $10^{-7}$ was achieved [41].

An absolute stability of $3 \times 10^{-9}$ was achieved with an etalon that was
shielded from atmospheric fluctuations [162]. The error signal was again obtained by frequency modulation. However, the FM of the output could be reduced to a neglible amount by modulating the mode selector's transmission
frequency instead of the cavity length. If the modulator's transmission frequency is modulated by $\delta f$, the output modulation is given by

$$d\nu = \frac{naR}{\mathcal{L}(1-R)} \, df \qquad (110)$$

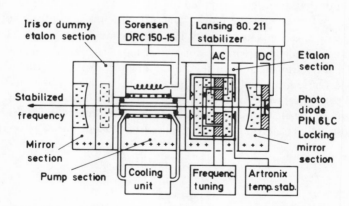

**Materials**: ⩵ Fused silica; ▨ Piezoceramic PZT 5; • Seals; ++ Invar

Figure 26

Mode selection and frequency stabilization of a Nd:YAG laser with FM modulation of
the mode selector transmission peak [162]. Absolute frequency stability $3 \times 10^{-9}$. Residual
FM on the output, $10^5$ Hz; residual AM, $10^{-3}$. Output power 103 mW. Etalon temperature
315 K with fluctuations $< 10^{-2}$ K. All sections match and can be assembled in any order.
The locking mirror (right-hand side) is mounted on an aluminum rod whose length is adjusted so that it compensates for thermal changes of the optical cavity length including the
rod. For this purpose, the aluminum rod and the laser rod are thermally coupled by the
cooling circuit (not shown).

where na is the optic length of the etalon, and R is the reflectivity of its surfaces. Since $na/\mathcal{L}$ is of the order of $10^{-2}$, the FM of the output is indeed small.
In principle, it can be made zero with a dummy antireflection-coated etalon
modulated in antiphase (Fig. 26).

## VI. Conclusions

In this review, emphasis is placed on the progress in the quantitative understanding of pump efficiency, thermal effects, fluorescence quenching, instabilities, mode locking, and single-frequency operation. Q-switching and crystal
growth have previously been adequately reviewed [164]. The future of Nd:YAG
as the most successful solid-state laser material [166] will depend on improvements with other materials mainly in two areas: on destructive effects for high-
power operation, and on flourescence quenching for integrated optics. It seems
that solids did not quite fulfill the expectations in the first area. It is possible, however, that neodymium ultraphosphates fulfill the expectations [22]
in the second area, for the Nd-O-P bonds provide an environment that shows
the upshift of the $^4I_{15/2}$ levels required for the absence of cross relaxation [165],
and $NdP_5O_{14}$, for instance, has much higher gain per unit length than Nd:YAG.

This review was completed in April 1973. In the meantime, progress with Nd
lasers has been made mainly in two areas: Stoichiometric Nd laser materials have
contradicted traditional views on concentration limits. With miniature Nd lasers
gains typical of semiconductor laser diodes have been reached, and optical gains
of 10 dB per optical wavelength can be expected [179]. High power Nd: glass
lasers were constructed for thermonuclear fusion experiments. Nd:YAG lasers
serve as oscillators (selection of a single pulse from a mode-locked pulse train).

## Acknowledgments

This review was written in part during a professorial assignment from Bell
Laboratories, Holmdel, New Jersey, to the University of Stuttgart, and in part
at the Max Planck Institute for Solid State Research. The author would like to
express his gratitude to A. G. Fox, Bell Laboratories; W. Eisenmenger, H. Haken,
and M. Pilkuhn, University of Stuttgart; and H. J. Queisser, Max Planck Institute,
Stuttgart, for their support and hospitality.

# List of Symbols

| | |
|---|---|
| A | Einstein coefficient; loss modulator amplitude |
| a | Damping constant; length |
| B | Drift parameter |
| b | Population ratio; distance |
| C | Hole parameter; elastooptic coefficient |
| c | Light velocity in vacuum |
| D | Energy diffusion constant, $cm^2/sec$ |
| d | Distance; thickness |
| E | Electric field |
| F | Free spectral range of axial mode selector |
| f | Focal length |
| $\delta f$ | Frequency detuning of modulator or mode selector |
| G | Power gain factor |
| g | Gain factor for spectral components |
| H | Heat generated in rod; power absorbed per unit volume |
| $H_T$ | Threshold pump density |
| h | Planck's constant |
| I | Radiation intensity, $W/cm^2$ |
| $I_s$ | Saturation parameter of Nd:YAG |
| k | Wavevector; Boltzmann constant |
| L | Round-trip cavity power loss, $0 < L \leqslant 1$ |
| $\mathcal{L}$ | Optical length of laser cavity |
| $\ell$ | Length of laser rod |
| M | Mode index (stabilization) |
| m | Mode index (mode locking) |
| N | Number of states per unit volume; concentration of Nd ions in YAG |
| $\mathcal{N}$ | Inversion density |
| n | Refractive index; inversion |
| $n_g$ | Group index |
| P | Laser output power |
| $P_L$ | Internal power in laser cavity |
| $\mathcal{P}$ | Excitation parameter |
| p | Thermal equilibrium population |
| $p_{ik}$ | Elastooptic constants |
| R | Pump rate; radius; power reflection coefficient |
| r | Radial coordinate; amplitude reflection coefficient |
| $r_0$ | Rod radius |
| T | Temperature; cavity power transmission, $0 < T \leqslant 1$ |
| t | Time |
| V | Signal amplitude |
| v | Velocity |
| $W_x$ | Cross-relaxation rate |
| W | Transition probability; pump power |
| w | Beam radius, defined as $(1/e)^2$ of the power drop |
| z | Distance along laser axis |
| $\alpha$ | Absorption; thermal expansion coefficient |

| | |
|---|---|
| $\beta$ | Branching ratio; gain saturation term |
| $\gamma$ | Nonlinear dispersion term |
| $\epsilon$ | Pump efficiency; modulation index |
| $\eta$ | Pump modulation index |
| $\kappa$ | Heat conductivity |
| $\lambda$ | Wavelength |
| $\nu$ | Frequency; Poisson's ratio |
| $d\nu$ | Change of carrier frequency |
| $\delta\nu$ | Axial mode spacing |
| $\Delta\nu$ | Full linewidth at one-half the peak intensity |
| $\overline{\Delta\nu}$ | Locking range; mean linewidth |
| $\xi$ | Loss modulation index |
| $\zeta$ | Pump rate |
| $\sigma_0$ | Peak cross section |
| $\sigma(\nu)$ | Cross section at the signal frequency |
| $\tau$ | Fluorescent lifetime |
| $\tau_r$ | Radiative lifetime |
| $\tau_s$ | Stimulated lifetime |
| $\tau_c$ | Signal round-trip time |
| $\tau_Q$ | Cold cavity photon lifetime |
| $d\tau$ | Change of cavity round-trip time |
| $\Phi$ | Phase retardation |
| $\phi$ | Phase angle; polar coordinate |
| $\psi$ | Phase |
| $\omega$ | Circular frequency |

# References

1. R. A. Statten, *J. Chem. Phys.*, **21**, 637 (1953).
2. L. F. Johnson and K. Nassau, *Proc. IRE*, **49**, 1704 (1961).
3. E. Snitzer, *Phys. Rev. Letters*, **7**, 444 (1961).
4. A. Yariv and J. Gordon, *Proc. IEEE*, **51**, 4 (1963).
5. J. E. Geusic, H.M. Marcos and L. G. van Uitert, *Appl. Phys. Letters*, **4**, 182 (1964).
6. B. Judd, *Phys. Rev.*, **127**, 750 (1962).
7. J. A. Konigstein and J. E. Geusic, *Phys. Rev.*, **136**, A711 (1964).
8. C. K. Asawa and M. Robinson, *Phys. Rev.*, **141**, 251 (1966).
9. M. J. Weber and T. E. Varitimos, *J. Appl. Phys.*, **42**, 4996 (1971).
10. J. Steffen, J.-P. Lörtscher and G. Herziger, *IEEE J. Quantum Electron.*, QE-8, 239 (1972).
11. D. W. Coffey and V. J. Norris, *Appl. Opt.*, **11**, 1013 (1972).
12. D. Maydan and R. B. Chesler, *J. Appl. Phys.*, **42**, 1031 (1971).
13. R. B. Chesler and D. Maydan, *J. Appl. Phys.*, **42**, 1028 (1971).
14. R. B. Chesler, M. A. Karr and J. E. Geusic, *J. Appl. Phys.*, **41**, 4125 (1970).
15. K. B. Steinbrügge, T. Henningsen, R. H. Hopkins, R. Mazelsky, N. T. Melamed, E. P. Riedel and G. W. Roland, *Appl. Opt.*, **11**, 999 (1972).
16. R. V. Alves, R. A. Buchanan, K. A. Wickersheim, and E. A. C. Yates, *J. Appl. Phys.*, **42**, 3043 (1971).
17. Kh. S. Bagdasarov and A. A. Kaminskii, *JETP Letters*, **9**, 303 (1969).
18. M. J. Weber, M. Bass, K. Andringa, R. R. Monchamp, and E. Comperichs, *Appl. Phys. Letters*, **15**, 342 (1969).
19. M. Bass and M. J. Weber, *Appl. Phys. Letters*, **17**, 395 (1970).
20. G. A. Massey and J. M. Yarborough, *Appl. Phys. Letters*, **18**, 576 (1971).
21. J. E. Miller, E. J. Sharp, and D. J. Horowitz, *J. Appl. Phys.*, **43**, 462 (1972).
22. H. G. Danielmeyer and H. P. Weber, *IEEE J. Quantum Electron.*, QE-8, 805 (1972).
23. B. Cockayne, *J. Crystal Growth*, **3-4**, 60 (1968).
24. A. A. Kaminskii and V. V. Osiko, *Izvest. Akad. Nauk. SSSR, Neorgan. Materialy*, **6**, 629 (1970). Transl. Plenum Publ., New York, UDC 546.01 (1970). See also Yu. K. Voronko and V. V. Osiko, *JETP Letters*, **5**, 295 (1967).
25. J. W. Strozyk, *IEEE J. Quantum Electron.*, QE-7, 467 (1971).
26. L. A. Riseberg and W. C. Holton, *J. Appl. Phys.*, **43**, 1876 (1972).
27. T. Kushida, *Phys. Rev.*, **185**, 500 (1969).
28. Z. T. Kiss and R. C. Duncan, *Appl. Phys. Letters*, **5**, 200 (1964).
29. L. F. Johnson, J. E. Geusic and L. G. van Uitert, *Appl. Phys. Letters*, **7**, 127 (1965).
30. G. O. Karapetyan, V. P. Kovalyov and S. G. Lunter, *Opt. and Spectr.*, **19**, 529 (1965).
31. Z. T. Kiss, *Phys. Rev. Letters*, **13**, 654 (1964).
32. D. L. Wood, J. Ferguson, K. Knox and J. F. Dillon, *J. Chem. Phys.*, **39**, 890 (1963).
33. W. F. Krupke, *IEEE J. Quantum Electron.*, QE-7, 153 (1972).
34. L. F. Johnson and A. A. Ballman, *J. Appl. Phys.*, **40**, 297 (1969).
35. P. H. Klein and W. J. Croft, *J. Appl. Phys.*, **38**, 1603 (1967).
36. J. D. Foster and L. M. Osterink, *Appl. Opt.*, **7**, 2428 (1966).
37. R. W. Dixon, *J. Appl. Phys.*, **38**, 5149 (1967).
38. E. G. Spencer, R. T. Denton, T. B. Bateman, W. B. Snow, and L. G. van Uitert, *J. Appl. Phys.*, **34**, 3059 (1963).
39. W. L. Bond, *J. Appl. Phys.*, **36**, 1674 (1965).
40. M. A. Gilleo and S. Geller, *Phys. Rev.*, **110**, 73 (1958).
41. H. G. Danielmeyer, *IEEE J. Quantum Electron.*, QE-6, 101 (1970).
42. B. G. Wyborne, *J. Chem. Phys.*, **32**, 639 (1960).

43. J. A. Konigstein, *J. Chem. Phys.*, **44**, 3951 (1966).
44. J. K. Neeland and V. Evtuhov, *Phys. Rev.*, **156**, 244 (1967).
45. A. A. Kaminskii and D. N. Vylegzhanin, *IEEE J. Quantum Electron.*, **QE-7**, 329 (1971).
46. T. Kushida and J. E. Geusic, *Phys. Rev. Letters*, **21**, 1172 (1968).
47. P. P. Feofilov, V. A. Timoteeva, M. N. Tolstoi, and L. M. Belyaev, *Opt. and Spectr.*, **19**, 451 (1965).
48. R. K. Watts, *J. Opt. Soc. Am.*, **61**, 123 (1971).
49. R. G. Smith, *IEEE J. Quantum Electron.*, **QE-4**, 505 (1968).
50. R. W. Wallace, *IEEE J. Quantum Electron.*, **QE-7**, 203 (1971).
51. M. Birnbaum, A. W. Tucker and P. J. Pomphrey Jr., *IEEE J. Quantum Electron.*, **QE-8**, 501 (1972).
52. R. W. Wallace and S. E. Harris, *Appl. Phys. Letters*, **15**, 111 (1969).
53. T. Kushida, H. M. Marcos and J. E. Geusic, *Phys. Rev.*, **167**, 289 (1968).
54. J. E. Geusic, Solid State Maser Research (Optical), Final Rept. AD-482-511, Aug. 1965.
55. J. R. Thornton, W. D. Fountain, G. W. Flint and T. G. Crow, *Appl. Opt.*, **8**, 1087 (1969).
56. L. A. Weaver, I. Liberman and C. H. Church, *J. Appl. Phys.*, **38**, 5405 (1967).
57. W. A. Specht, Jr., J. K. Neeland, and V. Evtuhov, *IEEE J. Quantum Electron.*, **QE-2**, 537 (1966).
58. H. G. Danielmeyer and E. H. Turner, *Appl. Phys. Letters*, **17**, 519 (1970).
59. H. G. Danielmeyer, *J. Appl. Phys.*, **42**, 3125 (1971).
60. G. Zeidler, *IEEE J. Quantum Electron.*, **QE-4**, 1016 (1968).
61. T. B. Read, *Appl. Phys. Letters*, **9**, 342 (1966).
62. J. H. Goncz and W. J. Mitchell, Jr., *IEEE J. Quantum Electron.*, **QE-4**, 330 (1967).
63. M. B. Davies, P. Sharman, and J. K. Wright, *IEEE J. Quantum Electron.*, **QE-4**, 533 (1968).
64. J. R. Oliver and F. S. Barnes, *IEEE J. Quantum Electron.*, **QE-5**, 225 (1969).
65. L. M. Osterink and J. D. Foster, *IEEE J. Quantum Electron.*, **QE-5**, 344 (1969).
66. I. Liberman, D. A. Larson, and C. H. Church, *IEEE J. Quantum Electron.*, **QE-5**, 238 (1969).
67. W. D. Fountain, L. M. Osterink, and J. D. Foster, *IEEE J. Quantum Electron.*, **QE-6**, 684 (1970).
68. H. G. Danielmeyer and J. M. Barro, *Appl. Opt.*, **10**, 1983 (1971).
69. G. D. Baldwin and I. T. Basil, *IEEE J. Quantum Electron.*, **QE-7**, 179 (1971).
70. M. Bass and A. E. Paladino, *J. Appl. Phys.*, **38**, 2706 (1967).
71. R. J. Keyes and T. M. Quist, *Appl. Phys. Letters*, **4**, 50 (1964).
72. R. B. Allen and S. J. Scalise, *Appl. Phys. Letters*, **14**, 188 (1969).
73. R. B. Allen, S. J. Scalise, and R. E. DeKinder, Jr., *IEEE J. Quantum Electron.*, **QE-5**, 345 (1969).
74. F. W. Ostermayer, Jr., *Appl. Phys. Letters*, **18**, 93 (1971).
75. F. W. Ostermayer, Jr., R. B. Allen, and E. G. Dierschke, *Appl. Phys. Letters*, **19**, 189 (1971).
76. J. F. Nester, *IEEE J. Quantum Electron.*, **QE-6**, 97 (1970).
77. R. B. Chesler, *Appl. Opt.*, **9**, 2190 (1970).
78. L. M. Osterink and J. D. Foster, *Appl. Phys. Letters*, **12**, 128 (1968).
79. J. D. Foster and L. M. Osterink, *J. Appl. Phys.*, **41**, 3656 (1970).
80. W. Koechner and D. K. Rice, *IEEE J. Quantum Electron.*, **QE-6**, 557 (1970).
81. W. Koechner and D. K. Rice, *J. Opt. Soc. Am.*, **61**, 758 (1971).
82. F. A. Levine, *IEEE J. Quantum Electron.*, **QE-7**, 170 (1971).
83. T. Kimura and K. Otsuka, *IEEE J. Quantum Electron.*, **QE-7**, 403 (1971).
84. W. C. Scott and M. DeWit, *Appl. Phys. Letters*, **18**, 3 (1971).
85. I. Liberman, *IEEE J. Quantum Electron.*, **QE-5**, 345 (1969).

86. P. W. Smith, M. V. Schneider, and H. G. Danielmeyer, *Bell Syst. Tech J.*, **48**, 1405 (1969).
87. H. G. Danielmeyer and W. G. Nilsen, *Appl. Phys. Letters*, **16**, 124 (1970).
88. M. Bass and K. Andringa, *IEEE J. Quantum Electron.*, QE-3, 621 (1967).
89. D. G. Carlson, *J. Appl. Phys.*, **39**, 4369 (1968).
90. H. G. Danielmeyer and F. W. Ostermayer, Jr., *J. Appl. Phys.*, **43**, 2911 (1972).
91. E. O. Amman and J. M. Yarborough, *Appl. Phys. Letters*, **20**, 117 (1972).
92. W. C. Scott and M. DeWit, *Appl. Phys. Letters*, **20**, 141 (1972).
93. J. E. Geusic, M. L. Hensel, and R. G. Smith, *Appl. Phys. Letters*, **6**, 175 (1965).
94. E. J. Woodbury, *IEEE J. Quantum Electron.*, QE-3, 509 (1967).
95. R. G. Smith and M. F. Galvin, *IEEE J. Quantum Electron.*, QE-3, 406 (1967).
96. D. G. Carlson and A. E. Siegman, *IEEE J. Quantum Electron.*, QE-4, 93 (1968).
97. R. B. Chesler, J. E. Geusic, and M. A. Karr, *IEEE J. Quantum Electron.*, QE-5, 345 (1969).
98. J. P. Budin and J. Raffy, *IEEE J. Quantum Electron.*, QE-5, 346 (1969).
99. A. Stein and R. A. Kaplan, *Appl. Phys. Letters*, **16**, 338 (1970).
100. R. B. Chesler, M. A. Karr, J. E. Geusic, *Proc. IEEE*, **58**, 1899 (1970).
101. G. D. Baldwin, *IEEE J. Quantum Electron.*, QE-7, 220 (1971).
102. M. DiDomenico, Jr., J. E. Geusic, H. M. Marcos, and R. G. Smith, *Appl. Phys. Letters*, **8**, 180 (1966).
103. L. M. Osterink and J. D. Foster, *J. Appl. Phys.*, **39**, 4163 (1968).
104. L. M. Osterink and J. D. Foster, *IEEE J. Quantum Electron.*, QE-4, 374 (1968).
105. S. K. Kurtz and S. L. Shapiro, *Phys. Letters*, **28A**, 17 (1968).
106. M. Bass and D. Woodward, *Appl. Phys. Letters*, **12**, 275 (1968).
107. T. S. Kinsel, J. E. Geusic, H. Seidel, and R. G. Smith, *IEEE J. Quantum Electron.*, QE-5, 326 (1969).
108. A. E. Siegman and D. J. Kuizenga, *Appl. Phys. Letters*, **14**, 181 (1969).
109. A. R. Clobes and M. J. Brienza, *Appl. Phys. Letters*, **14**, 287 (1969).
110. A. W. Smith, *Appl. Phys. Letters*, **15**, 194 (1969).
111. H. Statz and M. Bass, *J. Appl. Phys.*, **40**, 377 (1969).
112. A. R. Clobes and M. J. Brienza, *IEEE J. Quantum Electron.*, QE-6, 651 (1970).
113. D. J. Kuizenga and A. E. Siegman, *IEEE J. Quantum Electron.*, QE-6, 673 (1970).
114. D. J. Kuizenga and A. E. Siegman, *IEEE J. Quantum Electron.*, QE-6, 694 (1970).
115. D. J. Kuizenga and A. E. Siegman, *IEEE J. Quantum Electron.*, QE-6, 709 (1970).
116. A. E. Siegman and D. J. Kuizenga, *IEEE J. Quantum Electron.*, QE-6, 803 (1970).
117. D. L. Lyon and T. S. Kinsel, *Appl. Phys. Letters*, **16**, 89 (1970).
118. C. B. Hitz and L. M. Osterink, *Appl. Phys. Letters*, **18**, 373 (1971).
119. R. R. Rice, *J. Appl. Phys.*, **42**, 4109 (1971).
120. K. Otsuka and T. Kimura, *IEEE J. Quantum Electron.*, QE-8, 23 (1972).
121. T. J. Nelson, *IEEE J. Quantum Electron.*, QE-8, 29 (1972).
122. D. J. Kuizenga and M. F. Becker, *IEEE J. Quantum Electron.*, QE-8, 385 (1972).
123. K. Otsuka, *IEEE J. Quantum Electron.*, QE-8, 496 (1972).
124. R. G. Smith, K. Nassau and M. F. Galvin, *Appl. Phys. Letters*, **7**, 256 (1965).
125. D. P. Schinke, *IEEE J. Quantum Electron.*, QE-8, 86 (1972).
126. R. Polloni and O. Svelto, *IEEE J. Quantum Electron.*, QE-4, 375 (1968).
127. T. Kimura and K. Otsuka, *J. Appl. Phys.*, **40**, 5399 (1969).
128. T. Kimura and K. Otsuka, *IEEE J. Quantum Electron.*, QE-6, 764 (1970).
129. H. G. Danielmeyer, *J. Appl. Phys.*, **41**, 4014 (1970).
130. T. Kimura, K. Otsuka and M. Saruwatari, *IEEE J. Quantum Electron.*, QE-7, 225 (1971).
131. R. Polloni and O. Svelto, *IEEE J. Quantum Electron.*, QE-4, 481 (1968).
132. H. F. Mahlein and G. Schollmeier, *IEEE J. Quantum Electron.*, QE-6, 529 (1970).
133. H. Gerhardt, V. Bödecker, and H. Welling, *Z. Angew. Physik*, **31**, 11 (1970).
134. W. Culshaw and J. Kannelaud, *IEEE J. Quantum Electron.*, QE-7, 381 (1971).

135. D. A. Draegert, *IEEE J. Quantum Electron.*, **QE-8**, 235 (1972).
136. I. C. Chang, E. H. Lean, and C. G. Powell, *IEEE J. Quantum Electron.*, **QE-5**, 344 (1969).
137. I. C. Chang, E. H. Lean, and C. G. Powell, *IEEE J. Quantum Electron.*, **QE-6**, 436 (1970).
138. R. B. Chesler and D. Maydan, *J. Appl. Phys.*, **43**, 2254 (1972).
139. D. L. Dexter and J. H. Schulman, *J. Chem. Phys.*, **22**, 1063 (1954).
140. H. G. Danielmeyer, M. Blätte, and P. Balmer, *Appl. Phys.*, **1**, 269 (1972).
141. S. Singh, to be published.
142. I. C. Wanderleeden, to be published.
143. D. Röss, *Appl. Opt.*, **3**, 259 (1964).
144. D. Röss, *IEEE J. Quantum Electron.*, **QE-2**, 208 (1966).
145. C. H. Church and I. Liberman, *Appl. Opt.*, **6**, 1966 (1967).
146. B. Schuldt and R. L. Aagard, *Appl. Opt.*, **2**, 509 (1963).
147. K. Kamiro, T. Kano, and H. Matsuzawa, Rep. Res. Inst. Elect. Commun., Tokohu Univ., Japan, Vol. 20, p. 67 (1968).
148. R. B. Chesler and D. A. Draegert, *Appl. Phys. Letters*, **23**, 235 (1973).
149. C. M. Stickley, *IEEE J. Quantum Electron.*, **QE-2**, 511 (1966).
150. R. B. White, Y. C. Lee, and K. Nishikawa, *Phys. Rev. Letters*, **29**, 1315 (1972).
151. D. G. Carlson, *J. Appl. Phys.*, **39**, 4369 (1968).
152. J. E. Bjorkholm and H. G. Danielmeyer, *Appl. Phys. Letters*, **15**, 171 (1969).
153. H. G. Danielmeyer and H. P. Weber, *Phys. Rev.*, **A3**, 1708 (1971).
154. H. P. Weber and H. G. Danielmeyer, *Phys. Rev.*, **A2**, 2074 (1970).
155. P. W. Smith, *Proc. IEEE*, **58**, 1342 (1970).
156. S. E. Harris and O. P. McDuff, *IEEE J. Quantum Electron.*, **QE-1**, 245 (1965).
157. H. Haken and M. Pauthier, *IEEE J. Quantum Electron.*, **QE-4**, 454 (1968).
158. H. G. Danielmeyer, unpublished.
159. H. Bateman, in *Tables of Integral Transforms* (A. Erdely, ed.), Vol. 1, p. 15 (1954).
160. H. P. Weber and F. Mathieu, *IEEE J. Quantum Electron.*, **QE-3**, 376 (1967).
161. Yu. V. Troitskii and N. D. Goldina, *Opt. Spectr.*, **25**, 255 (1968).
162. H. G. Danielmeyer and W. N. Leibolt, *Appl. Phys.*, **3**, 193 (1974).
163. B. Hardiman, R. Bucksch, and P. Korczak, *Phil. Mag.*, **27**, 777 (1973).
164. D. Findlay and D. W. Goodwin, *Advances in Quantum Electronics* (D. W. Goodwin, ed.), Vol. 1, Academic Press, New York, 1970.
165. M. Blätte, H. G. Danielmeyer, and R. Ulrich, *Appl. Phys.*, **1**, 275 (1972).
166. *Laser Focus*, July 1972, p. 36.
167. L. G. van Uitert, E. F. Dearborn, and J. J. Rubin, *J. Chem. Phys.*, **47**, 547 (1967).
168. H. K. V. Lotsch and Ed. Matovich, *Optik*, **32**, 95 (1970).
169. D. Röss, in *Laser Handbook* (F. T. Arachi, and E. O. Schulz-Du Bois, eds.), North-Holland Publ., Amsterdam, 1972.
170. D. A. Draegert, private communication, March 1973.
171. H. Kogelnik and T. Li, *Appl. Opt.*, **5**, 1550 (1966).
172. R. A. Brandewil and C. L. Telk, *J. Opt. Soc. Am.*, **57**, 1221 (1967).
173. A. R. Clobes and M. J. Brienza, *Appl. Phys. Letters*, **21**, 265 (1972).
174. T. J. Nelson, *IEEE J. Quantum Electron.*, **QE-8**, 29 (1972).
175. W. Koechner, *IEEE J. Quantum Electron.*, **QE-8**, 656 (1972).
176. L. G. DeShazer and E. A. Maunders, *IEEE J. Quantum Electron.*, **QE-4**, 642 (1968).
177. R. B. Chesler and J. E. Geusic, in *Laser Handbook* (F. T. Arachi and E. O. Schulz-DuBois, eds.), North-Holland Publ., Amsterdam, 1972.
178. P. F. Liao and H. P. Weber, *J. Appl. Phys.*, **45**, 2931 (1974).

179. H. G. Danielmeyer, "Stoichiometric Laser Materials," in *Festkörperprobleme XV — Advances in Solid State Physics* (H. J. Queisser, ed.), Pergamon-Vieweg, Braunschweig, 1975.
180. S. Singh, R. G. Smith, and L. G. van Uitert, *Phys. Rev.,* **B10**, 2566 (1974).

*Chapter 2*

# Single-frequency Lasers

*Peter W. Smith*

Bell Laboratories, Incorporated
Holmdel, New Jersey

## 1.  Introduction

In their classic paper proposing optical maser operation, Schawlow and Townes [1] suggested that a sufficiently stable optical maser would tend to oscillate in just a single mode because of "the usual nonlinearities which would allow the most favored mode to suppress oscillations in those [modes] which are less favored." However, the early optical masers, or lasers as they are generally referred to, oscillated in many modes, and thus their output consisted of light at a number of closely spaced optical frequencies. Although the total frequency bandwidth of this group of modes is typically of the order of $10^{-4}$ to $10^{-5}$ of the laser frequency, there are still many scientific and communications applications for which greater spectral purity is required. Thus various methods of obtaining single-frequency laser operation have been developed. This chapter will present a tutorial review of these methods. Section II is a review of the subject of modes in laser resonators. Because most laser resonators will have a number of low-loss modes of different frequencies occurring within the frequency range over which the laser medium has gain, power will begin to build up in a number of different modes. To some extent these modes will draw power from the same laser atoms or molecules, and thus mode competition will have an effect on the steady-state laser output. In general, however, multifrequency operation will result unless some special method is used to favor one resonator mode to such an extent that oscillation takes place only at this mode frequency. Section III deals with laser gain saturation and output power. In particular, we clarify the role of mode competition in determining the selectivity requirements of a mode selector, and discuss the single-frequency output power that can be obtained. Section IV first examines frequency-selective devices that are relatively "coarse" in that they can be used to select a given laser line or narrow the frequency bandwidth of laser oscillation but are not sufficiently selective to produce single-mode operation. Next transverse- and longitudinal-mode-selective devices are discussed. In general, some combination of all three types of devices may be needed to produce single-frequency laser operation. Section V presents a few examples of single-frequency laser topics of current research interest.*

*Note added in proof:* This manuscript was submitted in September, 1971.

## II. Modes in Laser Resonators

In this section, the theory of laser resonator modes is briefly outlined. For a more complete discussion of the subject, the reader is referred to the excellent review article by Kogelnik and Li [2] on which our discussion of Gaussian beams is based, and to Chapter 5 of Volume 1 of this series.

### A. Gaussian Beams in Space

The propagation of light in free space can be described with the use of the scalar wave equation. A field component $\mu$ of the coherent light satisfies the equation

$$\frac{\partial^2 \mu}{\partial x^2} + \frac{\partial^2 \mu}{\partial y^2} + \frac{\partial^2 \mu}{\partial z^2} + k^2 \mu = 0 \tag{1}$$

where $k = 2\pi n/\lambda$ is the propagation constant of a plane wave of wavelength $\lambda$ in the medium of refractive index n.

For a beam whose deviation from a plane wave is not too great, one can write for light traveling in the +z direction

$$\mu = \psi(x, y, z) \exp(-jkz) \tag{2}$$

where $\psi(x, y, z)$ is the solution of the equation

$$\frac{\partial^2 \psi}{\partial x^2} + \frac{\partial^2 \psi}{\partial y^2} - 2jk \frac{\partial \psi}{\partial z} = 0 \tag{3}$$

and $j = \sqrt{-1}$. The most general solution to this equation, substituted into Eq. (2), gives

$$u = A_0 \left(\frac{w_0}{w}\right) H_m\left(\frac{\sqrt{2}\,x}{w}\right) H_n\left(\frac{\sqrt{2}\,y}{w}\right) \exp\left[-j(kz - \Phi) - (x^2 + y^2)\left(\frac{1}{w^2} + \frac{jk}{2R}\right)\right] \tag{4}$$

for a system with rectangular geometry, and

$$u = A_0' \left(\frac{w_0}{w}\right)\left(\frac{r}{w}\right)^\ell L_p^\ell \left(\frac{2r^2}{w^2}\right) \left(\begin{Bmatrix}\cos\\\sin\end{Bmatrix} \ell\theta\right) \exp\left[-j(kz - \Phi') - r^2\left(\frac{1}{w^2} + \frac{jk}{2R}\right)\right] \tag{5}$$

for a circularly symmetric system with cylindrical coordinates r, $\theta$, and z. Equations (4) and (5) describe what are known as Gaussian beams. The symbols $A_0$ and $A_0'$ represent normalizing constants that depend on the intensity of the light beam. The value of w is a measure of the radius of the beam and varies with z according to the relation

$$w^2 = w_0^2 \left[ 1 + \left( \frac{\lambda z}{\pi w_0^2} \right)^2 \right] \tag{6}$$

where $w_0$ is a constant for a given beam and is a measure of the minimum beam radius. $H_a(b)$ is the ath-order Hermite polynomial of argument b. $L_a^b(c)$ is a generalized Laguerre polynomial and a and b are the radial and azimuthal mode numbers. The symbol R represents the radius of curvature of the phase front of the beam; it varies with z according to the formula

$$R = z \left[ 1 + \left( \frac{\pi w_0^2}{\lambda z} \right)^2 \right] \tag{7}$$

The value of $\Phi$ is a measure of the phase shift of the Gaussian beam relative to a plane wave of the same wavelength. For rectangular symmetry,

$$\Phi = (1 + m + n) \arctan \left( \frac{\lambda z}{\pi w_0^2} \right) \tag{8}$$

and for circular symmetry

$$\Phi' = (1 + 2p + \ell) \arctan \left( \frac{\lambda z}{\pi w_0^2} \right) \tag{9}$$

In further discussion, we shall refer to the Gaussian beam with rectangular symmetry described by Eqs. (4), (6), (7), and (8). The transverse variation of $\mu$ depends on n and m, the order of the Hermite polynomials. For n = m = 0, the equations describe the so-called fundamental transverse mode. The amplitude distribution is a Gaussian function with 1/e radius of w, as illustrated in Fig. 1. The beam radius is $w_0$ at the beam waist, where the phase front is plane, and expands with a far-field diffraction angle of $\theta = \lambda/\pi w_0$, as illustrated in Fig. 2. Higher-order beam modes, characterized by the transverse mode numbers n and m, have more complicated amplitude distributions in the xy plane. These modes are often referred to as $TEM_{mn}$ modes by analogy with modes in waveguides. Figure 3 shows the x variation of $\mu$ for low values of the mode order m. Note that as one goes to higher-mode orders, the energy is spread further from the center of the beam. We shall see later how this allows us to discriminate against higher-order transverse modes in a laser resonator.

## B.   Transverse Modes of a Laser Resonator

A typical laser resonator is made up of two curved mirrors separated by a dis-

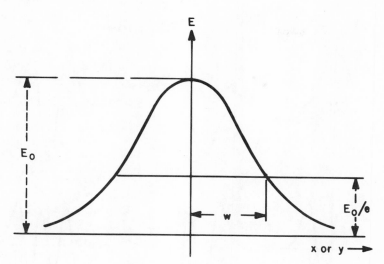

**Figure 1**
Cross-sectional amplitude distribution of a fundamental Gaussian beam.

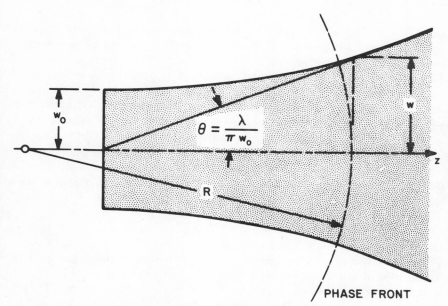

**Figure 2**
Gaussian beam spread as a function of the propagation coordinate z.

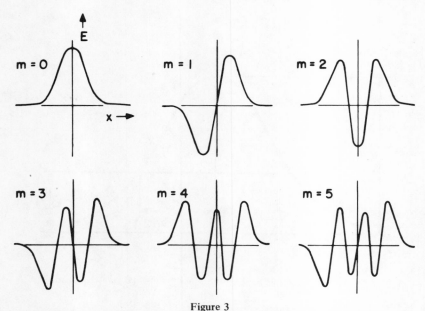

**Figure 3**

Cross-sectional amplitude distribution of some low-order Gaussian beam modes of the type $TEM_{mo}$.

tance L. A mode of a resonator is defined as a self-consistent field configuration. A Gaussian beam will be resonant in a laser resonator if (1) the curvature of its phase front coincides with the mirror curvature so that the beam is reflected back on itself, and (2) its wavelength is such that the round-trip phase shift in the resonator is an integral number of $2\pi$. We are assuming here that the mirrors are so large that essentially no power "leaks" out of the resonator. The effects of a finite aperture are discussed later in this section. Figure 4 shows a Gaussian beam mode of a resonator. Figure 5 shows the mirror separation L of two mirrors of radius $R_1$ and $R_2$ for which stable modes can be obtained, i.e., for which a Gaussian beam exists that satisfies condition 1 above. With a suitable Gaussian beam satisfying condition 1, we can determine the frequency of light required to satisfy condition 2. We find from Eqs. (4) and (8) that

$$\nu = \left(\frac{c}{2L}\right)\left\{(q+1)+\frac{1+m+n}{\pi}\arccos\sqrt{g_1 g_2}\right\} \tag{10}$$

The axial mode order q is the number of nodes in the axial standing-wave pattern (the number of half-wavelengths is $q + 1$), and $g_1 = 1 - L/R_1$, $g_2 = 1 - L/R_2$. Note that different transverse modes have different resonant frequencies. Thus in order to make a single-frequency laser, it is necessary in general to have not only axial but also transverse mode selection.

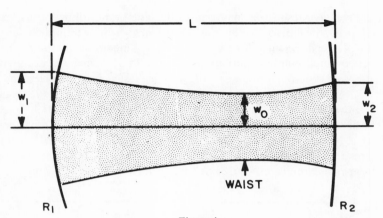

Figure 4
Gaussian beam mode of an optical resonator.

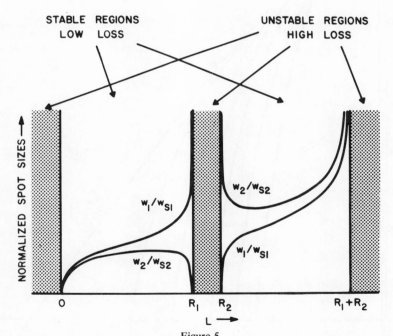

Figure 5
Spot size on resonator mirrors as a function of mirror spacing L for reflectors with radii $R_1$ and $R_2$. The spot size on mirror i, $w_i$, is normalized relative to the confocal spot size $w_{si} = \sqrt{R_i \lambda / \pi}$ (i = 1, 2) [3].

In any real laser resonator, some part of the laser beam will be lost by leaking around mirrors of finite size or by intercepting an aperture within the laser resonator. These diffraction effects will modify the modes within the resonator. With certain simplifying assumptions, Fox and Li [4-6] have made a computer calculation of the resonator mode configurations, resonant frequencies, and losses as a function of resonator geometry and size of limiting aperture. Figures 6 and 7 show the results of such calculations for the $TEM_{00}$ and $TEM_{10}$ modes [7]. The Fresnel number N ($= a^2/\lambda L$) is a measure of the size of the limiting aperture of radius a. Note that the $TEM_{10}$ mode has higher losses for a given N than the $TEM_{00}$ mode. This is because the $TEM_{10}$ mode has a larger spatial extent and thus the aperture intercepts a larger fraction of the power.

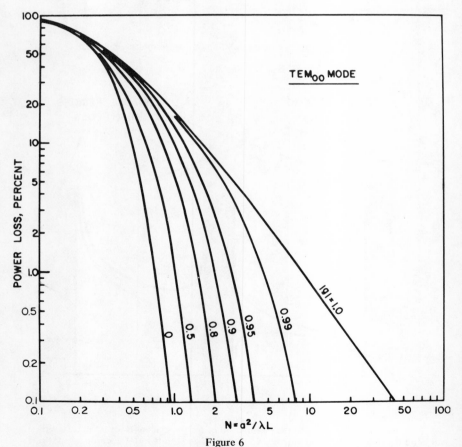

**Figure 6**
Diffraction loss per transit for the $TEM_{00}$ mode of a resonator with two circular mirrors of equal radii, as a function of the Fresnel number N for various values of g ($= 1 - L/R$) [7].

## C. Longitudinal Modes of a Laser Resonator

Equation (10) shows that for each transverse mode in the laser resonator there exists a set of resonances separated in frequency by c/2L. These are called the axial, or longitudinal, modes of the resonator. Each mode has a different number of half-wavelengths of light within the resonator but the same distribution of energy in the xy plane (perpendicular to the resonator axis).

## D. Laser Operation

To make a laser oscillator, it is necessary to introduce a medium exhibiting gain into the resonator. Energy will then build up in those resonator modes for

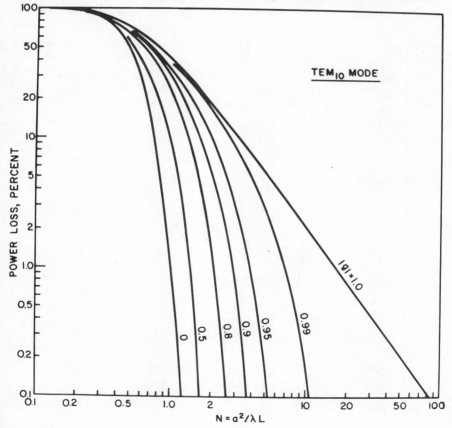

Figure 7
Diffraction loss per transit for the $TEM_{10}$ mode of a resonator with two circular mirrors of equal radii, as a function of the Fresnel number N for various values of g (= 1 - L/R) [7].

which the gain per transit exceeds the loss per transit. Resonator losses may be due to mirror transmission losses, diffraction losses, and scattering and absorption losses of the laser medium and the resonator mirrors. Figure 8 shows this situation for the case where several longitudinal modes corresponding to a single transverse mode are above threshold for oscillation. In the most general case, other sets of longitudinal modes corresponding to other transverse modes will also oscillate. Thus although the bandwidth of a single laser mode can be as narrow as a fraction of a hertz [8], the actual oscillation bandwidth of a laser with no mode control will be governed by the width of the gain curve, which may be several gigahertz for gas lasers in the visible region of the spectrum and much greater for solid-state lasers. The total output of the laser as a function of time will depend on the amplitudes, frequencies, and phases of the oscillating modes. Because the various oscillating modes may change their phase relationship as a function of time due to random fluctuations and effects in the laser medium, the output will vary in an uncontrolled way. It is possible to fix the amplitudes and the phase relationships of the oscillating modes (to mode-lock the laser) and thus obtain a well-defined output. This technique has been much used, especially to obtain a repetitive train of short light pulses. Reference 9 gives a recent review of mode-locking of lasers. There are many instances, however, when a stable, continuous, narrow-band light source is required. Then one requires a single-frequency, single-mode laser output.

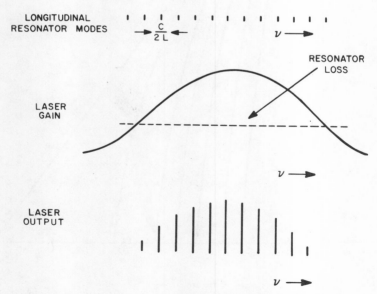

Figure 8
Laser oscillation on several longitudinal resonator modes [208].

## III.  Gain Saturation and Laser Power Output

Before considering single-frequency laser operation, it will be useful to examine gain saturation and mode competition in more detail. In particular, we are concerned with how the gain for one resonator mode is influenced by oscillation of the laser in some other mode. It is clear that if the radiation due to oscillation of a laser at one resonator mode appreciably saturates the gain available to the other resonator modes, the problem of mode selection will be less severe than if this were not the case. In this section, the ways in which gain saturation takes place in various laser media are reviewed.

### A.  Homogeneous and Inhomogeneous Line Broadening

A homogeneously broadened resonance line is one within which all the atoms respond in the same way to incoming monochromatic resonant radiation. Within an inhomogeneously broadened resonance line, however, different groups of atoms have different frequency responses, and thus only those atoms within groups that have a frequency response close to the frequency of the incoming radiation will interact appreciably with it. These remarks will be made clearer by referring to Fig. 9, which shows the saturation behavior of a homogeneous and an inhomogeneous resonance line under the influence of monochromatic radiation at the frequency indicated by the arrow. For an inhomogeneous line, it is possible to "burn a hole," i.e., saturate only those atoms with resonant frequencies close to that of the incident radiation.

It is instructive to examine results of a rate equation analysis of a simple laser amplifier. Such an analysis has been made by J. P. Gordon.* From this analysis, one finds that $2\gamma_h'$, the width of the hole "burned" in the inhomogeneously broadened gain curve by incident radiation of intensity I is given by the expression

$$2\gamma_h' = 2\gamma'\left(1 + \frac{I}{w_0}\right)^{1/2} \tag{11}$$

where $2\gamma'$ is the homogeneous linewidth (the width of the atomic response of an individual atom), and $w_0$, the saturation parameter, is a group of atomic constants and a measure of the radiation intensity required for a given degree of gain saturation.†

---

*Gordon's analysis is reproduced in *Quantum Electronics,* by Yariv [10].
†There is a possible source of confusion here as, to conform to the literature, we use the same symbol, $w_0$, to designate the minimum radius of a Gaussian beam.

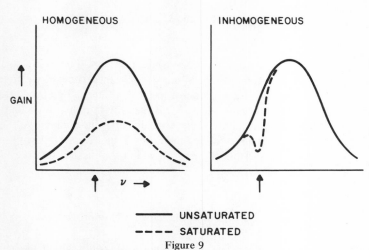

———— UNSATURATED

– – – – SATURATED

**Figure 9**

The saturation behavior of homogenously broadened and inhomogeneously broadened resonance lines under the influence of intense monochromatic radiation at the frequency indicated by the arrow [208].

Although a detailed treatment of the theory of laser operation is rather complicated [11], we can obtain physical understanding from a "hole-burning" model based on the description of gain saturation given above [12]. In the typical laser with a simple two-mirror resonator, the radiation in the resonator consists of approximately equal intensities of light traveling in each direction, and standing waves are formed in the resonator. If, for example, the laser medium is a gas whose gain curve is inhomogeneously broadened because of the Doppler effect due to the distribution of thermal velocities, then a single frequency of radiation in the resonator will, in general, interact with two groups of atoms — one group in resonance with the light traveling one direction, and the other group with light traveling in the opposite direction. Figure 10 illustrates this for the case of a steady-state laser oscillator for which the gain is saturated to equal the losses. Note that as the frequency of oscillation ($v_1$) is tuned to the atomic line center, both the forward- and backward-traveling waves interact with the same group of atoms. Thus at line center, fewer atoms contribute to the laser output and the power is reduced. This effect is evident in Fig. 10(c), which shows the so-called Lamb dip at the center of the output power-vs-frequency curve. The width of the Lamb dip at low laser powers gives a measure of the homogeneous linewidth, $2\gamma'$. Figure 11 shows values of $\gamma'$ vs gas pressure for the 6328-Å He-Ne laser line that were obtained from Lamb dip experiments [13]. Note the large pressure dependence of $\gamma'$. At sufficiently large pressures (~10 Torr for the 6328-Å He-Ne laser line), the homogeneous linewidth becomes larger than the inhomogeneous linewidth, and the line becomes essentially a homogeneously broadened line.

From the previous discussion, we have seen that radiation in a single resonator mode can interact with atoms over a total frequency range of the order of $2\gamma_h'$. If $\gamma_h'$ is much smaller than the gain bandwidth, then other resonator modes will be capable of sustaining oscillation if they occur at regions where the gain is not saturated. This is illustrated in Fig. 12. In Fig. 12(a) the gain saturation and laser output are shown for the case $\gamma_h' \ll$ inhomogeneous broadeneing. Three modes are above threshold for oscillation, and the laser output consists of radiation in these modes. In Fig. 12(b), we consider the case $\gamma' \gtrsim$ inhomogeneous broadening. In this case, although three modes were initially above threshold, radiation in the mode closest to line center has saturated the gain so that the other two modes are below threshold for oscillation, and we should expect the laser output to consist of single-frequency radiation at the frequency of the mode closest to line center.

There are some laser systems that do not behave according to the simple picture of inhomogeneous saturation by "hole burning." It has recently been shown that for the inhomogeneously broadened 6328-Å He-Ne laser line there is

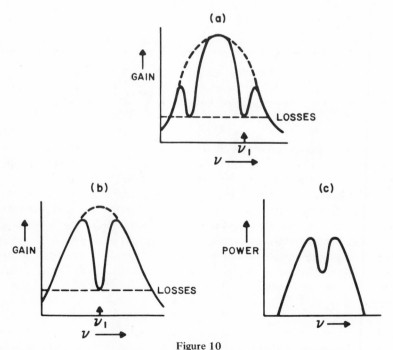

**Figure 10**
Plots of laser gain as a function of frequency for (a) a single mode at frequency $\nu_1$ away from atomic line center, and (b) a single mode at frequency $\nu_1$ at line center; (c) is a plot of single-mode output power as a function of frequency [208].

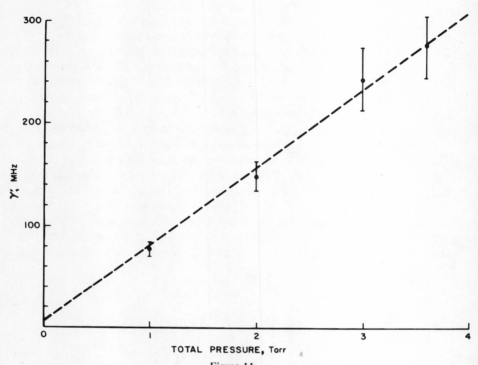

**Figure 11**
Experimental plot of the homogeneous linewidth parameter $\gamma'$ of the 6328-Å He-Ne laser line as a function of gas pressure [13].

a strong cross relaxation that redistributes the saturated atoms over the entire gain curve and thus leads to partially homogeneous line saturation [14]. Figure 13 shows how cross relaxation modifies gain saturation and leads to greater mode competition than would be expected from simple inhomogeneous line saturation.

There are many laser materials, for example Nd-doped yttrium aluminum garnet (YAG) and good-quality ruby, for which the resonance line broadening is almost entirely homogeneous. Thus one would expect on the basis of the previous discussion that single-frequency operation would always be obtained with these lasers. Multimode operation is usually observed, however, because of an effect known as spatial hole burning.

## B.   Spatial Hole Burning

Spatial hole burning was first discussed by Tang et al. [15], who pointed out that even for a completely homogeneously broadened line, there are atoms in a standing-wave laser that are situated in the nodes of the radiation standing-wave pattern in the resonator and thus cannot contribute to radiation in this mode. However, they will be stimulated to emit into another mode if it has standing-wave maxima where these atoms are situated. Figure 14 illustrates the spatial hole burning caused by a single frequency in a standing-wave resonator. If either the standing-wave pattern or the atoms of the active medium are moved so that

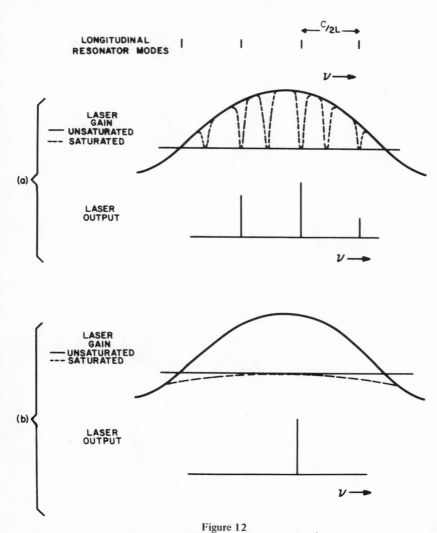

**Figure 12**

Laser gain saturation and output frequency spectrum for (a) $\gamma'_h \ll$ inhomogeneous broadening, and (b) $\gamma' \gtrsim$ inhomogeneous broadening.

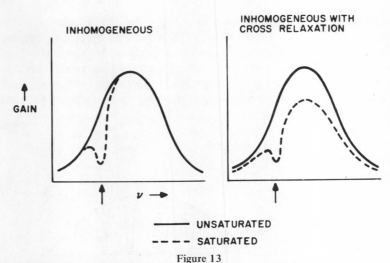

**Figure 13**
Inhomogeneous gain saturation (a) in the absence of cross relaxation, and (b) in the presence of cross relaxation.

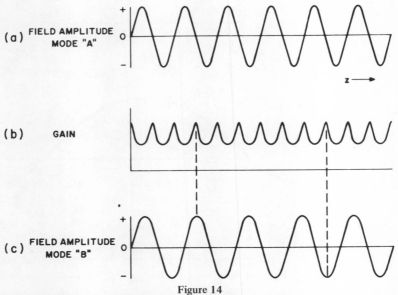

**Figure 14**
Spatial hole burning in a laser medium in a standing-wave resonator: (a) electric field of one longitudinal mode (mode A), (b) population saturation due to mode A, (c) electric field of adjacent longitudinal mode (mode B). Note that mode B will experience some gain as it can interact with atoms that are not saturated by mode A [208].

all the atoms, during their lifetime in the excited state, will encounter a standing-wave maximum of a given mode, then this spatial hole-burning effect will be averaged out, and one would expect to observe single-mode operation with a homogeneously broadened laser material. Tang et al. [15] reported what was apparently single-frequency operation of a ruby laser with a ring resonator when one direction of oscillation was suppressed so that there was no standing wave within the resonator. Other experiments have reported eliminating spatial hole-burning effects by physically moving the active medium [16, 17], using $\lambda/4$ plates [18, 19] or 45° rotators [20] to obtain different polarizations for the forward- and backward-traveling waves, and using electrooptic phase modulators within the laser resonator [21].

Danielmeyer [22] has shown that if the drift or diffusion rate for the atoms is large enough, spatial hole burning effects will be averaged out. Thus although spatial hole burning is important for solid-state lasers, the effect is usually negligible for gas lasers because the thermal velocities of most of the atoms are sufficient for the atoms to traverse several standing-wave maxima in an excited-state lifetime.

### C. Optimum Single-frequency Laser Geometry–Internal vs External Mode Selection

How can one use the facts discussed earlier in this section to design an efficient single-frequency laser? To some extent this will depend on what type of mode-selection scheme is used, but some general comments can be made. It will be assumed that we wish to maximize the available single-frequency laser output power.

From considerations of spectral hole burning, it is clear that the more homogeneous the resonance line, the greater the fraction of atoms that can contribute to the laser output. Thus, for example, increasing the gas pressure in a gas laser will increase $\gamma'$; this may improve the efficiency of single-frequency operation. Also, from Eq. (11) it is clear that $\gamma'_h$ can be increased by increasing I, the radiation intensity in the laser resonator. For lasers using materials for which spatial hole burning effects exist, more power can be obtained if one of the spatial averaging techniques described earlier is used.

If many modes of a laser resonator oscillate simultaneously, the modes will compete for the energy available from the atomic system if there is spatial and spectral overlap of their "region of influence." In this case, using a mode filter external to the laser resonator to select a single mode will be inefficient because energy that might have been contributed to the selected mode will have been given to other modes rejected by the mode filter. The use of some type of mode-selective device within the laser resonator to allow oscillation on only the desired resonator mode will result in greater output power. Only for the case where each oscillating laser mode interacts with a different group of atoms will an external mode-selection technique have a potential efficiency equal to an internal mode-selection scheme. In the following section a number of internal mode-selection schemes are discussed in some detail.

## IV. Single-frequency Laser Operation

### A.  Laser Line Selection and "Coarse" Frequency Selection Schemes

Many laser materials can be excited in such a way that a number of atomic or molecular transitions (or lines) exhibit gain, and thus can be used to obtain laser action. There are several relatively "coarse" frequency selection techniques that can be used to confine the laser oscillation to a single atomic or molecular line or to reduce the oscillation bandwidth of some of the very broad-band lasers such as dye lasers. We consider in this category those techniques that usually do not have sufficient selectivity to isolate a single resonator mode. Thus they must be used in conjunction with one or more of the other techniques described in parts B and C of this section if reliable single-frequency operation is desired.

Figure 15 shows schematically some commonly used frequency selection schemes. In each case, the arrow indicates the path taken by the unwanted radiation and the solid line indicates the laser oscillation. Figure 15(a) shows the simplest of these schemes. A typical laser mirror is composed of a multilayer dielectric structure that is highly reflecting at the laser wavelength. It may be possible to adjust the number and thickness of these layers so that the mirrors are highly transmitting at the unwanted wavelengths. Thus at those wavelengths, the laser resonator has a low "Q" and no oscillation will build up.

Figure 15(b) shows a prism used inside the laser resonator for frequency selection. This scheme has been used in particular with low-gain gas lasers because with a prism designed so that the laser beam enters and leaves the prism at the Brewster angle, very low prism insertion losses can be obtained. White [23] has used a prism in a He-Ne laser to observe oscillation on many laser lines that normally do not oscillate because of competition with the dominant 6328-Å transition. The prism resonator may be tuned to different frequencies by tilting the laser mirror at the prism end of the resonator.

When the laser medium has sufficient gain so that losses of the order of 10% can be tolerated, a diffraction grating can be used so that the first-order diffracted beam is reflected back into the laser resonator [24-26]. Such a system is shown in Fig. 15(c). Tuning may be accomplished by tilting the diffraction grating.

Figure 15(d) shows a laser with a gas cell within the resonator. A gas that is transparent at the desired laser wavelength but absorbing at an unwanted laser transition can be used to prevent radiation buildup at the unwanted wavelength. A good example of this technique is the use of methane gas in the resonator of a He-Ne gas laser to suppress oscillation on the high-gain 3.39-$\mu$m laser transition and enhance power output on the visible 6328-Å transition [27]. Because these two transitions have a common upper laser level, oscillation at 3.39 $\mu$m reduces the gain for the 6328-Å radiation. Methane absorbs strongly at 3.39 $\mu$m and is transparent in the visible portion of the spectrum. Enhancement of the 6328-Å output power by 20-30% can often be obtained by absorbing 3.39 $\mu$m with a methane cell in a He-Ne laser resonator. A similar technique has been used to discriminate between two high-gain lines near 3.39 $\mu$m [28]. Karlov et al. [29] have reported using a boron trichloride gas cell in the resonator to control the line on which a $CO_2$ laser would oscillate.

Figure 15(e) shows the use of a birefringent crystal filter (Lyot filter) to obtain a narrow spectral response. A Lyot filter consists of a length of birefringent material with polarizers on either side. High transmission occurs only for those wavelengths for which the rotation of the polarized light passing through the

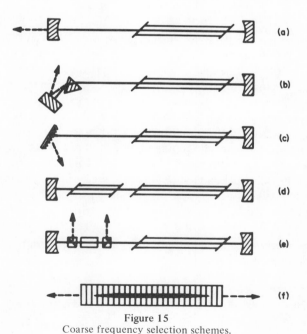

**Figure 15**
Coarse frequency selection schemes.

birefringent material is such that it is transmitted through the second polarizer with low loss. Using such a filter, Walther and Hall [30] obtained a dye laser output bandwidth of 0.01 Å, and Cirkovic et al. [31] obtained narrow linewidth emission from a ruby laser. If an electrooptic crystal is used as the birefringent element, the laser can conveniently be tuned by varying the voltage across the crystal.

Figure 15(f) shows schematically a new technique that was proposed by Miller [32] and Kogelnik and demonstrated by Kogelnik and Shank [33] and Kaminow et al. [34]. They showed that a phase grating within the (solid) laser medium can be used to form a "distributed feedback" resonator, which will have low losses only over a narrow band of frequencies. Output frequency widths of 0.1 Å have been reported using this structure with dye lasers that have gain bandwidths of the order of 200 Å. Shank et al. [35] have pumped an organic dye laser with two crossed coherent light beams. The interference of these beams produces a spatial modulation of both gain and index of refraction to create a distributed-feedback grating within the laser medium. The advantage of this system is that the frequency of the resonator formed by this distributed-feedback grating can be tuned by changing the angle between the two interfering pump beams. In this way tuning over a range of 640 Å was obtained.

## B.  Transverse Mode Selection

Most transverse mode selection schemes are based on the fact that different transverse modes have different spatial distributions transverse to the laser beam. A circular aperture, for example, will interrupt a progressively larger fraction of energy as one goes to modes of higher and higher order. Thus in theory, it appears that one could always obtain fundamental-transverse-mode operation by closing down a circular aperture inside the laser resonator until all transverse modes but the fundamental experience diffraction losses larger than the gain. Indeed, for low-gain gas lasers this is perhaps the commonest method of transverse-mode selection. Because in most cases there will be some mode competition (i.e., oscillation in the fundamental mode will reduce the available gain in the higher-order modes), it will not be necessary to introduce a loss for the second-order mode equal to the maximum gain. The loss for a given aperture size can be found from curves given, for example, in Ref. 7 (see also Figs. 5 and 6).* In general, however, the aperture size is simply adjusted until fundamental-transverse-mode operation is obtained.

---

*The justification for using curves calculated for an empty resonator is provided by Fox and Li (IEEE J. Quantum Electron. 2, 774 (1966)), who show that for low-gain lasers negligible distortion of the empty cavity modes results from the presence of the laser gain medium.

What will the diffraction loss for the desired fundamental mode be when the second-order mode is suppressed? One would like this to be as low as possible, i.e., one desires the maximum ratio of loss for second-order mode to loss for fundamental mode. Li [7, 36] has shown that this ratio depends on the laser resonator geometry. Figure 16 illustrates this dependence and shows that the maximum mode discrimination for a given Fresnel number is obtained with a confocal laser resonator (mirror spacing = mirror radius of curvature). Note that almost no mode selectivity is obtained with a plane-parallel resonator. Several authors have reported modifying the plane-parallel resonators of solid-state lasers to obtain regions with better mode-selective properties [37-39]. Evtuhov and Neeland [40] reported good mode selection in a ruby laser by making the resonator end reflector have high reflectivity only where the fields of the desired mode are high. Suematsu and Iga [41] used a similar technique.

To get the maximum output power in the fundamental transverse mode, it is desirable to have a large mode volume in the laser gain medium. Our requirements on the laser resonator geometry are now more complicated, for we wish to have simultaneously a large mode volume and a large mode selectivity. Several authors [42-46] have studied this problem. Sinclair [42] has also considered the sensitivity of the resonator diffraction losses to small changes in mirror tilt (alignment tolerance). He shows that for many situations a hemispherical resonator consisting of a curved mirror and a flat mirror spaced by a distance

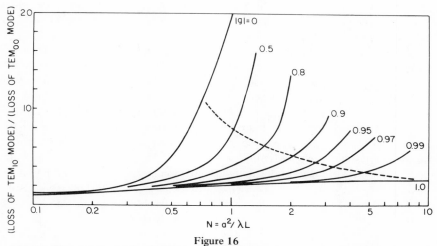

**Figure 16**
Ratio of losses per pass for the $TEM_{10}$ and $TEM_{00}$ modes in resonators with two mirrors of equal radii of curvature, as a function of the Fresnel number N for various values of $g$ (= 1 - L/R). The dashed line is a locus of points for which the loss for the $TEM_{00}$ mode is 1% per pass [7].

almost equal to the radius of curvature of the curved mirror offers the best compromise. Figure 17 shows the variation of mode volume and alignment tolerance with mirror curvature for a specific example assuming a planoconcave resonator (one flat and one concave resonator mirror). Figure 18 shows that for a near hemispherical resonator the alignment tolerance and mode volume are both high. From Fig. 16 it can be seen that a hemispherical resonator (for which $|g| = 0$) also has high mode discrimination.

Another resonator geometry that offers large mode volume and high mode selectivity is the "cat's eye" resonator [47, 48] shown in Fig. 19(a). The mode selectivity is that of a confocal resonator and the mode volume approaches that of a plane-parallel resonator as the size of the aperture is reduced. Li and Smith [48] have described experiments with a 6328-Å He-Ne gas laser using such a resonator.

Siegman [49] and Siegman and Arrathoon [50] have shown that unstable (high diffraction loss) optical resonators can be used with high-gain lasers to get single-transverse-mode laser operation (see also Ref. 51). Such a resonator is shown in Fig. 19(b). The disadvantage of such a system is that an appreciable power loss occurs even for the desired mode. This disadvantage is to some extent offset if the radiation "leaking" from the resonator around the resonator mirror can be used as the useful laser output.

There are a number of other techniques that have been used either alone or in combination to produce fundamental-transverse-mode laser operation. For high-gain solid state lasers, in general, the situation is complicated both by the high gain and by thermal effects [52] that change the mode volume in the laser resonator during a laser pulse. Fricke [53] analyzes in detail the thermal effects for a Nd-YAG laser.

Experimenters have found that reduction of the angular divergence of the beam is a useful method of mode control [54-56]. Use of rooftop prisms with angle slightly less than 90° to make a resonator has proved to be a useful method for obtaining single-transverse-mode operation of a ruby laser [57, 58]. Mode selection in a Nd:glass laser has been obtained by making the laser in the form of a slab waveguide [59]. Still other methods have been found useful in specific cases [45, 60-65]. Some of these transverse mode selection schemes are discussed in a review article by Hanna [66].

The selection of higher-order transverse modes can be accomplished by inserting a lossy element (e.g., a fine wire) into the laser resonator in such a position that it is at an electric-field minimum of the desired mode but will absorb an appreciable fraction of the radiation in other modes. For example, a single fine wire crossing the resonator axis and perpendicular to it will select the $TE_{01}$ mode (see field configurations in Fig. 3). In a similar way, other rectangular and circular symmetry modes can be selected [67, 68]. Collins and Giordmaine [69] have described high-order "bouncing ball" modes of rectangular

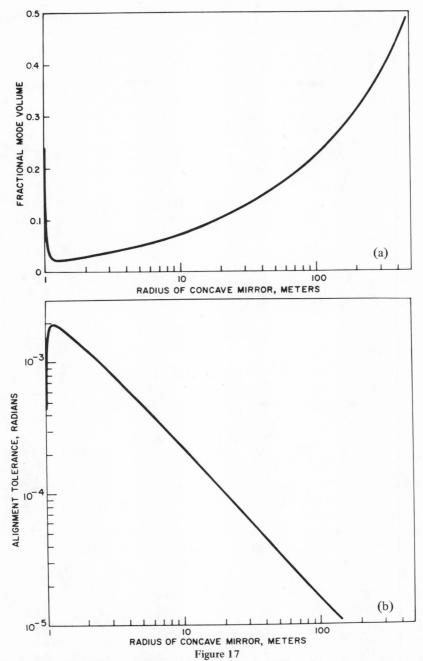

**Figure 17**
(a) Fractional mode volume vs radius of concave mirror for a plano-concave resonator, and (b) alignment tolerance vs radius of concave mirror for a plano-concave resonator. In both cases, a laser tube of length 1 m and diameter 3 mm is considered as aperturing the laser beam, and the mirror spacing is 1 m [42].

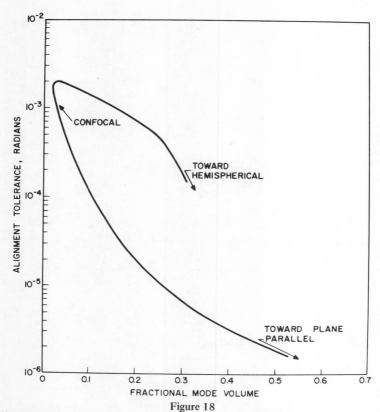

**Figure 18**

Alignment tolerance vs fractional mode volume for a plano-concave resonator with the same laser tube and mirror spacing as in Fig. 17 [42].

dielectric resonators such as a rectangular ruby rod, and have shown how mode selection can be achieved by suitably coating regions of high reflectivity on the surfaces of the resonator.

Before leaving the subject of transverse mode selection we shall discuss two different types of "dynamic" mode-selection schemes that permit switching from one set of transverse modes to another. Johnston, Li, and Smith [70] describe experiments in which a laser normally oscillating in the fundamental mode was switched to second-order-mode operation by injecting a low-power, second-order-mode signal of the correct frequency. In a similar way, any configuration of transverse modes might be made to oscillate by injecting a suitable low-level signal. For example, a laser oscillating in several transverse modes could be made to oscillate in only the lowest-order mode. With this technique, the frequency of laser oscillation is locked to the frequency of the injected signal, and this may be useful for some applications.

The "scanlaser" [71] furnishes an example of a different type of dynamic mode selection. Figure 20 shows an early version of such a device. The laser is designed so that many transverse modes can oscillate in the resonator with low diffraction loss. Oscillation is prevented, however, by the quartz plate, which rotates the plane of polarization of the incident light sufficiently so that the loss the light experiences in passing through the Brewster angle windows of the laser tube is larger than the laser gain. By focusing an electron beam onto a region of the KDP (potassium dihydrogen phosphate) slab in front of the laser mirror, one can create a small area of charge on the KDP surface and thus a field across the KDP. The local region of birefringence in the KDP can be made to just compensate for the birefringence introduced by the quartz slab. Thus a mode with radiation concentrated at this point on the KDP will experience low loss and can be made to oscillate. In this way, complicated patterns of high-order laser modes can be produced and the mode patterns can be rapidly changed by "writing" a new charge distribution on the KDP slab. Resolution of more than 200 spots per cm has been obtained with devices of this type.

## C. Longitudinal Mode Selection

Perhaps the most complex and interesting topic we shall cover concerns selecting radiation in a single longitudinal mode of the laser resonator. As shown

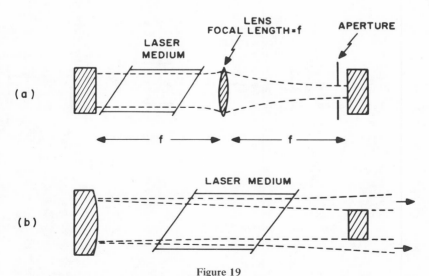

**Figure 19**
Resonators with high transverse-mode selectivity: (a) "cat's eye" resonator, and (b) one type of unstable resonator.

in Section II, the longitudinal modes of a simple two-mirror resonator are spaced in frequency by c/2L where c is the velocity of light and L is the distance between the mirrors. It is clear from Fig. 8 that by making the resonator losses sufficiently large, one can always arrange to have only one mode above threshold for oscillation, and the laser output will consist only of radiation at this frequency. If the longitudinal mode spacing is much smaller than the gain bandwidth, however, the laser must be operated so close to threshold that the output power will be very small. Single-frequency operation far above threshold can be achieved if the resonator length L is made sufficiently small that the longitudinal mode spacing is of the order of or greater than the gain bandwidth. Various researchers have described short, single-frequency He-Ne lasers oscillating at 6328 Å [72-77] or 1.15 μm [78] and ultrathin single-frequency semiconductor lasers [79]. In general, however, the output power of such lasers is very limited because of the limited length of active laser medium that the restrictions on the resonator length allow. Many types of laser would require such short lengths of active medium, or operation so close to threshold, that this method of single-frequency operation is not feasible. We are left, then, with two alternatives. We can allow the laser to oscillate in several longitudinal modes and then select, external to the laser resonator, a single mode for our use. The alternative method is to modify the resonator or place some element into the

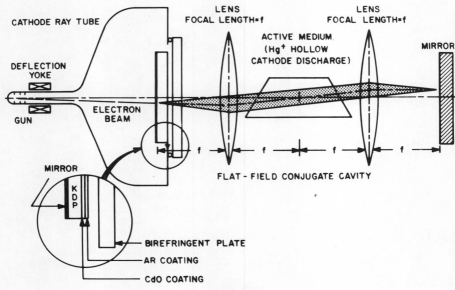

**Figure 20**
An early version of a scanlaser [71].

resonator to constrain the oscillation to a single longitudinal mode. We have seen (Section III) that it is usually possible to obtain higher single-frequency powers by using internal mode selection. The remainder of this section is devoted to a discussion of internal mode selection techniques. Magyar [80] has reviewed some mode-selection techniques for solid-state lasers.

The first type of internal longitudinal mode-selection techniques to be used were what might be called interferometric schemes. Some types of complex laser resonator using more than two mirrors was used to provide a resonant structure for which only one high Q (low-loss) resonator mode would be above threshold for laser oscillation. These schemes have the drawback that the maximum output power that can be obtained in a single frequency is limited, since a single frequency of radiation cannot in general interact with all of the atoms in an inhomogeneously broadened resonance line. Thus these inter-fermoetric schemes are potentially less efficient than some of the noninter-ferometric schemes (to be discussed later). In practice, however, the power outputs that have been achieved experimentally with the best interferometric and noninterferometric schemes are quite comparable. Figure 21(a) shows the first of these schemes, originally proposed by Kleinman and Kisliuk [81]. The two mirrors at the left-hand end of the laser resonator act as a reflector whose reflectivity varies with frequency. The response of such a Fabry-Perot interfer-ometer to incident radiation is well known [82]. The round-trip resonator loss as function of frequency is shown in Fig. 21(a). The vertical lines along the abscissa represent longitudinal resonances of the same laser resonator with a simple end reflector. The periodicity of the loss is $c/2d$, where c is the velocity of light and d is the spacing of the two left-hand mirrors. The reflectivity of the left-hand mirrors determines the width of the region of low loss. With this resonator, then, we have some control of the number of longitudinal modes that will be above threshold for oscillation. We can make d as small as we want and thus ensure that only one loss minimum will exist for which the laser gain exceeds the resonator losses. We cannot, however, choose mirror reflectivities that will make the region of low loss as narrow as we wish, and thus this scheme is useful only for lasers having a few modes within the oscillation bandwidth. This scheme has been analyzed in detail [81, 83-86] and experimental results have been reported for the 6328 Å He-Ne gas laser [87, 88], the argon ion laser [89], and solid-state laser [90-95]. Kobayashi and Matsui [96] have described a modification of this technique that involves placing a modulator in the Fabry-Perot interferometer. Under suitable conditions, they could achieve enhanced mode selectivity.

A somewhat narrower region of low loss is also possible with the device shown in Fig. 21(b). In this case, the width of the low-loss regions is a function of the mirror spacings at both ends of the laser resonator [97]. Although somewhat narrower low-loss regions are achievable with this scheme, the additional complex-ity makes it unattractive compared with some of the other schemes. Birnbaum and

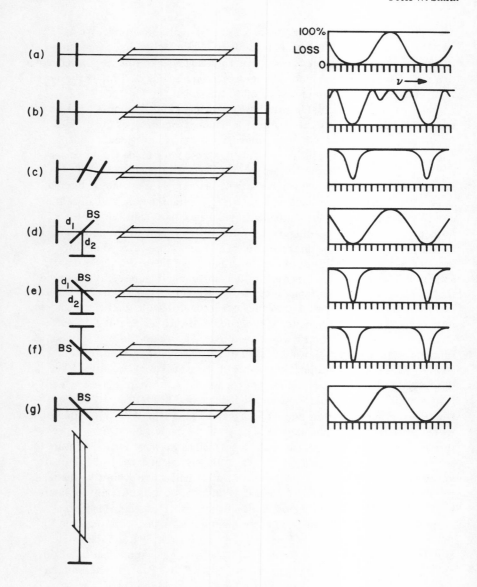

**Figure 21**

Schematic representations of some interferometric schemes for laser resonators with longitudinal mode selectivity. The curves to the right of each figure show the round-trip loss as a function of frequency for radiation in an empty resonator with perfect reflectors (reflectivity = 100%) and beamsplitters (reflectivity plus transmissivity = 100%). For comparison, the frequencies of the longitudinal modes of the same laser resonator with a simple end reflector are indicated [208].

Stocker [99, 100] and Pratesi and diFrancia [101, 102] have experimented with segmented ruby lasers where the ends of the ruby rod acted as low-reflectivity mirrors within the laser resonator. Although the oscillation frequency band-width was reduced, single-frequency operation was not obtained. Later results of Pratesi [103] appear to show single-frequency output from a 10-element pulsed ruby laser.

The so-called resonant reflector used to obtain narrow-band operation of solid-state lasers consists of several low-finesse etalons in tandem [104-108]. Watts [109] and Magyar [110] have proposed specific resonant-reflector systems, but a simple method of developing an optimum design does not seem to exist.

The scheme shown in Fig. 21(c) was suggested by Collins and White [111] and Manger and Rothe [112, 113], and has been analyzed by Kumagai and Matsuhara [98]. It has been used with some success with solid-state lasers [93-95, 111-118], gas lasers [114, 119, 120], dye lasers [121, 122], and parametric oscillators [123]. In this scheme, a tilted Fabry-Perot etalon is inserted at a small angle in the laser resonator. The reflectivity of the composite mirror consisting of the tilted etalon and the adja-cent end mirror corresponds closely to the transmission curve of a simple Fabry-Perot resonator. The advantage of this is that now we can not only control the spacing of the reflectivity peaks (which is just $c/2d$ where $d$ is the Fabry-Perot etalon spacing) but also make the peaks very narrow by selecting a sufficiently high reflectivity for the etalon mirrors. The only problem with this technique is that there is a "walkoff" loss associated with the tilt of the etalon. A certain etalon tilt is unavoidable, since operating the device depends on losing from the laser resonator the power reflected from the etalon. Thus the minimum resonator loss is increased because of the reduced transmission of a Fabry-Perot etalon at other-than-normal incidence. The losses associated with the tilted etalon have been estimated by Danielmeyer [115]. As we shall see, there exists a device that has the advantages of the tilted etalon scheme without the disadvantages of the increased loss for the favored mode. The tilted etalon scheme does, however, have the advantage of simplicity.

Figure 21(d) shows a Michelson interferometer used as a complex end reflector [124-126]. The loss minima are spaced by $c/2(d_1 - d_2)$, where $d_1$ and $d_2$ are the spacings of each mirror from the beam splitter (labeled BS in the diagram). The mode selectivity of this device is restricted because the Michelson inter-ferometer loss vs frequency is a sine function, and no value of beam splitter reflectivity will increase the sharpness of the loss minima. Fox [127] and Smith [128] originally described the device shown in Fig. 21(e), and several experimenters have used it to obtain single-frequency operation of gas lasers [128-136]. As before, the three left-hand mirrors can be thought of as a mirror of variable reflectivity. In this case, the reflectivity peaks are spaced by $(c/2)(d_1 + d_2)$. In contrast to the previous scheme, however, the width of the reflectivity peak and thus the width of the low-loss region can be made as narrow as desired by properly choosing the reflectivity of the beam splitter; high mode selectivity with low losses for the favored mode can thus be achieved with this device. Sinclair [137] has described how an off-axis confocal interferometer can function as a Fox-Smith interferometer; and he has demonstrated its use with an argon ion laser. The device shown in Fig. 21(f) has mode-selective properties identical to those of a Fox-Smith device if the beam splitter reflectivity and transmissivity are interchanged.

The last mode-selection device of the interferometric type that we will discuss is shown in Fig. 21(g). It was proposed by DiDomenico and Seidel, and its operation has been demonstrated with the He-Ne laser [138, 139]. White has described a similar device which uses a polarizing prism in place of the beam-splitter [140]. There is no simple way to picture the operation in terms of a mirror of variable reflectivity. It is essentially a vernier device and oscillation takes place at frequencies at which the longitudinal resonances of the two coupled resonators of almost equal length coincide. Rigrod [141] has made a comparison of the Fox-Smith interferometer and the scheme shown in Fig. 21(g), and has concluded that the Fox-Smith interferometer gives appreciably better mode selectivity. A general theory of these resonators has been attempted by Fontana [142].

To demonstrate how the mode properties of any of the lasers in Fig. 21 can be analyzed, we present an analysis of a laser using a Fox-Smith interferometer based on Ref. [128]. Figure 22 is a diagram of this device with the mirrors and mirror separations labeled. Consider a wave $\exp(j\omega t)$ incident from the left on mirror $M_2$ of Fig. 22. The wave that returns in the opposite direction to the incident one is

$$\tau_2^2 \rho_3 \left\{ 1 - \rho_3 \rho_4 \rho_2^2 \exp\left[\frac{4\pi j}{\lambda}(L_2 + L_3)\right] \right\}^{-1} \exp\left[j\omega t + \frac{4\pi j L_2}{\lambda}\right] \tag{12}$$

where $\rho_i$ is the field reflection coefficient and $\tau_i$ is the field transmission coefficient of mirror $M_i$, and $\lambda$ is the wavelength of the radiation. If the laser medium in arm $L_1$ has a roundtrip electric-field gain g, then the wave returning to mirror $M_2$ will be

$$g\tau_2^2 \rho_3 \rho_1 \left\{ 1 - \rho_3 \rho_4 \rho_2^2 \exp\left[\frac{4\pi j}{\lambda}(L_2 + L_3)\right] \right\}^{-1} \exp\left[j\omega t + \frac{4\pi j}{\lambda}(L_1 + L_2)\right] \tag{13}$$

In order for the radiation to be resonant, this wave must equal $\exp(j\omega t)$. Thus one obtains

$$g = \frac{1 - \rho_3 \rho_4 \rho_2^2 \exp\left[(4\pi j/\lambda)(L_2 + L_3)\right]}{\rho_1 \rho_3 \tau_2^2 \exp\left[(4\pi j/\lambda)(L_1 + L_2)\right]} \tag{14}$$

The requirement that the gain g be real gives the additional condition

$$\sin \frac{4\pi}{\lambda}(L_1 + L_2) = \rho_3 \rho_4 \rho_2^2 \sin \frac{4\pi}{\lambda}(L_1 - L_3) \tag{15}$$

The power gain G is

$$gg^* = G = \frac{(1 - \rho_3\rho_4\rho_2^2)^2 + 4\rho_3\rho_4\rho_2^2 \sin^2\left[(2\pi/\lambda)(L_2 + L_3)\right]}{\rho_3^2\rho_1^2\tau_2^4} \tag{16}$$

and the fractional power loss L is

$$L = 1 - \frac{1}{G} = 1 - \frac{\rho_3^2\rho_1^2\tau_2^4}{(1 - \rho_3\rho_4\rho_2^2)^2 + 4\rho_3\rho_4\rho_2^2 \sin^2\left[(2\pi/\lambda)(L_2 + L_3)\right]} \tag{17}$$

Let us consider the case $\rho_1 = \rho_3 = \rho_4 = 1$, $\rho_2^2 = \tau_2^2 = 0.5$. One sees from Eqs. (16) and (17) that for the case $L_2 + L_3 - m\lambda/2$, $L_1 + L_2 = n\lambda/2$, where m and n are integers, the gain is equal to 1 and there are no losses in the system. Thus mirror $M_2$ reflects no power out of the resonator. Let $\lambda'$ be another resonance of the system. Then from Eq. (15),

$$\sin\left(\frac{2\pi n\lambda}{\lambda'}\right) = 0.5 \sin\left[\frac{2\pi(n - m)\lambda}{\lambda'}\right] \tag{18}$$

The two sides of Eq. (18) are plotted in Fig. 23 for the case m = n/10. The intersections of the solid and dashed curves correspond to solutions of Eq. (18). Note that half the solutions are rejected as they correspond to negative gain.

Equation (18) has been solved numerically for the case m = n/10. It is found that for the next resonance away from the one with no loss, the loss given by Eq. (17) is L = 0.40.

If one estimates the absorption and scattering power losses at each mirror surface to be 0.2%, Eq. (17) can be used to find the theoretical loss for the "on resonance" frequency. A power loss of L = 0.016 is obtained. It is thus seen that even with a power reflectivity of 0.5 for $M_2$, the longitudinal mode selector discriminates strongly against unwanted resonator modes. Increasing the reflectivity of the beam splitter gives greater discrimination.

One significant problem with any of these interferometric mode selectors is that they depend on the precise tuning (within a small fraction of a wavelength) of two or more coupled optical resonators. We will briefly discuss feedback sys-

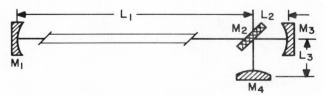

**Figure 22**
Laser resonator incorporating a Fox-Smith interferometer [128].

tems that "lock" together the resonances of these coupled resonators. (The problem of obtaining frequency stability of the laser output will be discussed in Section V.)

In most of the interferometric schemes shown in Fig. 21, there is one short resonator that, in effect, selects one of the modes of the long laser resonator. For many applications, it may be possible to accept the relative drift of the two resonators as long as the output power does not change too drastically while the long resonator modes are tuned through the mode-selective resonator's resonance. This will occur if mode competition in the laser medium is sufficient to allow a low-finesse mode-selective resonator to produce single-frequency operation. Single-frequency operation with a low-finesse tilted etalon in the laser resonator has been reported for He-Ne lasers [119], argon ion lasers [114], and solid-state lasers [114, 115]. A low-finesse three-mirror interferometer of the Fox-Smith type has also been used with an argon ion laser [132]. Rigrod and Johnson [132] used a coated solid quartz prism to form the mode-selector resonator. By placing this resonator in a temperature-controlled oven, they were able to keep a resonance of the mode selector stabilized to within ±3 MHz.

For more precise amplitude and frequency stability, some type of feedback system can be used to "lock" a resonance of the laser resonator to the peak of the mode-selector resonance. Feedback systems for this purpose have been described in Refs. 128-130. Figure 24 shows a block diagram of a typical system and Fig. 25 illustrates the principle of operation. The resonant frequency of the mode-selector resonator is modulated at an audio rate, and the output power is monitored with a detector. Figure 25 shows that when the laser output drifts to one side of the mode-selector response, the output will be amplitude-modulated at the audio frequency of the resonator modulation. At resonance, there will be no signal at this audio frequency. (But there will be one at twice the frequency.) On the other side of the mode-selector resonance, a

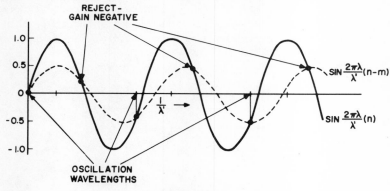

**Figure 23**
Graphical solution to Eq. (18) for the case m = n/10 [128].

fundamental signal of the opposite phase will be produced. Thus a phase-sensitive detector tuned to this audio frequency can be used to derive from the laser output a dc signal whose amplitude is proportional to the deviation from the center of the mode-selector resonance, and whose sign depends on the direction of this deviation. This signal, when suitably amplified, can be used to control the laser frequency by varying the length of the laser resonator so that the output is stabilized on the center of a mode-selector resonance. This system was shown [128] to be capable of locking the resonators together indefinitely if occasional adjustments were made to compensate for thermal expansion. Somewhat more sophisticated systems that lock the two resonators together without imparting an ac "dither" to the laser output are described in Refs. 129 and 130.

Before leaving the subject of interferometric mode selectors, it should be pointed out that some of the devices shown in Fig. 21 have ring-laser analogs [141, 143-145]. These are shown in Fig. 26. The device shown in Fig. 26(c) has been demonstrated experimentally with a He-Ne laser [143] and an argon ion laser [146]. A similar device is described in Ref. 145. All of these devices have mode-selective properties similar to their standing-wave laser counterparts, and will not be discussed further here.

Several noninterferometric schemes for obtaining longitudinal mode selection have been proposed. Some of these are illustrated in Fig. 27. Figure 27(a) shows a scheme that Massey et al. [147] proposed and demonstrated. (See also Ref. 148.) By internal phase modulation, it is possible to obtain a laser output whose mode amplitudes and phases correspond to the carrier and sidebands of an FM-modulated wave [149]. By passing the output of such an FM laser through a suitable demodulator, Massey et al. [147] showed that they could recover the "carrier"; i.e., all of the laser output light was converted to this single output

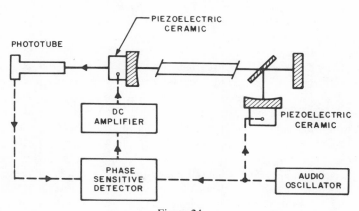

**Figure 24**

Block diagram of simple feedback system for locking a resonance of the main laser resonator to a resonance of the mode selector resonator [128].

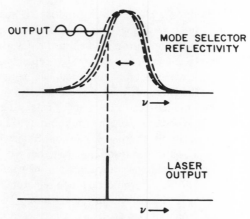

**Figure 25**
Mode selector resonator reflectivity as a function of frequency. With the laser frequency
as shown, modulation of the length of the mode selector resonator modulates the
amplitude of the laser output as shown schematically in the figure. The feedback system
locks the laser frequency to the peak of the mode selector reflectivity curve [128].

frequency. One advantage of this scheme is that in theory all of the multimode
output power can be obtained in this single-frequency output. Weber and
Mathieu [150] have proposed a rather complex scheme to produce single-frequency
output from an FM laser at the second harmonic of the laser frequency. Harris
and McMurtry [151] proposed and demonstrated yet another scheme utilizing the
FM laser. This scheme is illustrated in Fig. 27(b). An etalon is used as an end
reflector of the FM laser and is tuned to transmit at only one of the oscillating
mode frequencies. If sufficient modulator drive is used to maintain FM mode
amplitudes and phases within the laser resonator, all of the multimode output
power can be obtained in the single-frequency output.

Figure 27(c) shows schematically a scheme proposed by Chebotayev et
al. [152] and by Lee et al. [153]. A resonant absorber with laser atoms excited primarily to the lower laser level is used in the laser resonator to induce single-frequency
operation. Experiments have been reported with the 6328-Å He-Ne laser, with
a discharge of pure Ne used as the resonant absorber [152-154], and a theoretical
explanation of the results based on Lamb's theory of a gas laser has been
given [155]. The experiments have been carried out, however, in an excitation
region well above the region where Lamb's theory would be expected to be valid.

Troitskii and Goldina [156] proposed and demonstrated the technique of mode
selection shown in Fig. 27(d). A thin (fractional-wavelength) absorbing film will
preferentially absorb those modes that have standing-wave maxima at the film
position in the laser resonator. The mode with a standing-wave minimum at the
film will experience little loss and thus be favored. Troitskii and Goldina were

able in this way to obtain single-frequency operation of a 6328-Å He-Ne laser [156] and an argon ion laser [157]. Smith et al. [158] presented a detailed theory of the absorbing film mode selector and reported single-frequency operation of the argon ion laser and the Nd:YAG laser using thin metal films in the laser resonator. Troitskii [159] also has given similar theoretical treatment, comparing the absorbing film technique with other mode-selection schemes. He concluded that the technique is most useful for relatively low-power lasers, and other schemes must be used for efficient, high-power operation. Recently, the use of a nonabsorbing diffracting film for mode selection has been reported [161, 162].

There have been several reports of single-frequency, or narrow-bandwidth, operation of Q-switched lasers when a bleachable dye is placed in the laser resonator [60, 93, 106, 163-165]. Sooy [166] has explained this as a transient effect, where the first mode above threshold grows more rapidly than the others over several resonator transits and is the only mode to attain appreciable intensity within the duration of the pumping pulse. Recently, Nurmikko et al. [167] re-

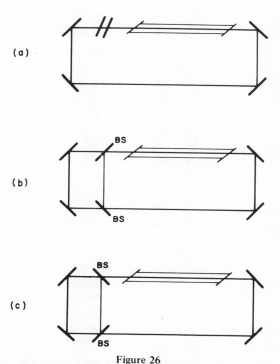

**Figure 26**
Ring laser analogs of the standing-wave laser mode-selecting devices shown in Fig. 21: (a) analog of Fig. 21(c); (b) analog of Fig. 21(d); (c) analog of Fig. 21(e).

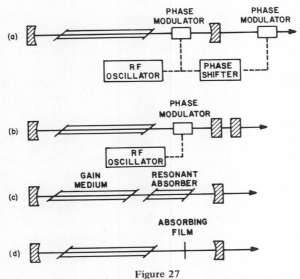

**Figure 27**
Some noninterferometric schemes for longitudinal mode selection.

ported single-frequency operation of a pulsed transverse-discharge high-pressure $CO_2$ laser, using $SF_6$ as a saturable absorber within the laser resonator.

There are two single-frequency techniques related to the power output considerations discussed in Section III. For a laser with a homogeneously broadened resonance line, the elimination of spatial hole burning may be all that is required to obtain single-frequency operation [15-21]. Such techniques have been proposed and demonstrated with the Nd:YAG laser [17,19,21] and the ruby laser [15,16, 18]. It is believed that the single-frequency operation of some optically pumped semiconductor lasers occurs because of the reduction of spatial hole burning, accountable by the large diffraction losses the radiation experiences in passing through the laser material [168]. For a laser with an inhomogeneously broadened resonance line, such as a gas laser, operation at sufficiently high gas pressure will cause the pressure-broadened homogeneous linewidth $\gamma'$ to become larger than the gain bandwidth, and spontaneous single-frequency operation will result. Smith [169] has observed such operation with a high-pressure He-Ne laser, and this effect is probably the explanation for the spontaneous single-frequency operation of an argon ion laser that Yarborough and Hobart [170], Bridges and Rigrod [171], and Borisova and Pyndyk [172] have reported. The experiments of Yarborough and Hobart are particularly noteworthy, as they obtained an output power of 2 W with 90% of the output in a single frequency.

A unique and as yet unexplained single-frequency technique was reported by Forsyth [173], who found that if the 4880-Å and 5145-Å radiation from an argon ion laser was resonated in separate cavities, single-frequency output could be obtained at 5145 Å.

DeShazer and Maunders [174] have reported narrow-band operation of a Nd:glass laser by injecting a beam of narrow-band light into the laser. Bondarenko et al. [175,176] obtained single-frequency operation of a Q-switched ruby laser by a similar technique. Birnbaum et al. [61] have also reported a related technique; they pumped a cw ruby laser with the 5145-Å output of an argon ion laser. They obtained single-frequency ruby laser oscillation in the $TEM_{00}$ mode. Bjorkholm and Danielmeyer [177] have obtained single-frequency oscillation of a pulsed parametric oscillator by injecting a signal from a single-frequency Nd:YAG laser into the parametric oscillator resonator. Single-axial-mode oscillation was also observed by Briquet et al. [178] with a Nd:glass laser pumped by second harmonic light from another Nd:glass laser. The reason for this is obscure, however, as the pumping light had a broad frequency bandwidth.

## V. Topics of Current Interest

There are several areas in which single-frequency lasers are being used in current studies. The choice of topics we shall examine is somewhat arbitrary and no attempt is made to be comprehensive. We shall outline some of the work that has been done and indicate the directions of current research.

### A. Frequency Stabilization and Frequency Standards

Schawlow and Townes [1] calculated the bandwidth of the radiation from a single mode laser. Their results imply that a typical single-frequency cw gas laser will have an output bandwidth of less than 1 Hz! Such narrow linewidths are not observed in practice because of environmental disturbances that cause variations in the optical length of a laser resonator, and hence in the laser output intensity and frequency. For example, a laser resonator made of invar (a metal with low thermal expansion coefficient) will change the frequency of its resonances in the visible region of the spectrum by $\sim$500 MHz for a 1°C change in ambient temperature. Small mechanical fluctuations are also serious, for a change in resonator length of half an optical wavelength will change the resonant frequency by $c/2L$ – the longitudinal mode spacing. This is 150 MHz for a 1-meter resonator.

One way to get stable laser output is to isolate the laser from mechanical, thermal, and atmospheric pressure disturbances. Jaseja et al. [8] were able, by operating their laser in an underground wine cellar, to obtain frequency bandwidths of less than 20 Hz over periods of a few tens of milliseconds, corresponding to a short-term frequency stability of about 1 part in $10^{13}$. In a typical laboratory environment, however, an unstabilized laser will have a frequency stability many orders of magnitude less than this. To improve the frequency stability of a laser beyond what is possible with a reasonable mechanical design for a stable laser resonator made of low-thermal-expansion material and shielded from acoustic disturbances, many workers have used some type of electronic feedback system. There are basically two types of feedback systems—those that stabilize the laser frequency to an external resonator (which can be made very stable as it is removed from the influences of the laser medium) and those that stabilize the laser frequency to some "absolute" frequency, determined by an atomic or molecular resonance. The former method has high sensitivity and good short-term stability but lacks long-term stability largely because of temperature detuning. The atomic resonance discriminator, on the other hand, lacks sensitivity because of the large atomic linewidth. To locate the atomic line center accurately, the signal-to-noise ratio must be increased by reducing the bandwidth of detection, thus limiting the response time of the entire system. For detailed treatment of such feedback systems, the reader is referred to review articles by White [179] and Birnbaum [180,181], and to Chapter 5 of Volume 2 of this series for a presentation of some of the many feedback control systems that have been proposed and demonstrated.

Recently Barger and Hall and their colleagues have developed a laser with a very high frequency stability and resettability [182,183]. They used as reference a resonance of the methane ($CH_4$) molecule, which coincides almost exactly with the 3.39-$\mu$m He-Ne laser line. Because the methane resonance frequency is insensitive to magnetic and electrical fields, and because the cross section is so large that appreciable absorption will occur in a low-pressure absorption cell where pressure effects are minimized and the absorption linewidth is very narrow, a frequency reproducibility of 5 parts in $10^{12}$ and a short-term frequency stability of greater than 1 part in $10^{13}$ have been achieved with this system [184]. Such lasers have been used for high-precision interferometry, and this type of system may some day become the new standard not only of length but also of frequency. (For a review of optical frequency standards see Ref. 185.)

### B.  Internal Modulation

In early studies of laser modulation systems, it was noted that high modulation efficiencies could be obtained by placing within the laser resonator a modulator that coupled out of the laser a fraction of the internal laser power. The reason for this is that for typical low-gain gas lasers, the optimum output coupling is of the order of a few percent [186], and thus a modulation voltage that would only produce a few percent modulation depth if the modulator were used outside the laser cavity, is sufficient to produce 100% modulated output at maximum output power when the same modulator is used within the laser [187]. Serious modulation distortion occurs, however, when the modulation frequency approaches the longitudinal mode-spacing frequency of the laser resonator [188]. To overcome this problem, Nash and Smith [189] used such an internal modulator within a 6328-Å He-Ne laser that used a Fox-Smith interferometer to obtain single-frequency operation. With such a device, these authors were able to show both theoretically and experimentally that negligible modulation distortion occurs when the output is modulated at the c/2L mode-spacing frequency of the long-laser resonator. The experimental modulator bandwidth was greater than 700 MHz and the driving power required was less than 0.4 mW per MHz of bandwidth. Some proposals for internal frequency modulation of such lasers have been discussed by Kupka [190].

### C. "Lamb Dip" Measurements

The shape of the so-called Lamb dip that occurs in the output power-vs-frequency tuning curve of a single-frequency gas laser (see Section II) depends on the homogeneous linewidth of the laser transition. Thus experimental observations of the output of single-frequency gas lasers as a function of resonator tuning can be used to measure the homogeneous linewidth of the transition as a function of gas pressure, mixture, etc. In particular, the effects of gas collisions

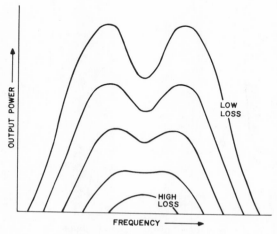

**Figure 28**

Single-frequency laser output vs frequency for different values of resonator loss.

can be studied in much greater detail than is possible with techniques that only observe the entire Doppler-broadened resonance line profile. Figure 28 shows a typical series of curves of output power vs tuning for various values of loss in the laser resonator. Since the first experimental observations by McFarlane et al. [78], Lamb dip studies have been reported for the He-Ne laser at $1.15\ \mu m$ [191, 192] and 6328 Å [13, 193, 194], the argon ion laser [133, 195, 196], and $CO_2$ and $N_2O$ molecular lasers [197, 198]. For most of these studies, laser resonators short enough to permit single-longitudinal-mode operation have been used; however, for the argon ion laser, experimenters have used a Fox-Smith interferometer to obtain single-frequency operation and have observed the output vs resonator length as the mode-selector resonator is tuned in order to obtain the form of the Lamb dip profile. Some related studies using single-frequency lasers are the two-wavelength experiments of Beterov et al. [199] and Hänsch and Toschek [200], the crossed-beam experiments of Shank and Schwarz [201] and Smith and Hänsch [14], and the modulated-frequency experiments of Bolwijn and his co-workers [202, 203].

### D.   Tunable Laser Sources: Laser Spectroscopy

Single-frequency lasers are sources of very intense narrow-band radiation that

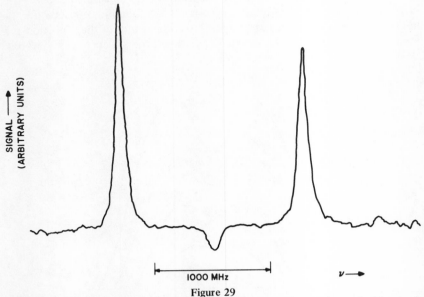

**Figure 29**

The sodium $D_2$ line, one component of the sodium D doublet, as observed with a tunable dye laser spectrometer. On this scale, the other component of the doublet would be situated a distance of roughly 20 m from this page.

would be ideal for spectroscopic studies if they were tunable over a sufficiently wide range. Most gas and even solid-state lasers, however, have relatively narrow gain bandwidths, and spectroscopic experiments can be done only on those systems that have a fortunate coincidence of resonance lines with the laser wavelength. (See, for example, Ref. 183). There are some lasers, however, notably dye lasers, that have very broad bandwidths, and by suitable single-frequency techniques, it has recently been demonstrated that one can obtain a very narrow-band, intense source that is tunable over most of the visible region of the spectrum. Hänsch and Schawlow [204] have built such a dye laser using a beam-expanding telescope to obtain a broad beam incident on a diffraction grating that is used as one end reflector, and also including a tilted Fabry-Perot etalon within the laser resonator. The dye solution is pumped by a pulsed nitrogen laser operating at 3371 Å. Figure 29 shows some preliminary results of laser spectroscopy of sodium vapor using this tunable dye laser.* The actual resolution capability of the system is higher than it appears from this figure, as most of the observed linewidth is believed to come from unresolved hyperfine splitting of the sodium $^3P_{3/2}$ state [204]. The experiment was performed using a crossed-beam technique first described by Smith and Hänsch [14]. This technique allows one to observe a response whose width is the homogeneous linewidth of a transition, and thus structure which is normally masked by Doppler broadening can be observed.

Other tunable single-frequency laser sources in the infrared region of the spectrum are the spin-flip laser [205] and the $Pb_{1-x}Sn_xTe$ diode laser [206]. Patel et al. [205] have described a single-frequency spin-flip laser tunable over the range of 10.9 to 13.0 $\mu$m by varying the applied magnetic field, and they have described the use of this laser to study the absorption spectrum of $NH_3$. Such a laser system has recently been used in air pollution studies and has been shown capable of detecting concentrations of NO in the atmosphere of less than 0.01 ppm [207]. Hinkley [206] has described the use of a single-frequency PbSnTe semiconductor laser tuned by varying the applied current to observe the absorption spectrum of $SF_6$ in the 10-$\mu$m region of the spectrum.

The development of tunable single-frequency lasers for spectroscopy is just reaching the stage where useful results can be obtained, and the next few years are likely to produce a rapid blooming of this important field.

---

*The author wishes to thank Prof. T. W. Hänsch of Stanford University for access to his experimental results prior to their publication.

## List of Symbols

| | | | |
|---|---|---|---|
| a | Radius of aperture | $r, \theta, z$ | Cylindrical coordinates |
| $A_0, A_0'$ | Field amplitude normalizing constants | R | Phase front curvature |
| | | $R_i$ | Curvature of mirror i |
| c | Velocity of light | w | Spot size of Gaussian beam |
| d | Mirror spacing | $w_0$ | Spot size of Gaussian beam at |
| g | Field gain | | beam waist |
| $g_i$ | $(= 1 - L/R_i)$ Resonator geometry parameter | $w_0$ | Saturation parameter |
| G | Power gain | $w_{si}$ | $(= \sqrt{R_i \lambda/\pi})$, i = 1, 2 Confocal spot size |
| $H_m, H_n$ | Hermite polynomials of order m, n | $\mu$ | Field component of light wave |
| | | $x, y, z$ | Cartesian coordinates |
| I | Radiation intensity | $\gamma'$ | Homogeneous linewidth |
| j | $\sqrt{-1}$ | $\gamma_h'$ | Radiation-broadened homogeneous linewidth |
| k | $(= 2\pi/\lambda)$ Propagation constant | | |
| $L_p^\ell$ | Laguerre polynomial of order $\ell$, p | $\theta$ | Far-field diffraction angle |
| | | $\lambda, \lambda'$ | Wavelengths |
| L | Length of laser resonator | $\nu$ | Frequency |
| L | Power loss | $\rho_i$ | Field reflection coefficient of mirror i |
| m, n | Transverse mode numbers | | |
| m, n | Integers | $\tau_i$ | Field transmission coefficient of mirror i |
| n | Refractive index | $\Phi, \Phi'$ | Phase shifts |
| N | $(= a^2/\lambda L)$ Fresnel number | $\psi$ | Field amplitude |
| q | Longitudinal mode number | $\omega$ | Circular frequency |
| Q | Quality factor of resonator | | |

## References

1. A. L. Schawlow and C. H. Townes, *Phys. Rev.,* **112**, 1940 (1958).
2. H. Kogelnik and T. Li, *Appl. Opt.,* **5**, 1550 (1966).
3. G. D. Boyd and H. Kogelnik, *Bell System Tech J.,* **41**, 1347 (1962).
4. A. G. Fox and T. Li, *Proc. IRE,* **48**, 1904 (1960); A. G. Fox and T. Li, *Bell System Tech. J.,* **40**, 453 (1961).
5. A. G. Fox and T. Li, *Proc. IEEE,* **51**, 80 (1963).
6  A. G. Fox and T. Li, *IEEE J. Quantum Electron.,* **2**, 774 (1966).
7. T. Li, *Bell System Tech J.,* **44**, 917 (1965).
8. T. S. Jaseja, A. Javan, and C. H. Townes, *Phys. Rev. Letters,* **10**, 165 (1963).
9. P. W. Smith, *Proc. IEEE,* **58**, 1342 (1970).
10. A. Yariv, *Quantum Electronics,* Wiley, New York, 1967.
11. See, for example, W. E. Lamb, Jr., *Phys. Rev.,* **134**, A1429 (1964).
12. W. R. Bennett, Jr., *Phys. Rev.,* **126**, 580 (1962).
13. P. W. Smith, *J. Appl. Phys.,* **37**, 2090 (1966).
14. P. W. Smith and T. Hänsch, *Phys. Rev. Letters,* **26**, 740 (1971).
15. C. L. Tang, H. Statz, and G. deMars, *Appl. Phys. Letters,* **2**, 222 (1963); *J. Appl. Phys.,* **34**, 2289 (1963); and C. L. Tang, H. Statz, G. A. deMars, and D. T. Wilson, *Phys. Rev.,* **136**, A1 (1964).
16. J. Free and A. Korpel, *Proc. IEEE,* **52**, 90 (1964).
17. H. G. Danielmeyer and W. G. Nilsen, *Appl. Phys. Letters,* **16**, 124 (1970).
18. V. Evtuhov and A. E. Siegman, *Appl. Opt.,* **4**, 142 (1965).

19. D. A. Draegert, to be published.
20. C. Bowness, U.S. Patent 3409843 (April 1964).
21. H. G. Danielmeyer and E. H. Turner, *Appl. Phys. Letters,* **17,** 519 (1970).
22. H. G. Danielmeyer, *J. Appl. Phys.,* **42,** 3125 (1971).
23. A. D. White, *Appl. Opt.,* **3,** 431 (1964).
24. B. H. Soffer and B. B. McFarland, *Appl. Phys. Letters,* **10,** 266 (1967).
25. T. J. Manuccia and G. J. Wolga, *IEEE J. Quantum Electron.,* **6,** 185 (1970).
26. W. Q. Jeffers, *Appl. Phys. Letters,* **11,** 178 (1967).
27. A. L. Bloom, W. E. Bell, and R. C. Rempel, *Appl. Opt.,* **2,** 317 (1963).
28. C. B. Moore, *Appl. Opt.,* **4,** 252 (1965).
29. N. V. Karlov, Yu. N. Petrov, and O. M. Stel'makh, *JETP Letters,* **8,** 224 (1968).
30. H. Walther and J. L. Hall, *Appl. Phys. Letters,* **17,** 239 (1970).
31. L. Cirkovic, D. E. Evans, M. J. Forrest, and J. Katzenstein, *Appl. Opt.,* **7,** 981 (1968).
32. S. E. Miller, *Bell System Tech J.,* **48,** 2059 (1969).
33. H. Kogelnik and C. V. Shank, *Appl. Phys. Letters,* **18,** 152 (1971).
34. I. P. Kaminow, H. P. Weber, and E. A. Chandross, *Appl. Phys. Letters,* **18,** 497 (1971).
35. C. V. Shank, J. E. Bjorkholm, and H. Kogelnik, *Appl. Phys. Letters,* **18,** 395 (1971).
36. T. Li, *Bell System Tech J.,* **42,** 2609 (1963).
37. J. A. Baker and C. W. Peters, *Appl. Opt.,* **1,** 674 (1962).
38. A. Okaya, *Proc. IEEE,* **51,** 1033 (1963).
39. J. G. Skinner and J. E. Geusic, in *Quantum Electronics III* (P. Grivet and N. Bloembergen, eds.), Columbia Univ. Press, New York, 1964, p. 1437.
40. V. Evtuhov and J. K Neeland, *IEEE J. Quantum Electron.,* **1,** 7 (1965).
41. Y. Suematsu and K. Iga, *Proc. IEEE,* **52,** 87 (1964).
42. D. C. Sinclair, *Appl. Opt.,* **3,** 1067 (1964).
43. A. V. Korovitsyn, L. D. Naumova, and Z. T. Lebedinskaya, *Radio Eng. Elect. Phys.,* **11,** 572 (1966).
44. I. M. Belousova and O. B. Danilov, *Soviet Phys.-Tech. Phys.,* **12,** 1104 (1968).
45. D. V. Gordeev, V. M. Grimblatov, Ye. P. Ostapchenko, and V. V. Teselkin, *Radio Eng. Elect. Phys.,* **14,** 1420 (1969).
46. A. L. Mikaelyan, A. V. Korovitsyn, and L. D. Naumova, *Radio Eng. Elect. Phys.,* **14,** 93 (1969).
47. J. M. Burch, *J. Opt. Soc. Am.,* **52,** 602 (1962).
48. T. Li and P. W. Smith, *Proc. IEEE,* **53,** 399 (1965).
49. A. E. Siegman, *Proc. IEEE,* **53,** 277 (1965).
50. A. E. Siegman and R. Arrathoon, *IEEE J. Quantum Electron.,* **3,** 156 (1967).
51. Yu. A. Ananev, N. A. Sventsitskaya, and V. E. Sherstobitov, *Soviet Phys. Doklady,* **13,** 351 (1968).
52. C. M. Stickley, *IEEE J. Quantum Electron.,* **2,** 511 (1966).
53. W. D. Fricke, *Appl. Opt.,* **9,** 2045 (1970).
54. L. G. DeShazer and E. A. Maunders, *Appl. Opt.,* **6,** 431 (1967).
55. N. G. Bondarenko, I. V. Eremina, and B. I. Talanov, *JETP Letters,* **6,** 1 (1967).
56. J. A. Giordmaine and W. Kaiser, *J. Appl. Phys.,* **35,** 3446 (1964).
57. G. Soncini and O. Svelto, *Appl. Phys Letters,* **11,** 261 (1967).
58. G. Soncini and O. Svelto, *IEEE J. Quantum Electron.,* **4,** 422 (1968).
59. R. P. Flam and E. R. Schineller, *Proc. IEEE,* **56,** 195 (1968).
60. J. M. McMahon, *IEEE J. Quantum Electron.,* **5,** 489 (1969).
61. M. Birnbaum, P. H. Wendzikowski, and C. L. Fincher, *Appl. Phys. Letters,* **16,** 436 (1970).
62. A. Stein, *Appl. Opt.,* **6,** 2193 (1967).
63. D. Roess, *Frequenz,* **17,** 61 (1963).
64. D. H. Arnold and D. C. Hanna, *Electron. Letters,* **5,** 354 (1969).
65. M. S. Lipsett and M. W. Strandberg, *Appl. Opt.,* **1,** 343 (1962).
66. D. C. Hanna, *Optics Tech.,* **2,** 122 (1970); *Optics and Laser Tech.,* **2,** 175 (1970).
67. A. Okaya, *Proc. IEEE,* **52,** 1741 (1964).
68. H. Kogelnik and W. W. Rigrod, *Proc. IRE,* **50,** 220 (1962); W. W. Rigrod, *Appl. Phys. Letters,* **2,** 51 (1963).
69. R. J. Collins and J. A. Giordmaine, in *Quantum Electronics III* (P. Grivet and N. Bloembergen, eds.), Columbia Univ. Press, New York, 1964, p. 1239.

70. W. D. Johnston, T. Li, and P. W. Smith, *IEEE J. Quantum Electron.,* **4**, 469 (1968).
71. See, for example, R. A Myers, *IEEE J. Quantum Electron.,* **4**, 408 (1968).
72. E. I. Gordon and A. D. White, *Proc. IEEE,* **52**, 206 (1964).
73. K. M. Baird, D. S. Smith, G. R. Hanes, and S. Tsunekane, *Appl. Opt.,* **4**, 569 (1965).
74. D. Gloge, J. Helmcke, and P. Runge, *Frequenz,* **18**, 367 (1964).
75. J. A. Collinson, *Bell System Tech J.,* **44**, 1511 (1965).
76. J. V. Ramsay and K. Tanaka, *Japan. J. Appl. Phys.,* **5**, 918 (1966).
77. C. F. Bruce, *Appl. Opt.* **10**, 880 (1971).
78. R. A. McFarlane, W. R. Bennett, and W. E. Lamb, *Appl. Phys. Letters,* **2**, 189 (1963).
79. G. E. Stillman, M. D. Stirkis, J. A. Rossi, M. R. Johnson, and N. Holonyak, *Appl. Phys. Letters,* **9**, 268 (1966).
80. G. Magyar, *Optics Tech.,* **1**, 231 (1969).
81. D. A. Kleinman and P. P. Kisliuk, *Bell System Tech J.,* **41**, 453 (1964).
82. See, for example, P. Jacquinot, *Rep. Progr. Phys.,* **23**, 267 (1960).
83. V. I. Perel and I. V. Rogova, *Opt. and Spectr.,* **25**, 401 (1968).
84. V. I. Perel and I. V. Rogova, *Opt. and Spectr.,* **25**, 520 (1968).
85. A. A. Bakeyev and N. V. Cheburkin, *Radio Eng. Elec. Phys.,* **14**, 1125 (1969).
86. G. Bouwhuis, *Philips Res. Repts.,* **19**, 422 (1964).
87. H. Kogelnik and C. K. N. Patel, *Proc. IRE,* **50**, 2365 (1962).
88. G. D. Currie, *Appl. Opt.,* **8**, 1068 (1969); G. D. Currie, *Rev. Sci. Instr.,* **40**, 1342 (1969).
89. E. Gregor, *Appl. Opt.,* **7**, 2138 (1968).
90. H. I. Pawel, J. R. Stanford, J. H. Wenzel, and G. J. Wolga, *Proc. IEEE,* **52**, 1048 (1964).
91. D. Roess, *Proc. IEEE,* **52**, 196 (1964).
92. W. B. Tiffany, *Appl. Opt.,* **7**, 67 (1968).
93. F. J. McClung and D. Weiner, *IEEE J. Quantum Electron.,* **1**, 94 (1965).
94. E. Snitzer, *Appl. Opt.,* **5**, 121 (1966).
95. N. M. Galaktionova, G. A. Garkavi, V. F. Egorova, A. A. Mak, and V. A. Fromzel, *Opt. and Spectr.,* **28**, 404 (1970).
96. T. Kobayashi and Y. Matsuo, *Appl. Phys. Letters,* **16**, 217 (1970).
97. N. Kumagai, M. Matsuhara, and H Mori, *IEEE J. Quantum Electron.,* **1**, 85 (1965).
98. N. Kumagai and M. Matsuhara, *Tech. Rept. Osaka Univ.,* **16**, 189 (1966).
99. M. Birnbaum and T. L. Stocker, *J. Appl. Phys.,* **34**, 3414 (1963).
100. M. Birnbaum and T. L. Stocker, *J. Appl. Phys.,* **37**, 531 (1966).
101. R. Pratesi and G. T. diFrancia, *Nuovo Cimento,* **34**, 40 (1964).
102. R. Pratesi and G. T. diFrancia, *Proc. IEEE,* **53**, 196 (1965).
103. R. Pratesi, *Appl. Opt.,* **6**, 1243 (1967).
104. H. F. Mahlein and G. Schollmeier, *Appl. Opt.,* **8**, 1197 (1969).
105. J. M. Burch, in *Quantum Electronics III* (P. Grivet and N. Bloembergen, eds.), Columbia Univ. Press, New York, 1964, p. 1187.
106. M. Hercher, *Appl. Phys. Letters,* **7**, 39 (1965).
107. E. I. Nikonava, E. N. Pavlovskaya, and G. P. Startsev, *Opt. and Spectr.,* **22**, 535 (1967).
108. R. M. Scotland, *Appl. Opt.,* **9**, 1211 (1970).
109. J. K. Watts, *Appl. Opt.,* **7**, 1621 (1968).
110. G. Magyar, *Rev. Sci. Instr.,* **38**, 517 (1967).
111. S. A. Collins and G. R. White, in *Lasers and Applications* (W. S. C. Chang, ed.), Ohio State Univ. Press, Columbus, Ohio, 1963, p. 96; S. A. Collins and G. R. White, *Appl. Opt.,* **2**, 448 (1963).
112. H. Manger and H. Rothe, *Phys. Letters,* **7**, 330 (1963).
113. H. Manger and H. Rothe, *Phys. Letters,* **12**, 182 (1964).
114. M. Hercher, *Appl. Opt.,* **8**, 1103 (1969).
115. H. G. Danielmeyer, *IEEE J. Quantum Electron.,* **6**, 101 (1970).
116. H. Manger, *Z. Agnew. Phys.,* **18**, 265 (1965).
117. D. Roess, *Appl. Phys. Letters,* **8**, 109 (1966).
118. M. P. Vanyukov, V. I. Isaenko, L. A. Luizova, and O. A. Shorokhov, *Opt. and Spectr.,* **20**, 535 (1966).
119. H. P. Barber, *Appl. Opt.,* **7**, 559 (1968).

120. L. H. Lin and C. V. LoBianco, *Appl. Opt.*, **6**, 1255 (1967).
121. A. J. Gibson, *J. Sci. Instr.*, **2**, 802 (1969).
122. D. J. Bradley, A. J. F. Durrant, G. M. Gale, M. Moore, and P. D. Smith, *IEEE J. Quantum Electron.*, **4**, 707 (1968).
123. L. B. Kreuzer, *Appl. Phys. Letters*, **15**, 263 (1969).
124. Yu. D. Kolomnikov, V. N. Lisitsyn, and V. P. Chebotayev, *Opt. and Spectr.*, **22**, 449 (1967).
125. T. Ulchida, U.S. Patent 3402365.
126. K. Kantor, A. Kiss, and T. Salamon, *Soviet Phys. JETP*, **25**, 221 (1967).
127. A. G. Fox, U.S. Patent 3504299.
128. P. W. Smith, *IEEE J. Quantum Electron.*, **1**, 343 (1965).
129. Y. Cho, T. Tajime, and Y. Matsuo, *IEEE J. Quantum Electron.*, **4**, 699 (1968).
130. P. W. Smith, *IEEE J. Quantum Electron.*, **2**, 666 (1966).
131. P. Zory, *J. Appl. Phys.*, **37**, 3643 (1966).
132. W. W. Rigrod and A. M. Johnson, *IEEE J. Quantum Electron.*, **3**, 644 (1967).
133. P. Zory, *IEEE J. Quantum Electron.*, **3**, 390 (1967).
134. L. Gorog and F. W. Spong, *RCA Rev.*, **30**, 277 (1969).
135. B. Dessus and P. Laures, *Ann. Telecomm.*, **24**, 164 (1969).
136. V. P. Belyaiev, V. A. Burmakin, A. N. Evtyunin, F. A. Korolyov, V. V. Lebedeva, and A. I. Odintzov, *IEEE J. Quantum Electron.*, **5**, 589 (1969).
137. D. C. Sinclair, *Appl. Phys. Letters*, **13**, 98 (1968).
138. M. DiDomenico, *Appl. Phys. Letters*, **8**, 20 (1966).
139. M. DiDomenico, *IEEE J. Quantum Electron.*, **2**, 311 (1966).
140. A. D. White, *Bell System Tech J.*, **45**, 339 (1966).
141. W. W. Rigrod, *IEEE J. Quantum Electron.*, **6**, 9 (1970).
142. J. R. Fontana, *IEEE J. Quantum Electron.*, **4**, 678 (1968).
143. P. W. Smith, *IEEE J. Quantum Electron.*, **4**, 485 (1968).
144. V. N. Kutin and B. I. Troshin, *Opt. and Spectr.*, **29**, 197 (1970).
145. V. Yu. Petrun'kin, M. G. Vysotskii, and R. I. Okunev, *Soviet Phys.-Tech. Phys.*, **14**, 694 (1969).
146. P. J. Maloney and P. W. Smith, *IEEE J. Quantum Electron.*, **8**, 744 (1972).
147. G. A. Massey, M. K. Oshman, and R. Targ, *Appl. Phys. Letters*, **6**, 10 (1965).
148. L. M. Osterink and R. Targ, *Appl. Phys. Letters*, **10**, 115 (1967).
149. S. E. Harris and O. P. McDuff, *Appl. Phys. Letters*, **5**, 205 (1964); S. E. Harris and R. Targ, *ibid*, **5**, 202 (1964).
150. H. P. Weber and E. Mathieu, *IEEE J. Quantum Electron.*, **3**, 376 (1967).
151. S. E. Harris and B. J. McMurtry, *Appl. Phys. Letters*, **7**, 265 (1965).
152. V. P. Chebotayev, I. M. Beterov, and V. N. Lisitsyn, *IEEE J. Quantum Electron.*, **4**, 788 (1968).
153. P. H. Lee, P. B. Schoefer, and W. B. Barker, *Appl. Phys. Letters*, **13**, 373 (1968).
154. I. M. Beterov, V. N. Lisitsyn, and V. P. Chebotayev, *Radio Eng. Elec. Phys.*, **14**, 981 (1969).
155. M. S. Feld, A. Javan, and P. H. Lee, *Appl. Phys. Letters*, **13**, 424 (1968).
156. Yu. V. Trotskii and N. D. Goldina, *JETP Letters*, **7**, 36 (1968).
157. V. I. Donin, Yu. V. Troitskii, and N. D. Goldina, *Opt. and Spectr.*, **26**, 64 (1969).
158. P. W. Smith, M. V. Schneider, and H. G. Danielmeyer, *Bell System Tech J.*, **48**, 1405 (1969).
159. Yu. V. Troitskii, *Radio Eng. Elec. Phys.*, **14**, 1423 (1969).
160. Yu. V. Troitskii, *J. Appl. Spectr.*, **12**, 425 (1970).
161. N. D. Goldina and Yu. V. Troitskii, *Opt. and Spectr.*, **28**, 319 (1970).
162. Yu. V. Troitskii, *Opt. and Spectr.*, **27**, 263 (1969).
163. B. H. Soffer, *J. Appl. Phys.*, **35**, 2551 (1964).
164. J. E. Bjorkholm and R. H. Stolen, *J. Appl. Phys.*, **39**, 4043 (1968).
165. V. Daneu, C. A. Sacchi, and O. Svelto, *IEEE J. Quantum Electron.*, **2**, 290 (1966).
166. W. R. Sooy, *Appl. Phys. Letters*, **7**, 36 (1965).
167. A. Nurmikko, T. A. DeTemple, and S. E. Schwarz, *Appl. Phys. Letters*, **18**, 130 (1971).
168. W. D. Johnston, Jr., *J. Appl. Phys.*, **42**, 2731 (1971).

169. P. W. Smith, *Appl. Phys. Letters*, 19, 132 (1971).
170. J. M. Yarborough and J. L. Hobart, *Appl. Phys. Letters*, 13, 305 (1968).
171. T. J. Bridges and W. W. Rigrod, *IEEE J. Quantum Electron.*, 1, 303 (1965).
172. M. S. Borisova and A. M. Pyndyk, *Radio Eng. Elec. Phys.*, 13, 658 (1968).
173. J. M. Forsyth, *Appl. Phys. Letters*, 11, 391 (1967).
174. L. G. DeShazer and E. A. Maunders, *IEEE J. Quantum Electron.*, 4, 642 (1968).
175. A. N. Bondarenko, G. V. Krivoshchekov, and V. A. Smirnov, *JETP Letters*, 9, 57 (1969).
176. A. N. Bondarenko, G. V. Krivoshchekov, and V. A. Smirnov, *Soviet Phys.-JETP*, 29, 975 (1969).
177. J. E. Bjorkholm and H. G. Danielmeyer, *Appl. Phys. Letters*, 15, 171 (1969).
178. G. Briquet, J. M. Jego, and A. Terneaud, *Appl. Phys. Letters*, 14, 282 (1969).
179. A. D. White, *IEEE J. Quantum Electron.*, 1, 349 (1965).
180. G. Birnbaum, *Proc. IEEE*, 55, 1015 (1967).
181. G. Birnbaum, *Electron Tech. (Poland)*, 2, 67 (1969).
182. R. L. Barger and J. L. Hall, *Phys. Rev. Letters*, 22, 4 (1969).
183. E. E. Uzgiris, J. L. Hall, and R. L. Barger, *Phys. Rev. Letters*, 26, 289 (1971).
184. J. L. Hall, private communication.
185. N. G. Basov and V. S. Letokhov, *Soviet Phys. Uspekhi*, 11, 855 (1969).
186. P. W. Smith, *IEEE J. Quantum Electron.*, 2, 62 (1966).
187. K. Gürs and R. Muller, *Proceedings of the Symposium on Optical Masers*, Polytechnic Press, Brooklyn, New York, 1963, p. 243; G. Grau and D. Rosenberger, *Phys. Letters*, 6, 129 (1963); T. Uchida, *IEEE J. Quantum Electron.*, 1, 336 (1965); A. D. Rugari and P. E. Nordborg, *Proc. IEEE*, 52, 852 (1964).
188. M. DiDomenico, Jr., *J. Appl. Phys.*, 34, 2870 (1964); I. P. Kaminow, *Appl. Opt.*, 4, 123 (1965).
189. F. R. Nash and P. W. Smith, *IEEE J. Quantum Electron.*, 4, 26 (1968).
190. J. Kupka, *Electron. Letters*, 4, 31 (1968).
191. A. Szöke and A. Javan, *Phys. Rev. Letters*, 10, 521 (1963).
192. A. Szöke and A. Javan, *Phys. Rev.*, 145, 137 (1966).
193. R. H. Cordover and P. A. Bonczyk, *Phys. Rev.*, 188, 969 (1969).
194. W. Dietel, *Phys. Letters*, 29A, 268 (1969).
195. D. A. Stetser, Tech. Rep., F920479-4 (1967).
196. A. I. Odintsov, V. V. Lebedeva, and G. V. Abrosimov, *Radio Eng. Elec. Phys.*, 13, 650 (1968).
197. C. Borde and L. Henry, *IEEE J. Quantum Electron.*, 4, 874 (1968).
198. K. Tan, H. T. Powell, and G. J. Wolga, *IEEE J. Quantum Electron.*, 5, 299 (1969).
199. I. M. Beterov, Yu. A. Matyugin, and V. P. Chebotayev, *JETP Letters*, 12, 120 (1970).
200. T. W. Hänsch and P. E. Toschek, *IEEE J. Quantum Electron.*, 5, 61 (1969).
201. C. V. Shank and S. E. Schwarz, *Appl. Phys. Letters*, 13, 113 (1968).
202. P. T. Bolwijn and C. Th. J. Alkemade, *Phys. Letters*, 25A, 632 (1967).
203. P. T. Bolwijn, *Phys. Letters*, 19, 384 (1965).
204. T. W. Hänsch and A. L. Schawlow, private communication.
205. See, for example, C. K. N. Patel, E. D. Shaw, and R. J. Kerl, *Phys. Rev. Letters*, 25, 8 (1970).
206. E. D. Hinkley, *Appl. Phys. Letters*, 16, 351 (1970).
207. L. B. Kreuzer and C. K. N. Patel, *Science*, 173, 45 (1971).
208. P. W. Smith, *Proc. IEEE*, 60, 422 (1972).

*Chapter 3*

# Helium-Neon Lasers and the Positive Column

*Raymond Arrathoon\**

Bell Laboratories, Incorporated
Murray Hill, New Jersey

*\*Present address:* Solarex Ltd., Troy, Idaho.

# I. Introduction

In January, 1961, simultaneous laser oscillation at five wavelengths in a helium-neon glow discharge was announced by Javan et al. [1]. This discovery heralded the advent of thousands of electrically excited laser transitions in gases. Prior to the initial operation of the helium-neon laser, Schawlow and Townes [2] had already delineated the essential features of optical regenerative amplification devices. By extending microwave maser principles [3] to the optical region, they had specified the conditions necessary for population inversion and the formation of a suitable cavity. Some forty years earlier, Tolman [4] had suggested that population inversion would result in the amplification of radiation due to stimulated emission. Both Tolman's proposal and the proposal of Schawlow and Townes were ultimately based on Einstein's [5] formalized description of stimulated emission processes.

That portion of the helium-neon discharge responsible for population inversion is referred to as the positive column. This discharge region is often called a plasma because the ions and electrons interact appropriately to produce a state of approximate charge neutrality. The electronic and ionic processes in the positive column were first discussed in detail by Schottky [6] and by Langmuir and Tonks [7]. Ladenburg [8] concurrently performed detailed experiments leading to a description of radiative processes and population mechanisms in a pure neon positive column. In retrospect, if Ladenburg had experimented with helium-neon mixtures as carefully as with pure neon, he might have observed perplexing population changes accompanied by superradiance at 3.39 $\mu$m. For the proper discharge conditions, this transition has such high gain that the deliberate formation of an optical cavity is often not essential to sustain coherent emission.

In 1940, Fabrikant [9], apparently unaware of the possibility of obtaining coherent oscillation from a stimulated emission amplifier, proposed that population inversion in a gas discharge might be achieved by using collisions of the second kind to depopulate the lower level. Almost twenty years later, Javan [10, 11] proposed using a gas discharge for the active medium in an optical maser. In this scheme, population inversion was to be collisionally induced either through direct electron-atom excitation or through second-kind atom-atom excitation. Sanders [12] simultaneously suggested using direct electron-atom excitation to generate population inversion. However, operation of the first helium-neon laser was subsequently achieved at five wavelengths in the vicinity of 1.15 $\mu$m based on Javan's [1] proposal for second-kind collisional excitation. White and Rigden [13] later obtained visible gas laser operation from another analogous group of helium-neon energy levels.

This chapter is primarily concerned with describing helium-neon lasers in terms of the basic populating mechanisms associated with second-kind collisional inversion. It is assumed that at a given point in space, the populating and depopulating mechanisms uniformly affect the statistics of all the atoms in a particular excited state. In general, treatments of stimulated emission are restricted to situations in which homogeneous processes directly affect the laser output. Emphasis is on relating many of the populating mechanisms to the actual physical characteristics of the positive column—specifically voltages, currents, partial pressures, and dimensions.

## II. Collision Processes and Stimulated Emission

### A. *Excitation Mechanisms*

In 1914, Franck and Hertz [14] directly demonstrated the existence of discrete energy levels in excited mercury atoms. They showed that free electons must possess a certain minimum kinetic energy in order to collisionally excite ground-state mercury atoms. This minimum kinetic energy corresponds to the potential energy of the first excited level. Electron-atom collisions, in which the potential energy of the atom is increased, became known as collisions of the first kind. In this type of collision, the impinging free electron can be exchanged with one of the bound electrons and transferred directly to an excited state. Alternatively, the impinging electron can remain unbound and one of the bound electrons can be transferred to the excited state. Later experiments by Maier-Leibnitz [15] showed that each excited atomic level had a particular structure associated with the dependence of electron-impact excitation on electron energy. Maier-Leibnitz succeeded in isolating this structure for the first few excited states of helium and neon. The results of his early experiments are redrawn in Fig. 1. The energy-dependent structures are termed excitation cross sections, and they provide a measure of the probability for direct electron excitation to each level. The cross sections of Fig. 1 indicate that the first helium singlet-to-triplet transition has a more sharply peaked energy dependence than the first helium singlet-to-singlet transition. This sharply peaked structure is characteristic of spin exchange transitions. (Details of electron-atom collision processes are reviewed in Massey and Burhop [16], McDaniel [17], and von Engel [18]).

The principle of microscopic reversibility or detailed balance, formulated by

Einstein [5] and expanded by Klein and Rosseland [19], requires that the excitation probability of a given excited state by a particular mechanism must equal the deexcitation probability of this state by the reverse mechanism. Physically, detailed balance implies that equilibrium must be achieved regardless of the presence of additional interaction mechanisms. Reversibility suggests that if an atom can gain potential energy in a collision with a fast electron, then a slow electron can gain kinetic energy in a collision with an excited atom. Collisions in which an electron gains kinetic energy from the potential energy of an excited atom are called collisions of the second kind. Second-kind collisions more generally refer to processes in which potential energy is partly or completely converted to kinetic energy. Thus, excitation transfer from a particular excited state to a lower excited state may also occur by second-kind collisions with atoms. As in electron-atom collisions, there is a definite structure, or energy-dependent cross section, associated with atom-atom collisional excitation transfer [20].

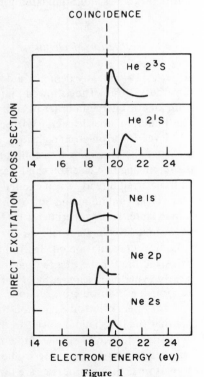

**Figure 1**

Direct excitation cross sections for the first few excited states of helium and neon, redrawn from the original work of Maier-Leibnitz [15]. A coincidence in energy between the He $2^3$S state and the Ne 2s states is indicated.

From detailed balance considerations, Klein and Rosseland [19] showed that the magnitude and energy dependence of the cross sections for first- and second- kind electron-atom collisions are connected by the relation

$$Q_2(E - E_n) = \frac{g_1}{g_2} \frac{E}{E - E_n} \, Q_1(E) \tag{1}$$

Here $Q_1$ is the first-kind collisional cross section for level one and $Q_2$ is the second-kind collisional cross section for level two; $g_1$ and $g_2$ are the respective level degeneracies; and $E_n$ is the energy difference, $E_2 - E_1$. The energy dependence of a typical exchange excitation cross section can be approximately expressed in the form [21]

$$Q_1(E) = Q_{10} \frac{E - E_n}{0.2E_n} \, \exp\left(-\frac{E - E_n}{0.2E_n}\right) \tag{2}$$

where $Q_{10}$ is the maximum value of the excitation cross section. This cross section is plotted in Fig. 2, together with its second-kind counterpart defined by Eq. (1). The second-kind collisional cross section is seen to have no minimum threshold; and it commonly peaks at very low energies [22].

When the electron energy distribution is Maxwellian, the population densities and the rates (sec $^{-1}$) for first- and second-kind collisions are related by a Boltzmann distribution [8].

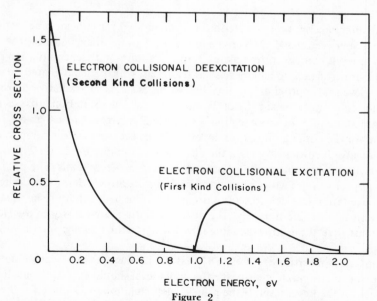

ELECTRON ENERGY, eV

**Figure 2**

Cross sections for collisions of the first and second kind in a typical spin exchange transition. The cross sections are related by detailed balance considerations.

$$\frac{N_2}{N_1} = \frac{Z_1}{Z_2} = \frac{g_2}{g_1} \exp\left(-\frac{E_n}{kT}\right) \tag{3}$$

In the next section, the magnitude of the rates $Z_1$ and $Z_2$ will be shown to be proportional to the overlap of the electron energy distribution and the appropriate cross section. The forward and reverse atom-atom collisional transfer rates are also related by a Boltzmann distribution, and the magnitude of these rates will depend on the overlap of the atomic kinetic energy distribution with the relevant cross section. For atom-atom collision processes, appreciable transfer usually requires that the average kinetic energy of the atoms should be comparable to the energy difference between excited states. At room temperatures, this is equivalent to requiring that the energy levels be nearly coincident. The coincidence restrictions do not apply to collisions resulting in the formation of a third body, i.e., Penning collisions [23]. In a helium-neon positive column, the electronic and atomic temperatures are quite different; typical atomic temperatures are less than 500 K [24, 25], and electron temperatures are in the vicinity of 85,000 K [26]. The two temperatures roughly indicate the levels most likely to be affected by atom-atom and electron-atom collisions.

## B. Inversion Considerations

The direct excitation cross sections presented in Fig. 1 indicate a near coincidence in energy between the He $2^3$S level and the third group of excited neon levels. This group of levels consists of four states, termed 2s states in Paschen notation [27]. The second group of excited neon levels has ten levels, which are designated 2p states. The 2p levels lie approximately 1 eV below the 2s states and radiative transitions are allowed between most pairs of 2s and 2p levels. The excitation cross sections of Fig. 1 show that the cross section for the He $2^3$S level is larger than the cross section for the entire group of Ne 2p levels. If the average electron temperature of the discharge is sufficiently high, the direct excitation rate to the He $2^3$S level may exceed the corresponding rate to the entire group of Ne 2p levels. The product of these respective rates with the relevant ground state atomic densities are the direct excitation rate densities (atoms/cm$^3$ sec). For high helium-to-neon ratios and comparable excitation rates, the direct excitation rate density to the He $2^3$S level must exceed the corresponding rate density to the entire group of Ne 2p levels.

Population inversion requires [28] that the product of the effective lifetime and the total excitation rate density for the upper level should exceed the analogous product for the lower level. If the primary depopulation mechanism for the He $2^3$S state is second-kind collisional transfer to the Ne 2s state, the total rate density at which atoms are excited to the 2s states will be at least as great as the direct excitation rate density to the $2^3S$ state. In addition, when the effective lifetime ratio between a particular pair of 2s and 2p levels is greater than unity, population inversion may result. Actual inversion will be determined by the relative contribution of other excitation mechanisms to the total excitation rate density of each level.

Population inversion depends on the intrinsic properties of the atoms as well as on the properties of the discharge. One approach towards describing the required discharge conditions is to begin by delineating the pressure conditions restricting such inversion. A partial energy-level diagram of helium and neon [27] is presented in Fig. 3. The lowest excited helium levels, the $2^3S$ and $2^1S$ states, can relax to the ground state only by nonradiative relaxation mechanisms. Since nonradiative relaxation times are usually orders of magnitude longer than radiative relaxation times, these states are long-lived and are called metastables. At low currents, the primary relaxation mechanisms for the helium metastables are atom-atom transfer collisions to adjacent neon levels and diffusion to the walls of the discharge vessel. (At constant temperature, the fundamental diffusion mode loss rate is inversely proportional to pressure [21]). In contrast to the helium metastables, the neon 3s and 2s levels can relax radiatively to the lower p levels; however, the strongest relaxation route for the 3s and 2s states is direct radiative relaxation to the ground state. Javan [1] proposed that a favorable lifetime ratio between the 2s and 2p states could be obtained by using radiation trapping to increase the effective lifetime of the 2s states. Radiation trapping has been extensively discussed by Holstein [29] and results in a decrease of the transition rate between an upper and lower level due to the reabsorption of emitted photons by neighboring lower-level atoms. This effect is significant only when the population density of the lower level is much larger than the upper-level population density. To obtain the required degree of ground state radiation trapping, the unexcited neon density must exceed a certain minimum value. The neon density should further be large enough to ensure that transfer collisions, rather than wall diffusion, are the primary deexcitation mechanisms for the helium metastable levels. Figure 3 indicates that this situation will also result in significant trapping of the radiation originating from the first group of excited neon levels, the 1s states. As the neon pressure is increased, nonradiative relaxation mechanisms will become increasingly important in determining the lifetime of the 1s states, and these populations will become relatively large. At high neon pressures, trapping of radiation from the 2p-1s transitions will result and the 2p-level effective liftimes will increase. Eventually, the lifetime ratio between the 2s and 2p levels will become small enough to destroy population inversion. The same effect may be produced at high helium pressures due to a decrease in the diffusion rate of the 1s states. The result will be an increase of the 1s level populations and the 2p level lifetimes. Concurrently, in this pressure region the lifetimes of the 2s and 3s states will decrease due to atom-atom transfer collisions [30-31]. Another consequence of high helium pressures is lowering of the electron temperature [26]. At low electron temperatures, the energy discrepancy between the He $2^3$S state and the Ne 2p levels becomes a significant factor in determining the relative excitation rate densities. At all

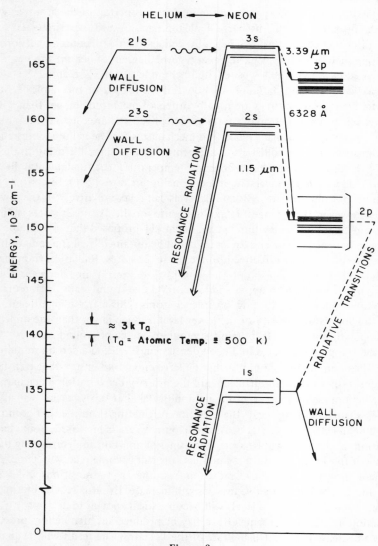

**Figure 3**
Helium-neon energy-level diagram illustrating the primary current independent relaxation mechanisms. [Adapted from [27].]

pressures, large helium-to-neon ratios are generally required to maintain favorable upper-to-lower-level excitation rate densities.

The preceding considerations crudely define the pressure limitations leading to second-kind collisional inversion. Discharge-current considerations are equally important and they will be discussed in detail in the next section. One of the remarkable characteristics of the helium-neon laser discharge is that most of the pressure limitations could have been equally well described as tube-diameter limitations. Gordon and White [32] showed that the primary excitation transfer mechanisms can be expressed in terms of pressure-diameter products. This principle of similarity is applicable over a wide range of conditions [26].

## C. Spectroscopic Qualifications

Helium and neon are the lightest of the noble gases, respectively possessing two and ten electrons. Many of the spectroscopic considerations that apply to the coupling of electrons in these atoms also determine the behavior of electron-atom and atom-atom collision processes in a helium-neon discharge. In the unexcited state, helium has a completely filled K shell with a single subshell containing two electrons. The orbital angular momentum of each of the electrons in this subshell is zero and the electrons have opposite spin angular momenta. When one of the electrons is excited to the next highest shell, the spin angular momenta of the two electrons tend to couple together strongly and may be treated as a unit with respect to the similarly coupled orbital angular momenta of the two electrons [33, 34]. This type of coupling is termed L-S coupling and forms the total angular momentum J associated with a given energy level. The number of energy levels in a given subshell depends on the possible values of S coupled to the possible values of L. For each principle quantum number n, the excited subshells are designated S, P, D, F, etc., corresponding to an orbital angular momentum of 0, 1, 2, 3, etc. For L-S coupling, the excited states are generally divided into groups of multiplicity $2S + 1$, and radiative transitions between groups of different multiplicity are strictly forbidden. The notation $n^{2S+1}L_J$ is commonly used to describe the excited levels. For an atom with an even number of electrons, the total spin will be either zero or one and the excited states may be divided into singlets and triplets. Figure 4 indicates the first few excited states of helium.

The lowest excited s and p states of neon are also shown in Fig. 4. For neon, j-1 coupling [35] provides a more accurate description of the excited states than L-S coupling. Here j represents the total angular momentum of the nine electrons in the inner shells, while 1 represents the orbital angular momentum of the excited electron in an outer subshell. Because a p electron is excited, the inner quantum number can be either 1/2 or 3/2. The heavier noble gas

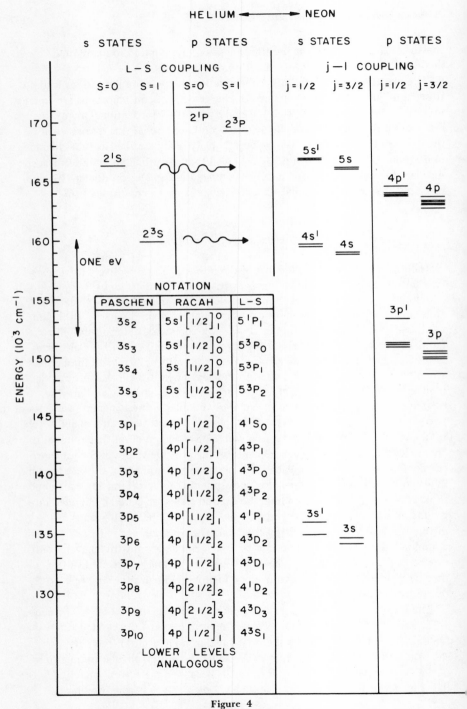

**Figure 4**

Spectroscopic coupling schemes and energy levels in the helium-neon system. The equivalent Paschen, Racah, and L-S notations are indicated.

excited subshells are commonly grouped by inner quantum number j, and this convention [36] is retained in Fig. 4. In Racah notation [37], a quantum number K is formed by coupling j to 1, and the total angular momentum of the atom J is formed by coupling K to the spin of the outer electron. The excited subshell designations are primed or unprimed depending on whether j is 1/2 or 3/2. The notation is n1 [K] J for states of even parity and n1 [K] $^{o}_{J}$ for states of odd parity. All relevant radiative transitions between subshells are of the electric dipole variety and require a change in parity, i.e., a change in the total orbital angular momentum. Most of the literature involving neon has relied upon the less precise Paschen notation, although L-S notation has also been used frequently. Paschen designations are used throughout this chapter. The relation among the various notations is presented in Fig. 4.

In the L-S coupling scheme, the cross sections for collisions of the first kind have shapes that are characteristic of the change in spin accompanying the excitation process. When electron exchange occurs and the spin is altered, the cross section is likely to be sharply peaked near threshold. For excitation processes in which the spin is not altered, the cross sections vary relatively slowly above threshold. These cross sections are usually strongest for transitions that are optically allowed. For atom-atom transfer collisions, the primary selection rule is that spin be conserved. This is the Wigner spin rule [38], which is particularly applicable for L-S coupling conditions. Although the validity of this rule has been contested [16], recent work has provided additional support in favor of spin conservation [39].

Atom-atom transfer collisions involving the helium metastables are particularly important in populating the 3s and 2s neon levels. There are three main groups of radiative transitions from these upper levels, consisting of 2s-2p, 3s-2p, and 3s-3p lines. Oscillation between levels in each of these groups, respectively, was first obtained by Javan et al. [1], White and Rigden [13], and Bloom et al. [40]. The paper announcing the first successful helium-neon laser [1] established that the Ne $2s_2$ and $2s_3$ levels were at least partially populated by collisions of the second kind with the He $2^3$S level. In afterglow experiments, the discharge excitation was abruptly removed and the decay rate of the $2s_2$ and $2s_3$ levels was observed to be identical to the decay rate of the He $2^3$S state. This indicated that the helium metastable was indeed transferring population to the neon levels, although more extensive measurements in an active discharge later showed that this transfer rate was comparable to the direct excitation rate of the 2s levels [41]. The importance of differences between resonant-transfer and direct excitation processes in neon was demonstrated by Patel [42]. He observed an improvement of nearly two orders of magnitude in output power at 1.15 $\mu$m in going from a pure neon discharge to a helium-neon discharge. The discharge electron temperatures and number densities were, however, quite different for the two cases. Surprisingly, the transfer cross sections from the $2^3S$ level to the $2s_2$ and $2s_3$ states were later found to be almost identical [43]. In the L-S coupling scheme, the $2s_2$ level is a singlet and the $2s_3$ level is a triplet. Helium-triplet-to-neon-singlet transfer violates the Wigner spin rule. Bennett [41] explained this violation on the basis of a breakdown of L-S coupling rules for neon.

In contrast to the $2s_2$ level, the Ne $3s_2$ level is preferentially populated over the more nearly coincident $3s_3$ level [43]. Here, the Wigner spin rule appears to be highly significant in determining transfer cross sections from the He $2^1S$ level to the Ne 2s levels. White and Gordon [44] showed that there was an exact current-dependent correspondence between the steady-state population of the $2^1S$ metastable level and the $2s_2$ level. They concluded that oscillation on the visible 3s-2p transitions, particularly at 6328 Å, occurred almost exclusively because of atom-atom transfer collisions. The $3s_2$ level is also the upper level of the 3.39-$\mu$m transition in the 3s-3p group. The progressive discovery of various helium-neon transitions are reviewed in several excellent references [28, 41, 45-47]. One notable exception is the recently obtained green helium-neon laser transition [48] at 5434 Å.

The L-S coupling scheme provides a fairly accurate description of the helium excited state interactions; however, for neon even j-1 coupling does not accurately describe the appropriate interactions. The apparent consequences of the breakdown of these coupling schemes are violations of the selection rules [49] and inaccuracies in the theoretical calculation of transition probabilities. Other coupling schemes for neon are now considered to be more realistic [50].

## D.  Transient Excitation Processes

Enhanced 1.15-$\mu$m laser output has been observed at relatively high pressures in pulsed helium-neon discharges [51-53]. Increased power output has been obtained during the period of initial discharge breakdown, as well as in the afterglow region [53]. The maximum output occurred in the afterglow, where a total peak power of 84 watts was obtained from at least four emitting 2s-2p transitions [51]. We are primarily concerned here with transient enhancement processes dependent on atom-atom transfer from the helium metastable levels.

When the discharge is pulsed on, the initial period of excitation is characterized by relatively high electron temperatures [52]. During this period, the He $2^3S$ level becomes populated much more rapidly than the Ne 2p levels. If the neon pressure is sufficiently high, atom-atom collisions will rapidly transfer population from the $2^3S$ level to the Ne 2s levels. As the populations of the upper and lower laser levels increase, the absolute value of the population difference may become relatively large and an increase in power output will be observed. The high-pressure limitations described in part B of this section eventually contribute to the termination of the laser pulse. Two-body pressure-dependent lifetime limitations are particularly severe for the upper level of the 6328-Å laser transition [31], and the initial increase of the population rate to the He $2^1$S level is not sufficient to provide significant improvements in 6328-Å output. Lower-level lifetime restrictions, however, are not necessarily significant in limiting transient laser operation. When the excitation rate densities are favorable, population inversion and stimulated emission can be maintained over times comparable to the lifetime of the upper level. The net transfer of population from the upper to the lower level, during stimulated emission, eventually causes the lower-level population to increase to the point at which population inversion is destroyed. Transient laser operation has even been obtained from the 2p levels to the 1s metastable levels [54, 55] in pulsed neon discharges.

Boot et al. [51] obtained 84 W in the afterglow of a pulsed helium-neon discharge from several simultaneously oscillating 2s-2p transitions. Maximum power was achieved at a helium pressure of 240 Torr, a neon pressure of 5 Torr, and a peak current of 35 A. These currents and pressures are extraordinarily large compared to typical helium-neon operating conditions. The results of Boot et al. are even more surprising than would be expected from the pressure limitations discussed in part B of this section, when the additional losses introduced by three-body collision processes are considered. At pressures of several hundred Torr, there is substantial volume destruction of the He $2^3$S metastable level due to three-body collisions [56, 57]. Three-body processes of this sort involve collisions of the excited state with two ground state atoms. The collisions result in a volume destruction of the excited states that is proportional to the square of the pressure. (Simple two-body atom-atom collisions result in volume destruction that is linearly proportional to pressure.) The extremely high transient output power obtained at high pressures can, however, be explained on the basis of exceedingly large excitation rate densities to the He $2^3$S level. In addition, the population of the 2p levels will decay more rapidly than the population of the $2^3$S state in the afterglow and this will also help to produce enhanced population inversion [1].

The two most probable processes for supplying large excitation rate densities to the $2^3$S level in a high-pressure afterglow are electron-ion recombination [51] and spin-exchange collisional deexcitation [58]. Electron-ion recombination, resulting in excited state formation, is a process that grows increasingly probable as the electrons move less rapidly relative to the ions and as the ion density or current increases [18, 59, 63, 64]. In the afterglow, the electron temperature drops rapidly and the electron-ion recombination rate increases dramatically. The result is an increase of the excitation rate densities to the helium metastable levels, either by radiative cascade from higher excited levels formed by recombination, or by direct recombination to the metastable states themselves.

The excitation cross sections of Fig. 2 shows that the electron collisional de-excitation cross sections for spin-exchange transitions increase sharply at low electron temperatures, i.e., during the afterglow. In fact, afterglow spin exchange deexcitation from the He $2^1$S level to the $2^3$S level is known to produce enhancement of the $2^3$S population [58]. Moreover, detailed balance considerations and Eq. (3) predict that the He $2^1$S population will be quite small compared with the $2^3$S population at low electron temperatures. Equivalently, the relaxation rate of the He $2^1$S level will be relatively rapid due to spin-exchange deexcitation. The net effect is to produce a large afterglow enhancement in 1.15-$\mu$m output, but no afterglow enhancement in 6328-Å.

## III. Positive Column Parameters

### A. Electron Collisional Rate Integrals

The positive column of a helium-neon laser discharge can be visually characterized as a region of uniform luminosity extending along the tube axis. The column can be electrically described as that portion of a glow discharge that is a plasma, i.e., a region in which approximate charge neutrality is maintained and in which the Debye length is smaller than the container boundaries [60]. In equilibrium, the electron-ion production rate must equal the electron-ion loss rate throughout the positive column. A first consideration is the rate integrals describing equilibrium electron-ion production. (The elementary theory of the positive column is reviewed in Refs. 18, 60-62.)

The rate integrals describing electron-ion production are identical in form to the integrals describing the rates for electron-atom collisions of the first and second kind [18]. These integrals are also analogous to the integrals used to describe atom-atom collisions [20]. The integrals depend on the overlap of the relevant velocity distribution function with the appropriate cross section. One approach towards understanding the formulation of these integrals is to begin by describing the collision cross sections, probabilities, and frequencies in terms of monoenergetic particles.

In the monoenergetic situation, the electrons and atoms may be considered to be moving at velocities $v_1$ and $v_2$, respectively. A two-body electron-atom collision probability $P_c$ can be defined by the relation

$$\sigma N_0 = p P_c \tag{4}$$

where $P_c$ is the number of electron-atom collisions per electron per cm per Torr at 273 K. Here p is the actual pressure times 273/T; $N_0$ is the ground state atomic density in atoms per $cm^3$; and $\sigma$ is the collision cross section in $cm^2$. Each side of Eq. (4) is dimensionally represented in units of inverse centimeters and is numerically equal to the inverse of the mean free path. When the reciprocal of the mean free path is multiplied by the velocity of the electron relative to the velocity of the atom, the number of collisions per electron per second is obtained. Then

$$\sigma N_0 v = f_c \tag{5}$$

where v is the relative velocity and $f_c$ is the collision frequency. The product of the collision frequency and the electron number density yields the number of collisions per second per $cm^3$,

$$\sigma v N_e N_0 = R_c \tag{6}$$

The quantity $R_c$ is the collision rate density and is dimensionally equivalent to the rate density discussed in Section II, B. When the collisions are inelastic, the product

$$\sigma v N_e = Z \tag{7}$$

represents the rate of depletion ($sec^{-1}$) of the population of the initial state. For a particular pair of levels, the forward and reverse depletion rates are related by the detailed balance considerations of Eq. (3); correspondingly, in the absence of additional interaction mechanisms $Z_1 N_1$ must equal $Z_2 N_2$. The quantity Z is sometimes expressed

$$\alpha N_e = Z \tag{8}$$

where $\alpha$ is a rate coefficient in $cm^3 \ sec^{-1}$.

The monoenergetic definitions can be extended to include the actual energy-dependent parameters. In reality, inelastic electron-atom collision cross sections have definite energy-dependent structures. Furthermore, the electrons and atoms have each their particular velocity distribution functions. The monoenergetic collision rates of Eq. (7) can be generalized by summing the product $\sigma v N_e$ over vanishingly small energy increments. The resulting integrals are termed rate integrals. The product of the appropriate rate integral with the population of the initial state yields a rate density that may represent ionization from the initial state, excitation to an excited state, or deexcitation from the initial state. The rate integrals are often expressed in the form [63, 64]

$$Z = \alpha N_e = N_e \int \sigma(v) v f(v) \, dv = \frac{R_c}{N_0} \tag{9}$$

where f(v) is the normalized relative velocity distribution function with average velocity $\bar{v} = \int v f(v) \, dv$. Since the electron velocities are always much higher than the velocities of the atoms, the relative velocity distribution may be regarded simply as the electron velocity distribution.

When the primary mechanism for kinetic energy exchange among the atoms is elastic collision, the normalized atomic velocity distribution function can be represented by a Maxwellian [65]. This distribution can be written

$$f(v) \, dv = 4\pi \left(\frac{m}{2\pi kT}\right)^{3/2} \exp\left(-\frac{mv^2}{2kT}\right) v^2 \, dv \tag{10}$$

where kT is equal to the kinetic energy of the most probable atomic velocity. The atomic velocity distribution of both helium and neon is nearly always Maxwellian in typical helium-neon laser discharges. When the atoms of each of the two atomic species are in equilibrium at a common temperature, the relative velocity distribution function can be expressed in terms of a single Maxwellian with reduced mass [65], $m = m_1 m_2 /(m_1 + m_2)$. Equation (9) is then also valid for excited state transfer collisions between atoms of two species, provided that $N_e$ is replaced by the ground state density of the unexcited species and m is replaced by the reduced mass.

A Maxwellian velocity distribution can also be represented as an energy distribution:

$$f(E) \, dE - \frac{2}{\sqrt{\pi}} \; \frac{E^{1/2}}{(kT)^{3/2}} \; \exp\left(-\frac{E}{kT}\right) dE \tag{11}$$

with average energy $\bar{E} = 3kT/2$. In the optimum pressure-diameter region for helium-neon laser operation [32], a Maxwellian electron energy distribution is only approximately realistic [66]. If such a distribution is assumed, Eq. (9) can be rewritten

$$Z = \alpha N_e = N_e \left(\frac{2}{m}\right)^{1/2} \int \sigma(E) E^{1/2} \, f(E) \, dE = \frac{R_e}{N_0} \tag{12}$$

The calculation of ionization rates has historically been approached in terms of ionization probabilities rather than ionization cross sections [18]. This method is essentially the converse of the approach adopted here and begins with the right rather than the left side of Eq. (4). The calculation assumes an energy-dependent ionization probability $P_i$ that varies linearly above threshold. This probability is defined:

$$P_i = \frac{300 \, a(E - E_i)}{e} \tag{13}$$

where a is the number of ion pairs produced per electron per cm per Torr per volt at 273 K, $E_i$ is the ionization energy in ergs, and e is the electron charge in esu. Integration of the collision frequency with a Maxwellian electron number density distribution yields the ionization rate density. This is equivalent to replacing $\sigma(E)$ in Eq. (12) by $P_i(E)$ and multiplying the resulting expression by the reduced pressure. The ionization rate denisity $R_i$ becomes

$$R_i = 600ap \frac{m}{e} \frac{1}{\sqrt{\pi}} \left(\frac{2kT_e}{m}\right)^{3/2} \exp\left(-\frac{E_i}{kT_e}\right)\left(1 + \frac{1}{2}\frac{E_i}{kT_e}\right)N_e \qquad (14)$$

where $T_e$ is the electron temperature. The ionization rate density is related to another parameter of particular interest in electron-ion rate equations, the electron-ion production rate. This production rate,

$$z = \frac{R_i}{N_e} \qquad (15)$$

represents the number of ionizations per second per electron. In part C of this section, the electron-ion production rate will be related to the electron-ion loss rate.

### B. Inelastic Electron Collisional Cross Sections

The energy-dependent structure of inelastic electron-atom collisions has been examined both theoretically and experimentally. In the present discussion, the primary emphasis is placed on a description of experimentally determined cross sections in terms of closed-form classical and empirical expressions. Detailed theoretical calculations are quite specialized and are not included here. (Various schemes for theoretical calculations are reviewed or referenced in Seaton [67].

The simplest closed-form approximation to the excitation or ionization cross section is one in which the cross section is assumed to be energy-independent. If a Maxwellian velocity distribution is assumed, Eq. (9) then yields

$$Z = \alpha N_e = N_e \sigma \bar{v} = N_e \sigma \left(\frac{8kT_e}{\pi m}\right)^{1/2} \qquad (16)$$

The actual inelastic collision cross sections exhibit pronounced energy dependences. Experimentally obtained direct excitation cross sections for the first few excited states of helium [68] are indicated in Fig. 5. The cross sections clearly demonstrate the characteristic spin-shape behavior discussed in Section II-C. Above the excitation energy threshold, the cross sections can be approximated by the closed-form expression [21]

$$\sigma(E) = C_1 Q_{10} \left(\frac{E - C_2 E_t}{C_3 E_t}\right) \exp\left(-\frac{E - C_2 E_t}{C_3 E_t}\right) \qquad (17)$$

where $C_1, C_2, C_3$ are appropriate constants [21], $E_t$ is the threshold excitation energy, and $Q_{10}$ is the maximum value of the excitation cross section. The excitation cross sections for neon can be approximated in a similar manner, and values for these cross sections are available in the literature [69]. The cross sections for second-kind collisional deexcitation, i.e., superelastic collisons, are related to the excitation cross sections by Eq. (1).

The high-energy portion of a Maxwellian distribution at a temperature of 80,000 K is also indicated in Fig. 5. This temperature is typical of the temperature obtained in the optimum pressure-diameter region for helium-neon laser operation and roughly corresponds to an average electron energy of 10 eV. Experimental evidence indicates that a Maxwellian distribution is an excellent approximation to the actual distribution function for electron energies below 35 eV [66]. The rapid falloff of the distribution function of Fig. 5 at higher electron energies suggests that most of the contribution to the He $2^1$S and $2^3$S excitation rate integrals comes from electrons with energies below 35 eV. This behavior may be exploited in the numerical calculation of excitation rate integrals by substituting a Maxwellian distribution for the actual electron energy distribution function.

Electron-atom ionization cross sections can often be approximated in terms of the classical Thompson ionization cross section [64]. Ionization may occur by electron impact with an atom in an excited state or by electron impact with an atom in the ground state. The Thompson cross section for ground state ionization is defined by the relation

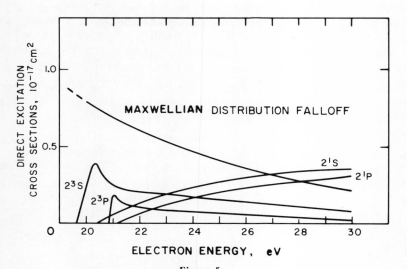

**Figure 5**

Detailed structure of the direct excitation cross sections for the first few excited states of helium [68]. The high-energy portion of a Maxwellian distribution function at an electron temperature of 80,000 K is also indicated on this figure.

$$\sigma(E) = 4\pi a_0^2 \ \frac{E_h^2}{E} \ (E_i^{-1} - E^{-1})$$

(18)

where $a_0$ is the Bohr radius, $E_h$ is the ionization energy of the hydrogen atom, and $E_i$ is the ionization energy of the ground-state atom. When electron energies below 40 eV are considered, the value of the Thompson cross section is within 25%-50% of experimentally obtained results for both helium and neon [70]. Experimental measurements and theoretical calculations [71] show that the Thompson cross section is of comparable accuracy when applied to stepwise ionization collisions from the first few excited states of helium and neon. In this case, $E_i$ must be replaced by the difference between the ionization energy and the energy of the particular excited state.

The Thompson cross section can also be used for the determination of stepwise inelastic collision cross sections between optically connected states. Distorted wave calculations have been derived for such stepwise excitation processes and the results can be approximated by the expression [64]

$$\sigma(E) = 12\pi a_0^2 \frac{E_h^2}{E} (E_n^{-1} - E^{-1})f_{ik}$$

(19)

where $f_{ik}$ is the oscillator strength and $E_n$ is the energy separation between excited levels. (The oscillator strengths for certain helium and neon transitions are tabulated in Ref. 72.) Equation (19) yields results that are somewhat less accurate than those obtained from Eq. (18). When the stepwise excitation cross sections are applied to helium at low energies, they are within a factor of two of recent $2^1S$-$2^1P$, $2^3S$-$2^3P$ calculations [16]. The Thompson $2^1S$-$2^1P$ excitation and $2^1S$ ionization cross sections for helium are plotted in Fig. 6. A Maxwellian electron energy distribution is superimposed on the stepwise excitation and ionization cross sections. The magnitudes of the cross sections and the respective degrees of overlap with the energy distribution indicate that stepwise excitation rates greatly exceed stepwise ionization rates. The effectiveness of stepwise excitation as a depopulation mechanism, however, also depends on the rate of repopulation back from the higher excited state.

### C. Component and Composite Electron Temperatures

In the positive column of a helium-neon discharge, the electron-ion production rate must equal the electron-ion loss rate. Electron-ion production occurs primarily by electron impact excitation from the ground state, and electron-ion loss occurs principally by ambipolar diffusion. The balance between these two processes determines the electron temperature. Other possible ion loss mechanisms, such as recombination or molecular conversion processes [59, 73], are relatively unimportant. Other possible ion production mechanisms, such as stepwise ionization or

metastable-metastable collisions [59, 73], are also unimportant. The positive column
container can be regarded as a cylinder in which the Debye length is much shorter
than the characteristic radial diffusion length. The electron mean free path is
also shorter than the characteristic diffusion length. Owing to interaction between electrons and ions, a space charge field is established. This field affects
the free diffusion of the charged particles: the more rapid diffusion of the
electrons is retarded, and the slower diffusion of the heavy ions is accelerated.
In the limit of ambipolar diffusion [73], the continuity equations governing the
respective electron and ion particle flow rates can be equated. This is the
situation that exists in the optimum laser discharge region; however, helium-
neon lasers can be made to operate in discharge regions for which many of the
preceding conditions are invalid. (In this and subsequent sections, the validity
of these assertions for the optimum pressure-diameter region will be tested.)

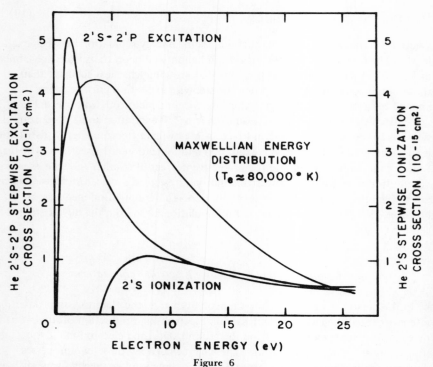

**Figure 6**
Thompson stepwise ionization and excitation cross sections for the He $2^1$S state. The
stepwise excitation cross section refers to $2^1$S-$2^1$P transfer. A Maxwellian distribution
function at an electron temperature of 80,000 K is superimposed on the figure.

The DAB equations [74] describing ambipolar flow in a three-component plasma can be represented as

$$\underline{\Gamma}_a = N_a \underline{v}_a = \mu_a N_a \underline{E} - \underline{\nabla}(D_a N_a) \tag{20}$$

$$\underline{\Gamma}_b = N_b \underline{v}_b = \mu_b N_b \underline{E} - \underline{\nabla}(D_b N_b) \tag{21}$$

$$\underline{\Gamma}_e = N_e \underline{v}_b = -\mu_e N_e \underline{E} - \underline{\nabla}(D_e N_e) \tag{22}$$

$$\underline{\nabla} \cdot \underline{\Gamma}_e = \underline{\nabla} \cdot (\underline{\Gamma}_a + \underline{\Gamma}_b) = z_e N_e \tag{23}$$

$$z_e N_e = z_e(N_a + N_b) = (z_a + z_b)N_e \tag{24}$$

where the subscripts a, b refer to positive ions of species a, b and the subscript e refers to free electrons. Here v is the drift velocity due to the sum of the electric field and concentration gradient, N is the number density, E is the electric field, $\mu$ is the mobility, and D is the diffusion coefficient. The ambipolar diffusion coefficient, $D_a$, is defined by the equation

$$\underline{\Gamma} = \underline{\Gamma}_e = \underline{\Gamma}_a + \underline{\Gamma}_b = -\underline{\nabla}(D_a N_e) \tag{25}$$

which may be obtained by eliminating the electric field from Eqs. (20), (21), and (22).

In the axial discharge direction, the concentration gradient is negligible and ambipolar diffusion theory is not applicable. The discharge current is mainly carried by electrons rather than ions. The electrons are injected into one end of the positive column and removed from the other end at an equal rate. The axial electron drift velocity becomes

$$v_d = \mu E \tag{26}$$

Classically, the electron mobility is inversely proportional to $f_c$, the collision frequency for momentum transfer [60]. The appropriate relations are

$$\mu = \frac{e}{m} \frac{1}{f_c} = \frac{e}{m} \frac{\lambda_e}{v_e} \tag{27}$$

where $\lambda_e$ is the electron mean free path and $\bar{v}_e$ is the average random thermal velocity of the electrons. Equation (27) implicitly assumes that $\bar{v}_e \gg v_d$. In certain gases, particularly helium, the electron collision frequency and the electron mean free path are nearly independent of the electric field. Since the mean free path is inversely proportional to pressure, Eqs. (26) and (27) predict that the drift velocity of electrons in helium will be linearly related to E/p, the ratio of electric field to pressure. Conversely, at constant drift velocity, E/p is a function of the electron temperature and is proportional to $\bar{v}_e$. Quite conveniently, in a 5 : 1 helium-neon discharge, the positive column characteristics are largely determined by the helium [75]. This allows some consistency checks of empirically determined relations with classical mobility theory.

The ionic mobilities in a mixture of gases are related by Blanc's law,

$$\frac{1}{\mu_a} = \frac{f_1}{\mu_{aa}} + \frac{f_2}{\mu_{ab}} \tag{28}$$

where $\mu_{aa}$ is the mobility of gas a in gas a, $\mu_{ab}$ is the mobility of gas a in gas b, and $f_1, f_2$ are the ratios of the partial pressure of each gas to the total pressure. When the velocity distribution is Maxwellian and the electron-atom collisional interaction involves an $r^{-4}$ potential [17], the respective ratios of the diffusion coefficients to the mobility are given by the Einstein relations

$$\frac{D_e}{\mu_e} = \frac{kT_e}{e} \tag{29}$$

$$\frac{D_a}{\mu_a} = \frac{D_b}{\mu_b} = \frac{kT_a}{e} = \frac{kT_b}{e} \tag{30}$$

in which the units of D are commonly $cm^2$ per sec and the units of $\mu$ are inversely proportional to pressure. Experimentally, the electron temperature has been found to be essentially independent of radial position in pure helium, as well as pure neon, positive columns [76]. Such evidence suggests that the diffusion and mobility coefficients are also independent of radial position and this assumption is made in the DAB treatment [74].

If Eqs. (20) - (24), (29), and (30) are combined, the equation

$$\nabla^2 N_e + \frac{e}{kT_e} \left[ \frac{z_a}{\mu_a} + \frac{z_b}{\mu_b} \right] N_e = 0 \tag{31}$$

can be obtained, provided that $\mu_e \gg \mu_{a,b}$ and $kT_e \gg kT_{a,b}$. For $N_e = 0$ at the tube walls, the radial solution of Eq. (31) is

$$N_e = N_0' \sum_{i=1}^{\infty} A_i J_0 \left( x_i \frac{r}{R} \right) \tag{32}$$

where $X_i$ is the ith root of $J_0$, the zero-order Bessel function of the first kind, R is the tube radius, and $N_0'$ is the axial number density. The characteristic diffusion length $\Lambda_i$ of an infinite cylinder is

$$\frac{1}{\Lambda_i} = \frac{X_i}{R} = \frac{e}{kT_e} \left[ \left( \frac{z_a}{\mu_a} + \frac{z_b}{\mu_b} \right) \right]^{1/2} \tag{33}$$

The characteristic diffusion length decreases for the higher-order modes and the lowest-order mode is usually dominant. In the afterglow, the higher-order modes will decay more rapidly than the fundamental. The radial profile of the lowest-order mode, $X_i = 2.405$, is indicated in Fig. 7. When the electron-ion production rates from Eqs. (14) and (15) are substituted in Eq. (33), a functional relation is obtained that defines the electron temperature solely in terms of the fractional partial pressures of the component gases and the pressure-diameter product. This relation, together with the appropriate constants, is given by Young [75]. A plot of electron temperature, for several helium-neon ratios, as a function of the pressure diameter product (pd) is presented in Fig. 8. The electron temperature of a 5 : 1 helium-neon discharge is seen to be quite close to that of a pure helium discharge. For high helium-to-neon ratios, the electron temperature is thus only a function of pd.

Despite the assumptions that ambipolar diffusion theory is valid and that the ionization probability varies linearly above threshold, the theoretical values of Fig. 8 are in approximate agreement with the experimental results of Labuda [26, 77]. In these experiments, Labuda performed rigorous measurements of helium-neon electron temperatures and number densities as a function of current, pressure, and

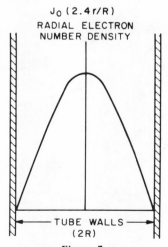

$J_0(2.4r/R)$
RADIAL ELECTRON
NUMBER DENSITY

TUBE WALLS
(2R)

**Figure 7**
Radial electron number density profile for the lowest-order mode, $J_0(2.4r/R)$.

tube diameter. The helium-to-neon ratios were almost invariably chosen to be 5:1 and the measurements were conducted in 2-, 3-, 5-, and 6-mm-bore tubes. The pressure-diameter products were restricted to the region 2-5 Torr-mm and the maximum tube currents were maintained below 100 mA. Over the entire pressure and diameter measurement region, the electron temperatures were found to be essentially independent of current and a function only of pd; the electron number densities were found to vary linearly with current. On integrating the product of the axial drift velocity and the radial number density over the cross section of the discharge, Labuda obtained an expression for the axial discharge current. A fit of this expression to the experimental data [77], together with auxiliary E/p measurements, can be written as

$$v_d = \frac{2.405/J_1(2.405)}{(\pi/2)1{,}000\,ed^2}\ \frac{I}{N_e} = (10.6 \times 10^6)\ \frac{1}{pd} \tag{34}$$

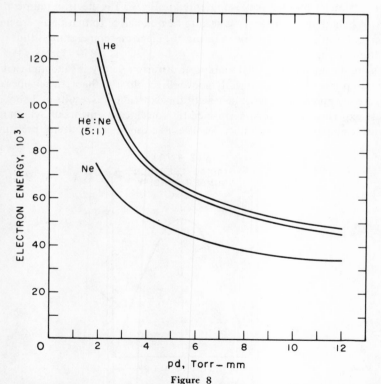

**Figure 8**

Ambipolar diffusion theory calculations of the positive column electron temperature as a function of the pressure-diameter product, pd. Curves are presented for pure helium, pure neon, and for a 5 : 1 helium-to-neon ratio.

$$\frac{I}{d} \propto \frac{N_e}{p} = (17.3 \times 10^8) \frac{I}{d} \tag{35}$$

$$\frac{E}{p} = \frac{10}{pd} \tag{36}$$

where $v_d$ is in cm/sec, d in cm, p in Torr, e in coulombs, I in mA, $N_e$ in electrons/cm$^3$, and E in V cm, and $J_1(2.405)$ is the first-order Bessel function of argument 2.405. The values presented in Eqs. (34) and (36) are fairly accurate, as they yield the proper collision frequency [60, 77] and electron mean free path [18] for a helium-dominated plasma. E/p is apparently only a function of pd, as the electron temperature is. The measurements indicate that similarity [32] and scaling laws [26] apply to the helium-neon laser.

The agreement between theory and experiment suggests that ambipolar diffusion theory is reasonably valid in the optimum pressure-diameter discharge region. Moreover, the experimentally obtained values of electron temperature and number density indicate that the Debye length is typically a small fraction of a millimeter, which is consistent with the initial assumption of charge neutrality. On the negative side, the electron drift velocity is more than 10% of the average electron thermal velocity and thus classical mobility theory is somewhat suspect. In addition, at the optimum value of 3.6 Torr-mm (for dc-excited 6328-Å operation), one of the ambipolar diffusion criteria is not strictly fulfilled. Here the mean free path is approximately equal to the characteristic diffusion length and the average electron does not make many collisions before reaching the wall boundary. Some care must therefore be exercised in the use of ambipolar diffusion theory for the helium-neon situation.

## IV. Descriptions of Population Mechanisms

### A. Qualitative Models

A precise, a priori determination of the optimum laser discharge conditions depends on a knowledge of the inversion mechanisms. A preliminary description of the necessary discharge conditions was originally presented by Javan, in conjunction with his proposals for the achievement of population inversion in a gas discharge [10]. Inversion was to be effected either by direct electron excitation or by resonant-transfer collisions (see Section II, B). Javan and Bennett subsequently formed a more explicit picture of the appropriate inversion mechanisms, based on experiments immediately preceding and following successful helium-neon laser operation at 1.15 $\mu$m [1]. They concluded that collisions between unexcited neon atoms and He $2^3$S metastable state atoms resulted in a significant amount of population transfer to the Ne $2s_2$ level. These transfer collisions, together with diffusion, seemed to constitute the primary current-independent depopulation mechanisms for the He $2^3$S state. Furthermore, depopulation of the Ne $2s_2$ level appeared to be dominated by radiative relaxation to the Ne 2p states. Gordon and White developed an analogous picture regarding He $2^1$S - Ne $3s_2$ level interactions [32, 44]. In a relatively detailed description, these investigators took current-dependent saturation of the He $2^1$S and Ne $3s_2$ populations into account by including the effects of electron collisional deexcitation in their analysis. (The general form of this particular model still provides an accurate framework for observed phenomena related to 3.39-$\mu$m or 6328-Å operation.) At about this time, Bennett proposed a four-level model for 1.15-$\mu$m operation that relied on a somewhat different mechanism for explaining current-induced gain saturation, namely, a build up of the lower-level population [45]. Arecchi [78], Asami [79], and Kawabe et al. [80] developed systems of rate equations, which explicitly included stimulated emission terms. Rate equation analyses were also employed by Schulz duBois [81], E. I. Gordon et al. [82], J. P. Gordon [83], and Tobias [84] to describe stimulated emission induced gain saturation. (Other descriptions of gain saturation [85-88], as well as density matrix formulations in weak [89] and strong saturation limits [90], are available in the literature.) As before, the discussion here will be limited to a description of models that are applicable in the absence of stimulated emission. Throughout this section, an attempt is made to develop and justify rate equations that specify the relevant level interactions and populations.

In equilibrium, the mechanisms that determine the positive column excited-state population balance are primarily diffusion, spontaneous emission, and two-body inelastic collisions. Diffusion and spontaneous emission are thermodynamically irreversible loss mechanisms. However, inelastic collisions are intrinsically reversible. These collisions can be arbitrarily classified into ionizing and nonionizing varieties. Electron-atom ionizing collision rates can be related to electron-ion recombination rates [59, 63, 64]. For typical positive column conditions, excited state formation by recombination can be shown to be negligible compared with formation by other processes. As for two-body nonionizing collisions, the excitation and deexcitation rates are related by the detailed balance considerations of Section II, A. If we neglect collisions between pairs of unexcited or excited atoms and ignore the formation of noble gas molecules, nine nonionizing two-body collisional reactions in a helium-neon discharge can be enumerated. Five of these reactions can be represented as

$$He^* + Ne \rightleftharpoons Ne^* + He \tag{37}$$

$$\text{He}^* + \text{Ne} \rightleftharpoons \text{He}^{**} + \text{Ne} \tag{38}$$

$$\text{He}^* + \text{He} \rightleftharpoons \text{He}^{**} + \text{He} \tag{39}$$

$$\text{He}^* + e \rightleftharpoons \text{He}^{**} + e \tag{40}$$

$$\text{He}^* + e \rightleftharpoons \text{He} + e \tag{41}$$

and another four can be obtained by permuting helium and neon symbols in each of Eqs. (38) - (41). Here a single asterisk refers to an excited state and a double asterisk refers to either a higher or a lower excited state. Any rate equation for a particular level clearly involves a minimum of five excitation and five deexcitation terms if interaction with even one other excited state (in each of the two species) is permitted. As the number of interacting excited states is increased, a profusion of ever more complex rate equations is generated. Since a real system almost invariably has many interacting levels, a precise solution of helium-neon excited state interactions is obviously extremely difficult to achieve. Fortunately, the states associated with 1.15-$\mu$m, 3.39-$\mu$m, and 6328-Å operation can be described in an approximate way by essentially decoupling the relevant levels from the majority of neighboring states. Estimates of the relative magnitudes of the various coupling processes can be obtained from experimental observations of discharge parameters and excited state populations.

Labuda [26, 77] and White and Gordon [44] made the first accurate measurements of the appropriate discharge and excited state conditions. Some of these experimental results are illustrated in Figs. 9 and 10, which respectively provide quantitative values for the electron number density and the He $2^1$S metastable

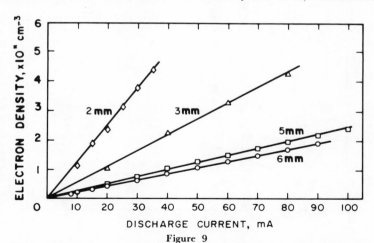

Figure 9

Verification of the linear relation between the electron number density and the current [26]. The data for each tube diameter were taken at a pressure-diameter product of 3.6 Torr-mm (5 : 1 mix).

level population. These measurements were conducted on dc excited helium-neon discharge tubes, in the optimum pressure-diameter region for 6328-Å operation. (The description here will be restricted to dc excited discharges, but is also crudely applicable to rf excited discharges. However, rf discharges often yield results that are difficult to interpret due to spatial inhomogeneities in excitation rates. Some differences in excitation and operating properties are briefly discussed in Section IV, C and in Section VI.) If we assume a Max-wellian electron energy distribution and various Thompson cross sections, the measured discharge conditions and metastable state populations can be used to estimate the relative importance of direct ionization from the ground state, as opposed to stepwise ionization from the heavily populated helium singlet state (see Section III). The results indicate that the ratio of singlet stepwise ionization to direct ground state ionization is typically less than 1%. Since the He $2^1$S, He $2^3$S, and Ne 1s metastable population densities are all comparable and are at least one to two orders of magnitude larger than the densities of other excited states, most of the ionization must be generated directly from the ground state. The experimental data also indicate that the He $2^1$S density is less than one part in $10^4$ of the ground state density and that the fractional ionization of the neutrals is less than one part in $10^5$. The current dependence of the upper-laser-level population, the Ne $3s_2$ level, almost exactly follows the current dependence of the He $2^1$S-level population. Both levels exhibit

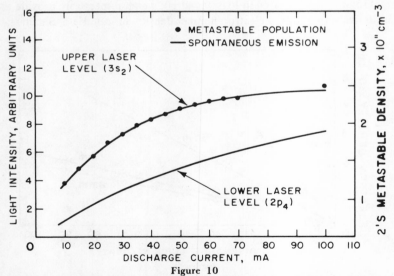

**Figure 10**

Demonstration of the current-dependent correspondence between the population densities of the He $2^1$S level and the Ne $3s_2$ level [44]. In these measurements, a 6-mm bore tube was operated at a pressure-diameter product of 4.2 Torr-mm (6 : 1 mix).

the characteristic current-dependent saturation behavior that Ladenburg [8] first observed, specifically

$$N_m \text{ or } N_2 = \frac{I}{BI + C} \tag{42}$$

where $N_m$ is the metastable density, $N_2$ is the upper-laser-level density, $I$ is the current, and $B$ and $C$ are constants. The lower-laser-level population (either the $3p_4$ or $2p_4$ state) varies almost linearly with current. Hence, the small signal gain at 3.39 $\mu$m (in db), which is proportional to the population difference between the upper- and lower-laser levels, can be fitted to an expression of the form

$$G = \frac{C_1 I}{1 + C_2 I} - C_3 I \tag{43}$$

For particular levels, the preceding experimental evidence can be used to begin eliminating some of the nonionizing collision mechanisms as numerically insignificant relative to the dominant populating and depopulating processes. Here, depopulating processes are defined as the reactions proceeding from left to right in Eqs. (37) - (41), whereas populating processes proceed in the reverse direction. Both the forward and reverse reactions presented in Eqs. (38) and (39) can be deduced to be negligible for the He $2^1$S level, essentially from the following detailed balance argument. If atom-atom reactions (38) and (39) with the lower He $2^3$S state were the dominant production and depletion mechanisms for the He $2^1$S state, then Eq. (3) indicates that the relative population of the singlet metastable level would be negligible compared with the population of the triplet metastable level at typical atomic temperatures of 300 to 500 K. Alternatively, atom-atom production and depletion reactions (38) and (39) with higher states should be insignificant because very few atoms would be likely to exchange the required kinetic energy at a significant rate. Consequently, reactions (38) and (39) involving the He $2^1$S level can be dismissed as physically unimportant processes. Direct transfer to the ground state via electron-atom depletion reaction (41) must also be insignificant. Indeed, if this were not the case, the metastable state and the ground state would be in Boltzmann equilibrium at the electron temperature. This would imply an excited state population only an order of magnitude less than the ground state population. Finally, the observed form of Eq. (42) indicates that electron-atom production reaction (40) must be negligible also. (Since the electron number density is linearly proportional to current, significant production by electron-atom collisions with other excited states would involve terms of order $I^2$ or higher.) The potential depletion reactions for the He $2^1$S state thus reduce to depletion by diffusion, electron-atom ionizing collisions, electron-atom nonionizing inelastic collisions, and forward resonant-transfer collisions (with neon atoms).

He $2^1$S production can proceed by direct electron excitation, by radiative cascading from higher levels, and by reverse resonant-transfer collisions.

The preceding considerations were initially incorporated by Gordon and White in their qualitative rate equation analysis of He $2^1$S- and Ne $3s_2$-level population densities [32, 44]. They concluded that the only reasonable explanation for the identical current-dependent behavior of the He $2^1$S and Ne $3s_2$ levels had to be based on two suppositions: first, that the Ne $3s_2$ level was populated almost exclusively by resonant transfer collisions with the helium metastable state, and second, that the neon level was primarily depopulated by current-independent mechanisms. (Temperature variation with current in their experiments was rather minor due to their relatively large-bore tube, 6 mm, and the fairly low operating currents.) For steady-state conditions, their qualitative rate equations may be written:

$$\frac{dN_m}{dt} = 0 = \alpha_m N_e N_{he} - \beta_m N_e M_m - Z_r N_m + Z_r N_2 - D\nabla^2 N_m \tag{44}$$

$$\frac{dN_2}{dt} = Z_r N_m - Z_r N_2 - AN_2 \tag{45}$$

$$\frac{dN_1}{dt} = \alpha_1 N_e N_{ne} - KN_1 \tag{46}$$

where $N_1$ is the population density of the $2p_4$ or $3p_4$ level, $N_2$ is the $3s_2$ population density, and $N_m$ is the $2^1$S population density. The $\alpha$'s refer to excited state production by direct electron excitation or by direct electron excitation to a higher level followed by radiative cascade; the $\beta$'s refer to the sum of two-body inelastic depletion processes; and the unprimed and primed $Z$'s refer to forward and reverse resonant-transfer collision rates. (Because dissimilar species are involved, the Boltzmann factor of Eq. (3) should be weighted by the relative abundance of each species.) The quantity A is the inverse effective radiative lifetime of the Ne $3s_2$ level, K is a constant, and D is the diffusion coefficient for the helium singlet metastable state. The diffusion term $D\nabla^2 N_m$ can be approximately represented as $D(2.405/R)^2 N_m$ if a zeroth-order Bessel function is assumed for the electron number density distribution and if either the metastable distribution is also assumed to be a zeroth-order Bessel function or the solution is restricted to the region along the cylindrical discharge axis. Both A and K are presumed to be constant for pressure and for the pressure-diameter product (pd), and the $\alpha$'s and $\beta$'s are also presumed to be pd-invariant. The ground state helium and neon densities, $N_{he}$ and $N_{ne}$, are proportional to pressure, as the forward and reverse resonant transfer rates (at constant helium-to-neon ratios) are. The diffusion coefficient D is inversely proportional to pressure. A solution of Eqs. (44) - (46) for the population difference $N_2 - N_1$ can be cast into the observed current-dependent form of Eq. (43).

A question arises whether the simplified rate equations (44) - (46), although consistent with the observed current dependence of Eq. (43), are consistent with the observed pressure and diameter dependence of the unsaturated 6328-Å or 3.39-μm gain. Equations (44) - (46) suggest that at a constant pressure-diameter product and partial pressure ratio, the decibel gain can be expressed solely in terms of various constants, the electron number density, and the total pressure. Ignoring the diffusion term, Gordon and White cast the gain into the form [32]

$$G_{db} = \frac{K_1(p^2/A)(N_e/p)}{1 + K_2(N_e/p)(p/Z_r)(1+Z_r'/A)} - K_3(p^2)\frac{N_e}{p} \qquad (47)$$

where $K_1$, $K_2$, and $K_3$ are constants and the transfer rates $Z_r$, $Z_r'$ are directly proportional to pressure. Optimizing the gain with respect to the quantity $(N_e/p)$ yields the optimum value of $N_e$ (or current density) at a given pressure. In the limit of very low pressures,

$$\frac{Z_r'}{A} \ll 1 \text{ and } \left(\frac{N_e}{p}\right)_{opt} = \text{constant} \qquad (48)$$

Substituting these results in Eq. (47) yields a maximum gain that is proportional to $p^2$. At the high pressure extreme,

$$\frac{Z_r'}{A} \gg 1 \text{ and } \left(\frac{N_e}{p}\right)_{opt} \propto \frac{1}{p} \qquad (49)$$

Eq. (47) predicts a maximum gain that is directly proportional to p. Since $N_e/p$ ∝ I/d [see Eq. (35)], constant pd conditions in the low pressure limit suggest that the optimum discharge current varies directly with the tube diameter. High pressure conditions, on the contrary, imply that the optimum discharge current varies with the square of the tube diameter. Experimentally, $(N_e/p)_{opt}$ appears to be approximately constant, decreasing slightly with increasing pressure. (The optimum current is known to be approximately proportional to the tube diameter but to increase somewhat more rapidly than the first power of the diameter for large-bore tubes.) This suggests that the ratio of $Z_r'$ to A must be less than 1, in accordance with conditions (48). If a diffusion term is included in Eq. (47), consistency with conditions (48) is still achieved. However, the maximum gain at 6328 Å or 3.39 μm has been observed to vary approximately linearly with pressure and this implies that the ratio of $Z_r'$ to A must be greater than 1. Since conditions (48) and (49) are mutually contradictory, either there is an error in the formulation of Eq. (47) or, as Gordon and White suggest, actual optimum operation lies somewhere between the two extreme conditions.

Despite the problems regarding pressure dependence, the current-dependent form for the gain, as given by Eq. (43), has been repeatedly verified for the

6328-Å, 1.15-$\mu$m, and 3.39-$\mu$m transitions [91]. In all three cases, the discharge conditions were somewhat arbitrarily chosen to be identical. Regarding the 1.15-$\mu$m transition, Bennett demonstrated that He $2^3$S-level transfer was only responsible for supplying about half the total excitation rate to the Ne $2s_2$ level, while the remainder was due to direct electron excitation [41]. The importance of direct electron excitation for the $2s_2$ level, as opposed to the $3s_2$ level, is illustrated in Fig. 11. The $3s_2$ level density is always seen to bear the same ratio to the He $2^1$S-level density, indicating population by atom-atom transfer collisions; however, the $2s_2$-level density has a component that increases linearly with the He $2^3$S density, indicating additional population by direct electron excitation. [The presence of this component does not alter the essential form of Eq. (43).] As opposed to Eq. (43), Bennett chose a completely different approach for describing 1.15-$\mu$m gain [45]. In his model a quadratic dependence of the excitation rate density to the lower-laser level was deduced. Excitation-dependent gain saturation occurred because the lower-level population eventually increased more rapidly than the upper-level population. It was postulated that the quadratic lower-level excitation rate occurred either

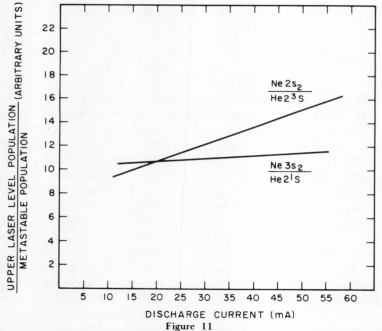

**Figure 11**

Relative population measurements in a 6-mm bore tube at a pressure-diameter product of 3.6 Torr-mm (7 : 1 mix). In contrast to the Ne $3s_2$ level, direct electron excitation to the Ne $2s_2$ level is apparently significant.

by stepwise excitation from the Ne 1s metastable levels or by radiation trapping of the lower-level relaxation rate. A direct comparison between this model and the model of Eq. (43) is somewhat difficult to make because the discharge conditions are not clearly correlated. The 1.15-$\mu$m transition optimizes at similar discharge currents to the 6328-Å transition, but at approximately twice the helium pressure [28, 92]; consequently, the electron number density is higher and the electron temperature is lower. If these differences are hypothetically extended still further, eventually conditions similar to those occurring in pure neon discharges will be realized. A considerable amount of work on pure neon positive columns by Russian workers, notably Kagan and co-workers [93] and Frish and Revald [94], indicates that stepwise excitation is a significant populating mechanism for the Ne 2p levels. This is not surprising, since it can be expected that the relative importance of direct electron excitation to higher neon levels will decrease as the electron temperature is decreased. Nonetheless, Fig. 10 establishes that for helium-neon discharges at pd = 3.6 Torr-mm, the Ne $2p_4$-level population does not vary quadratically with current. Since unpublished measurements by this author indicate that the Ne 1s metastable populations do not saturate over this current regime, stepwise excitation is clearly not important here; however, at higher helium pressures, saturation of the 1s metastable densities does occur at much lower currents. In support of Bennett's observations concerning the maximum 1.15-$\mu$m gain, there is now some evidence that the maximum gain ($G_{opt}$), even at 6328 Å or 3.39 $\mu$m, will vary approximately as $C_0 p \cdot p^2$ or as $K_0 N_e \cdot N_e^2$ if a very minor modification is introduced in the rate equation for the $3s_2$-level population (see the next part of this section). Unfortunately, complications introduced by the higher operating pressures of the 1.15-$\mu$m transition reduce the validity of the various scaling considerations. Because the 6328-Å and 3.39-$\mu$m transitions have proved more tractable, the main emphasis in the subsequent quantitative discussions is limited to levels associated with these lines.

## B.  Quantitative Formulations

A rigorous description of the He $2^1$S and Ne $3s_2$-level populations requires that even weak coupling with other levels be considered. This coupling introduces large numbers of radiative and nonradiative terms into the system rate equations. The level equations themselves actually form an infinite series, since each additional level interacts with still other levels. A precise numerical solution of the exact helium-neon system equations has not yet been attempted, primarily because numerical estimates of the relevant parameters are not even remotely available. An alternative approach is to seek a solution to a limited number of rate equations, which are considered as being decoupled from the main body of equations. If the theoretically derived populations exhibit both qualitative and quantitative agreement with experimental observations, the decoupled rate equations can be assumed to be approximately realistic. Ideally, the numerical values for terms substituted in the rate equations should be determined solely by the appropriate atomic constants and by the gross characteristics of the physical system. These characteristics include discharge currents, voltages, partial pressures, and dimensions.

Ohi [95], Sakurai et al. [96], and Herziger et al. [97] have tried to use some of the known system characteristics and atomic constants in three- or four-level rate equation analyses of the upper- and lower-laser-level populations. The various numerical analyses employed either empirically determined parameters or experimentally obtained populations. The problem with this approach is that ad hoc, or empirical, substitutions for unknown terms can lead to models that are not necessarily connected with physical reality. Additional physical inaccuracies inevitably arise from the use of a simple three- or four-level model in a system where multiple cascading and collisional interaction effects are obviously important. In an effort to avoid these problems, Arrathoon [21] restricted his quantitative analysis to levels associated only with the upper-laser-level population. The calculations were based almost exclusively on atomic and system parameters. Far from verifying the simplified qualitative features of previous models, these calculations seemed to indicate the presence of unexpected processes linking the levels in question to other nearby levels. Nonetheless, the implications of this particular formulation are essentially consistent with the general features of the qualitative analysis discussed earlier.

Along the discharge axis, Eqs. (44) and (45) can be solved simultaneously to obtain

$$N_m = \frac{\alpha_m N_e N_{he}}{\beta N_e + Z_r [A/Z_r' + A)] + D(2.405/R)^2} \tag{50}$$

$$N_2 = \frac{Z_r}{Z_r' + A} N_m \tag{51}$$

As discussed in the first part of this section, these equations seem to show the appropriate current dependence and to a lesser extent the appropriate pd scaling considerations. Comparing the numerical values of $Z_r'$, the reverse resonant transfer rate, and A, the effective inverse radiative lifetime of the Ne $3s_2$ level, immediately suggests that $Z_r'$ is typically small relative to A. (The degeneracy factors relating $Z_r$ and $Z_r'$ were omitted in Refs. 21 and 32.) Yet for the proper gain scaling considerations to hold, $Z_r'$ should at least be comparable to A. This difficulty can be resolved by including an additional pressure-dependent term in the total relaxation rate for the Ne $3s_2$ level. The additional term represents the net atom-atom collisional depletion rate from the $3s_2$ level to all other nearby neon levels. Indeed, the presence of significant excitation transfer from the upper-laser level to adjacent neon levels has long been suspected [98] and progressively confirmed [31, 99], although the precise levels to which transfer occurs have not been clearly identified. When this term is added to the quantity A in Eqs. (50) and (51), the pd scaling inconsistencies discussed earlier are largely eliminated.

Somewhat more difficult problems are associated with the evaluation of the current-dependent terms in Eq. (50). The direct excitation rate integral of Eq. (12) is quite sensitive to the particular shape of the helium metastable-level excitation cross section. This sensitivity arises because only the sharply decreasing high-energy tail of the electron energy distribution overlaps the above threshold region of the excitation cross section (see Fig. 5). The sharp falloff of the electron energy distribution at higher energies and the rapid decrease in magnitude of the direct excitation cross sections of more highly excited states suggest that the helium metastable levels are primarily populated by direct excitation from the ground state, rather than by cascading from higher levels. For either of the helium metastable states, the $\alpha$ of Eq. (5) may therefore be approximated by the respective direct excitation rate coefficients. Substituting Eqs. (11) and (17) into Eq. (12) yields

$$\alpha N_e = 6.69 \times 10^7\, E_t^{1/2} \left(\frac{E_t}{kT_e}\right)^{3/2} \exp\left(1 + \frac{C_2 - 1}{C_3}\right)\left(\frac{C_1}{C_3}\, Q_{10}\right) \frac{\exp(-E_t/kT)}{[(C_3 E_t/kT_e) + 1]^3}$$

$$\times\, N_e \left[C_3(1 - C_2)\left(\frac{C_3 E_t}{kT_e} + 1\right)^2 + C_3^2(2 - C_2)\left(\frac{C_3 E_t}{kT_e} + 1\right) + 2C_3^3\right] \quad (52)$$

where $E_t, kT_e$ are in eV. The He $2^3 S$ constants are [21] $E_t = 19.8$ eV, $C_1 \cong 0.7$, $C_2 \cong 0.85$, $C_3 \cong 0.2$, and $Q_{10} \cong 0.045\pi a_0^2$ ($a_0$ is the Bohr radius), and the constants for the He $2^1 S$ level are $E_t = 20.6$ eV, $C_1 \cong C_2 \cong 1$, $C_3 \cong 0.5$, and $Q_{10} \cong 0.018\pi a_0^2$.

The discussion of Eqs. (40) and (41) in the first part of this section indicated that metastable depletion is likely to occur via stepwise deexcitation to a higher or lower level or via stepwise ionization. The stepwise excitation or ionization rate integrals are not as sensitive to cross-sectional shape as the direct excitation rate integrals because the electron energy distribution is relatively slowly varying in the overlap region (see Fig. 6). From Eqs. (11), (12), and (19) the stepwise excitation rate becomes

$$\beta N_e = 1.31 \times 10^{-5}\, N_e \frac{f_{ik}}{(kT_e)^{3/2}} \left\{ \frac{\exp(-E_n/kT_e)}{E_n/kT_e} - \left[ -E_i\left(-\frac{E_n}{kT_e}\right)\right]\right\} \quad (53)$$

where $-E_i(E_n/kT_e)$ is the exponential integral and $E_n$, $kT_e$ are in eV. Stepwise coupling from the He $2^1S$ to the $2^1P$ level or from the $2^3S$ to the $2^3P$ level is far stronger than coupling from the He $2^1S$ or $2^3S$ states to higher levels. The $2^1S$-$2^1P$ coupling constants are $f_{ik} = 0.376$ and $E_n = 0.602$ eV, while the $2^3S$-$2^3P$ constants are $f_{ik} = 0.539$ and $E_n = 1.14$ eV. Current-dependent depletion can also occur via $2^1S$-$2^3S$ interactions, but the cross sections are relatively small [16] and the interaction rates are not particularly large for steady-state discharge conditions. The stepwise ionization rate is almost identical in form to that given by Eq. (53), except for a factor of $3f_{ik}$ and the replacement of $E_n$ by the stepwise ionization energy. The singlet and triplet metastable-state stepwise ionization energies are 3.97 eV and 4.76 eV, respectively. Some numerical values for parameters in Eqs. (50) and (51) are presented in Table 1. The calculations were made for constant pd conditions, as a function of tube diameter.

Preliminary estimates of various current-dependent metastable depletion mechanisms by Wada and Heil [66] seem to indicate that these mechanisms were negligible compared with current-independent processes. This conclusion, in turn, appears to be inconsistent with the observed metastable saturation characteristics of Fig. 10. Later calculations by Arrathoon [21] suggest that He $2^1S$-$2^1P$ or He $2^3S$-$2^3P$ stepwise excitation is one plausible mechanism large enough to account for the observed saturation characteristics. As shown in Fig. 12, the He $2^3S$-state calculations are also in good agreement with frequency pushing experiments (see Section VI, B). The present state of atomic and system parameter determination, together with the approximate nature of the formulation, limits the accuracy of this sort of calculation to a factor of two.) However, for He $2^1S$-$2^1P$ stepwise excitation to be a significant relaxation mechanism, other mechanisms must be invoked to explain a depletion rate from the He $2^1P$ level that exceeds the radiative cascade rate back to the He $2^1S$ level. The most probable such mechanisms appear to be successive stages of electron-atom collisional depletion, involving both allowed and exchange transitions [21], and helium-neon atom-atom transfer collisions, involving various highly excited neon states [21, 100]. Singlet triplet atom-atom exchange collisions are unlikely at any stage, however, as long as L-S coupling conditions are valid. (Barring spin-spin interactions, spin flips will not occur unless the spin of an electron is affected by orbital forces.)
Ionikh and Frish [101] have also suggested that electron-atom depletion of the He $2^1S$ state occurs by electron exchange transfer to the higher helium triplets. Here again, cascading from higher triplets to the triplet metastable state must be considered. Since the saturation characteristics of the helium metastable singlets and triplets are similar, still other mechanisms must be invoked to explain metastable triplet saturation. One such mechanism involves radiation trapping, which may reduce the He $2^3P$-$2^3S$ repopulation rate [21].

**Table 1**

Numerical Values for the Parameters Appearing in Eqs. (50) and (51) at a Pressure-Diameter Product of 3.6 Torr-mm (5 : 1 mix).

| Term | Units | Sources | Diameter | | |
|---|---|---|---|---|---|
| | | | 1 mm | 3 mm | 6 mm |
| I | mA | | | | |
| $N_0$ | atoms/cm$^3$ | | $7.24 \times 10^{16}$ | $2.41 \times 10^{16}$ | $1.21 \times 10^{16}$ |
| $N_e$ | electrons/cm$^3$ | Eq. (35), Ref. 77 | $6.23I \times 10^{10}$ | $6.92I \times 10^{9}$ | $1.73I \times 10^{9}$ |
| $\beta_1 N_e$ | sec$^{-1}$ | Eq. (53)/3f$_{ik}$ | $7.85I \times 10^{3}$ | $8.73I \times 10^{2}$ | $2.18I \times 10^{2}$ |
| $\beta_2 N_e$ | sec$^{-1}$ | Eq. (53) | $1.40I \times 10^{5}$ | $1.56I \times 10^{4}$ | $3.89I \times 10^{3}$ |
| $Z_r$ | sec$^{-1}$ | Ref. 23 | $1.42 \times 10^{6}$ | $4.76 \times 10^{5}$ | $2.38 \times 10^{5}$ |
| $Z_j'$ | sec$^{-1}$ | Eq. (3), Ref. 23 | $9.36 \times 10^{6}$ | $3.12 \times 10^{6}$ | $1.56 \times 10^{6}$ |
| $Z_r + A$ | sec$^{-1}$ | Ref. 31 | $4.41 \times 10^{7}$ | $2.71 \times 10^{7}$ | $2.28 \times 10^{7}$ |
| $Z_d$ | sec$^{-1}$ | Ref. 57 | $4.63 \times 10^{5}$ | $1.54 \times 10^{5}$ | $7.71 \times 10^{4}$ |
| $\alpha N_e N_0$ | atoms/(cm$^3$ · sec) | Eq. (52) | $2.36I \times 10^{17}$ | $8.74I \times 10^{15}$ | $1.09I \times 10^{15}$ |
| He $2^1$S | atoms/cm$^3$ | Eq. (50) | $\dfrac{1.51 \times 10^{11}}{1 + 0.94I}$ | $\dfrac{1.51 \times 10^{10}}{1 + 0.029I}$ | $\dfrac{3.71 \times 10^{9}}{1 + 0.014I}$ |
| He $2^1$S (I $\to \infty$) | atoms/cm$^3$ | Eq. (50) | $1.6 \times 10^{12}$ | $5.2 \times 10^{11}$ | $2.6 \times 10^{11}$ |
| Ne $3s_2$ | atoms/cm$^3$ | Eq. (51) | $\dfrac{4.8I \times 10^{9}}{1 + 0.094I}$ | $\dfrac{2.7I \times 10^{8}}{1 + 0.029I}$ | $\dfrac{3.8I \times 10^{7}}{1 + 0.014I}$ |
| Ne $3s_2$ (I $\to \infty$) | atoms/cm$^3$ | Eq. (51) | $5.1 \times 10^{10}$ | $9.3 \times 10^{9}$ | $2.7 \times 10^{9}$ |

**Note:** In these calculations the electron temperature is taken to be 90,000 K and the atomic temperature is assumed to be 400 K.

Finally, the formulation of Eq. (50) assumes that the distribution of electrons and excited states can be described by a zeroth-order Bessel function. At high levels of excitation, the radial metastable density profile tends to flatten. This results in a sharper concentration gradient to the discharge wall, and appears to an observer as an enhanced current-dependent metastable depletion rate. At this time, the appropriate depletion mechanism has not been clearly identified and may yet be caused by some unexpected process.

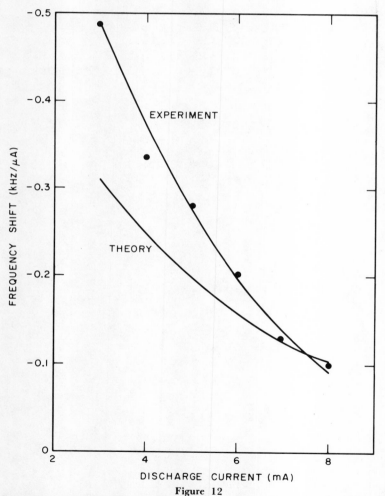

**Figure 12**

Comparison of the calculated and experimental values of the excitation-induced off-resonant dispersive shifts at 1.15 $\mu$m [21]. The calculations are based on variations in the He $2^3$S population, resulting in index changes of the He $2^3$S-$2^3$P 1.08-$\mu$m transition.

As far as a quantitative description of the Ne $2p_4$-level population is concerned, at least seven more coupled rate equations appear to be required for even a crudely realistic model; however, the accumulation of experimental data on two-body inelastic cross sections (see Refs. 20, 23, 31, 41, 45, 93, and 102-106) and on radiative lifetimes (see Section V,B) is proceeding so rapidly that much more accurate quantitative models for the helium-neon system are becoming feasible. Most of the atom-atom and electron-atom cross-sectional data are unfortunately of the velocity-averaged variety and therefore of dubious value in a realistic model (see Section V,A). Once the appropriate equations have been obtained, radial solutions of the excited state populations should also be determined. Solutions of the required type are commonly expressed in terms of series expansions and become exceedingly complicated rather quickly. In terms of physical understanding, a reduction of the upper- and lower-level populations to a relatively simple form is perhaps more meaningful. Nevertheless, a considerable increase in the complexity of present numerical models is essential for a reasonably accurate calculation of optical gain.

## C. Power and Pressure Limitations

The inelastic collision of metastable helium and neutral neon atoms plays a significant role in the excitation of over twenty-five visible and infrared neon laser transitions. If care is taken to suppress certain stimulated emission effects associated with cavity tuning [107], level interactions [40, 108, 109], and dispersive shifts (see Section VI,B), the power output of each transition can be regarded as a monotonically increasing function of the gain. Since the gain is proportional to the difference in population between the upper- and lower-laser levels, the population mechanisms developed up to this point can provide a crude indication of the physical conditions required for maximum laser output. For simplicity, the arguments will be restricted to the more than fourteen laser transitions originating from the Ne $3s_2$ level.

The current dependence of the gain at 6328 Å and 3.39 $\mu$m is given by Eq. (43):

$$G = \frac{C_1 I}{1 + C_2 I} - C_3 I \qquad (54)$$

This equation clearly demonstrates that the gain, and hence the power output, passes through some maximum as a function of current. For optimum pd conditions in a dc excited discharge, the maximum 6328-Å incremental gain (in nepers) has been determined experimentally to be [110]

$$G_m = \frac{3.0 \times 10^{-4} \ell}{d} \qquad (55)$$

where $\ell$ is the discharge length and d is the discharge-tube diameter. At 3.39 $\mu$m, the incremental gain may be approximately 65 times as large [82], so that gains in excess of 50 dbm can be achieved [82, 111]. Despite the large disparity in gain for the two transitions, the maximum power output is basically determined by the rate at which atoms can be supplied to the common upper level; consequently, power output at the longer wavelength is usually comparable to or less than power output obtainable at 6328 Å [28]. In an rf excited system, the optimum discharge conditions vary somewhat from the conditions required for dc excitation [112], although similar power output vs current constraints are applicable. In fact, the first helium-neon laser of Javan et al. [1] used 28-MHz rf excitation, but this type of operation was fairly quickly superceded by dc excitation (see Section VI).

Since increasing the discharge current is apparently of limited usefulness in terms of enhancing the laser output, raising the discharge pressure appears to be an obvious alternative. At higher pressures, the total number of excited atoms, as well as the absolute value of the upper- and lower-level populations, appears likely to increase. However, raising the pressure above the value required by optimum pd constraints fails to improve the laser output. Three factors are primarily involved; first, the electron temperature decreases with increasing pressure, which tends to reduce the excitation of the upper-laser level compared with the lower-laser level; secondly, inelastic transfer from the upper-laser level tends to diminish the upper-level lifetime; and finally, the heightened direct excitation rate density and reduced diffusion rate cause an enhancement of the Ne 1s metastable level densities, which results in radiation trapping and an increase in the lower-laser-level lifetime. This latter restriction requires a relatively high helium-to-neon ratio (perhaps 20 : 1) for total pressures well above optimum. The first restriction allows a relatively low helium-to-neon ratio (perhaps 3 : 1) for large-bore low-pressure tubes [113]. At pressures appreciably below optimum pd requirements, helium metastable diffusion losses become significant enough to lower the power output.

The preceding considerations indicate that the range of possible pressure and current variation is severely constrained. By increasing the tube diameter at constant pd, however, one can make the laser output larger. In this case, the gain drops approximately inversely with the tube diameter, and the cross-sectional area of the discharge grows with the square of the diameter. The combined effect is to produce an output that varies roughly in direct proportion to the tube diameter [113]. Well above threshold, the output increases linearly with length [114]. A typical optimum output for a 100-cm by 6-mm cylindrical discharge might be 100 mW. In practice, cylindrical discharges above 15 mm in diameter are seldom employed because of stability limitations. Actually, most helium-neon discharges are operated in the range 1-6 mm, for mode control purposes.

Various other techniques have been used in attempts to increase the laser gain per unit length. One of the most successful of these [115] relies on the use of the light helium isotope, $He^3$. At constant temperature, $He^3$ atoms have a higher average velocity than $He^4$ atoms and this results in an improved rate of resonant transfer to the upper neon level [see Eq. (16)]. Another way of augmenting the resonant transfer rate is to increase the physical temperature [24, 25, 116]. Raising the temperature by several hundred degrees has produced a 30 - 40% improvement in power output [116]. At still higher temperatures, the output diminishes because of He $2^1$S or Ne $3s_2$ collisional transfer to adjacent neon levels and because of heightened helium metastable diffusion losses. (High physical temperatures are generally avoided because they are usually accompanied by accelerated gas cleanup and degraded cathode performance.) Other output improvement techniques have relied on the addition of selected impurities [28, 41] or on variations in discharge geometry [117] and excitation [118, 119]. Impurity-based schemes appear to be the most promising and depend either on decreasing the lifetime of the lower-laser level or on altering the ambipolar electron temperature balance. In the latter case, the average value of the electron temperature distribution may be altered, as well as the distribution shape itself. For example, if substantial numbers of monoenergetic electrons are emitted in Penning collisions, the distribution shape may be considerably affected. At present, all impurities appear to affect laser operation adversely; consequently, great care is routinely taken to eliminate impurities from helium-neon systems. Attempts at altering the electron-ion loss rates by using magnetic fields have also failed to produce significant improvements in power output characteristics [120, 121]. Although previous efforts to increase the intrinsic gain or power output have proved somewhat ineffective, it is not inconceivable that more significant progress will be made in the near future. One such possibility may involve the transient or cw use of electron beams to control the electron density and temperature independently.

## V. Investigations of Atomic Parameters

### A. Metastable State Decay

The metastable state relaxation mechanisms presented in the previous section involve only two-body inelastic collisions and wall diffusion. The collisions result in simple bound-free or bound-bound transitions among neutral atomic states. Several other types of collisional relaxation mechanisms should also be enumerated. At gas pressures that are substantially higher than those encountered in helium-neon laser discharges, two- and three-body collisions may result in significant metastable level depopulation by the formation of stable and unstable noble gas molecules [56, 57], or by collision-induced radiative transitions [57, 122]. If the metastable state concentration is very high, metastable-metastable collisions may also be important [73, 122, 123]. Furthermore, the addition of foreign gases into a helium-neon discharge may depopulate the metastable levels via Penning reactions [23, 122, 124-127]. As far as radiative relaxation is concerned, the Ne $1s_2$ and $1s_4$ "quasi-metastable" levels [8] may also decay by resonance-trapped relaxation to the ground state. (For certain helium-neon laser discharges, the resonance-trapped radiative relaxation rate may be comparable to the diffusion rate [128].) Ebbinghaus [129], Biondi [122], and Phelps and Molnar [56] were among the first investigators to analyze helium metastable-state relaxation mechanisms. The decay processes for the Ne 1s states were later studied in detail by Dixon and Grant [130] and by Phelps [131]. Following the advent of the helium-neon laser, other researchers examined the magnitude [1, 23] and structure [20] of helium-neon resonant-transfer cross sections.

The most popular techniques for evaluating metastable-state relaxation parameters are based either on time-resolved static afterglow methods [1, 23, 56, 57] or on flowing afterglow methods [23, 132]. The two principal static afterglow measurement techniques rely either on direct metastable-level population determination through absorption measurements [57] or on indirect population determination through resonant-transfer induced emission measurements [1]. In both types of static afterglow methods, the discharge is pulsed off and the time decay of the metastable populations is monitored. The decay is exponential and the time constant of this exponential is determined by the inverse sum of the various rates (sec$^{-1}$) for the metastable level depopulation processes.

In a real system, electron-ion buildup and decay times are finite and afterglow population or depopulation processes can be appreciable [133]. Moreover, noble gas molecules such as $He_2^+$, $Ne_2^+$, and $HeNe^+$ may complicate the analyses [134]. The afterglow mechanisms may include radiative or collisional cascading and electron-ion recombination. By restricting attention to times moderately late in the afterglow and reducing the initial electron-ion density sufficiently, real system complications can often be eliminated. (Late afterglow measurements also help to ensure that the fundamental diffusion mode is dominant [56]. When the discharge conditions are appropriately adjusted and the measurement techniques are sufficiently refined, quite accurate measurements of metastable-state relaxation mechanisms can be obtained. Using a relatively sensitive optical-absorption afterglow technique, Phelps was able to determine the pressure-dependent destruction rates of helium metastable states in pure helium [57] (Fig. 13). Because the various decay processes have different pressure-dependent characteristics, the individual relaxation rates are separable.

Afterglow absorption techniques can also be used to obtain the decay rates of metastable levels in the presence of foreign gas inpurities. Adding neon or other gases to a helium discharge may radically alter the helium metastable-state relaxation rate. From measurements of decay times as a function of foreign gas concentration, helium-neon resonant transfer cross sections and Penning cross sections can be determined [23]. When one of the foreign gas impurities is neon, measurements of impurity-induced metastable state depletion rates can rely on stimulated emission [135, 136] or spontaneous emission techniques [1]. In the latter method, use is made of resonant-transfer collisions to monitor helium metastable state lifetimes through neon-level spontaneous emission measurements. Here the respective decay rates of the Ne $3s_2$ and Ne $2s_2$ populations are directly proportional to the decay rates of the He $2^1$ S and He $2^3$ S populations, provided that the neon-level lifetimes are relatively short compared with the metastable-state lifetimes. By adjusting conditions in a helium-neon discharge to a regime where He $2^3$ S-level depletion occurs predominantly by diffusion and by resonant transfer collisions, Javan et al. were able to evaluate the magnitude of the metastable depletion processes on the basis of the pressure dependence of the overall relaxation time [1]; the forward resonant-transfer rate is directly proportional to neon pressure and the diffusive relaxation rate is inversely proportional to the total pressure (Eq. (28) should be applied for varying helium-to-neon ratios).

The relatively recent introduction of flowing afterglow systems by Schmeltekopf and co-workers [23, 132] has provided an added impetus to the study of He $2^3$ S collisions. Flowing afterglows differ from static afterglows in that the temporal decay of the discharge is displayed spatially. At each point in the spatial display, there is a one-to-one correspondence with the temporal

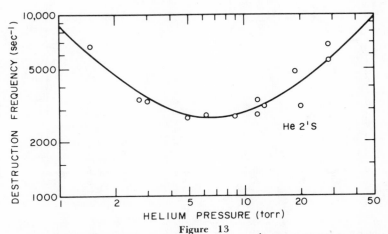

**Figure 13**

Pressure-dependent destruction frequency of the He $2^1$ S state from time-resolved afterglow absorption measurements [57].

behavior of an equivalent pulsed discharge. The display is maintained by pumping the plasma along at nearly supersonic speeds, and foreign gases can be introduced downstream from the discharge source. These systems have the attractive feature of being able to control the He $2^3$S density independently of the foreign gas concentration. Flowing afterglows are particularly well suited for the study of relative collision cross sections [127], although the method has been used to obtain absolute cross sections for a number of He $2^3$S collisions [23, 132].

The resonant-transfer cross sections obtained in emission or absorption afterglow measurements have up until recently been simple velocity-averaged quantities. Substitution of the experimentally obtained decay rates into the atomic analog of Eq. (16) yielded the energy-independent cross sections. However, at atomic temperatures differing from the initial measurement conditions, energy-independent cross sections do not give realistic estimates of the decay rates [20, 137]. The inaccuracies occur because there is an energy-dependent structure associated with the collision cross section. Strictly speaking, this structure must be extracted from the atomic analog of Eq. (9). A first attempt to isolate the

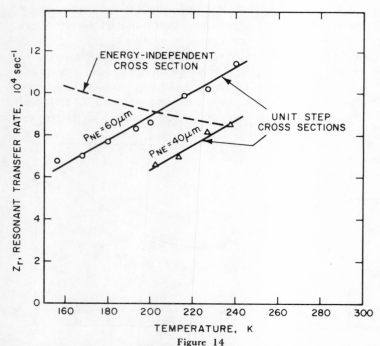

**Figure 14**

Temperature-dependent destruction frequency of the He $2^1$S state from time-resolved afterglow emission experiments [20].

structure of the He $2^1$S-Ne $3s_2$ transfer cross section was made by Arrathoon in a temperature-dependent afterglow-emission experiment [20]. As indicated in Fig. 14, a unit-step cross section with a threshold energy corresponding to the energy difference between the initial and final states was adjusted to fit the observed metastable decay rates. (Discharge conditions were altered so that the He $2^1$S afterglow lifetime was determined almost exclusively by resonant-transfer collisions.) Figure 14 apparently indicates that the use of an energy-independent cross section at varying temperatures can lead to serious errors in evaluating resonant-transfer rates. The indiscriminate application of such cross sections is clearly inadvisable. Temperature variations in the diffusion coefficients are also significant but can be crudely estimated on the basis of a $T^{1.75}$ dependence [21, 56] (at constant pressure).

## B. Radiative and Collisional Relaxation

The radiative relaxation rates of the first few groups of He I and Ne I excited states are at least one or two orders of magnitude larger than the metastable-state relaxation rates encountered in a typical positive column. The determination of fast radiative relaxation rates in the noble gases has been, and continues to be, a subject of intensive investigation. Most of the direct and indirect methods for fast radiative lifetime measurements in helium and neon have previously been reviewed by Bennett [45]. Since then, three varieties of direct measurements and three varieties of indirect measurements have developed significantly. Two of the indirect methods rely on the Hanle effect [138] and the beam foil technique [139] and a third is based on the lineshape characteristics of an operating laser [140]. The first of the direct methods depends on the modulated electron-excitation phase-shift technique [141]. The second is based on pulsed electron-excitation multichannel time-decay methods [45], and the third depends on monochromatic (optical) perturbation time-decay techniques [31, 142, 143]. Various types of collision cross sections can also be deduced from the six types of lifetime measurements and these cross sections will be respectively discussed in connection with the relevant lifetime measurement techniques. Since transition probabilities are also essential atomic parameters, some current sources will be cited at the end of this section.

The zero-field level crossing, or Hanle effect, is based on the absorption and reradiation of incident light in the presence of a static magnetic field. Classically, the polarization of the scattered light is altered due to the effect of Larmor precession on the spatial orientation of the emitted electric field. In the simplest form of a Hanle measurement, the intensity of the perpendicular component of the scattered light, as a function of the applied magnetic field, has a Lorentzian lineshape. The full width at half maximum of the Lorentzian can be expressed in terms of the mean-level lifetime [138]. Decamps and Dumont have extended the theory of Hanle measurements in a gas discharge to describe the fluorescent behavior of pairs of excited levels that are resonantly illuminated by a laser beam [144]. Experimentally, they obtained values for the depopulation and depolarization rates of the Ne $3s_2$, $2s_2$, and $2p_4$ levels as functions of both helium and neon pressure. The experimental results were also expressed in terms of velocity-averaged cross sections. In the absence of radiation trapping (coherence narrowing), Decamps depopulation rates are physically identical to the sum of the radiative and inelastic collisional relaxation terms, as they would appear in a rate equation analysis. At low pressures, the depopulation rates yield the vacuum-ultraviolet untrapped natural lifetimes of the levels [45]. The depolarization or dealignment rates are determined directly from the Hanle curve and consist of the sum of the effects due to inelastic collisions, radiative relaxation, and precession-perturbing elastic collisions. Although the values that Decamps and Dumont obtained appear to be approximately correct, there is some disagreement with cross sections obtained in other experiments [31, 145], possibly because the applied magnetic field changes both the electron-ion loss rate and the discharge excitation conditions.

Magnetic-field difficulties are not encountered in the beam foil technique [139], which has been used with some success in determinating neutral neon lifetimes [146]. The method relies on the passage of a single or multiply ionized high-energy atomic beam through a thin foil. At the foil, some of the beam energy is converted to heat and the rest produces various stages of excitation and ionization in the transmitted beam. For a given excited state, the intensity-vs-distance variation from the foil can be used to determine the level decay rate. Assousa et al. have used this technique to obtain some reasonable estimates of neon 2p-level lifetimes [146]. The method appears to be unsuitable for determining collisional decay rates and is susceptible to cascade errors and data normalization problems; however, the technique does provide a powerful tool for examining highly excited states of multiply ionized atoms.

Another class of indirect lifetime measurements, which is in a particularly dynamic state of development, is based on the line shape dependent output characteristics of a gas laser [30, 140]. In the limit of a collisionless system, Lamb's theory of the gas laser [89] provides a basis for the experimental determination of lineshape parameters. For example, in certain circumstances, the width of the Lamb dip can be used to extract natural linewidths [140, 147]. The effects of "hard" and "soft" collisions were first introduced by Szoke and Javan [30, 140] into a slightly modified form of Lamb's theory. Hard collisions were defined as interactions resulting in large velocity or phase shifts and an interruption in the coherent interaction of the atomic wave function with the laser field; soft collisions resulted only in small velocity or phase shifts and no disruption of coherent interaction. A hard collision lineshape parameter (analogous to the Lorentzian linewidth obtained from spontaneous emission measurements) was defined that was equal to the sum of natural broadening, inelastic collisional broadening, and elastic hard collisional broadening effects. The soft collisional lineshape parameter was defined as equal to the sum of the hard collisional parameter and elastic soft collisional effects. Physically, hard collisions manifest themselves primarily as an increase in the Lorentzian component of the Doppler broadened line, whereas soft collisions appear principally as shifts in the central frequency of the Lorentzian component [148]. By fitting pressure-dependent single-mode tuning data to their theory, Szoke and Javan were able to obtain both parameters for the 1.5-$\mu$m transition. Their natural linewidth, together with a knowledge of the Ne $2p_4$-level lifetime, provides a determination of the vacuum-ultraviolet untrapped lifetime of the Ne $2s_2$ level. Similar measurements by Cordover and Bonczyk [149] on the 6328-Å transition provide the untrapped lifetime of the Ne $3s_2$ level. However, the $3s_2$ and $2s_2$ hard linewidths obtained in these experiments are not in good agreement with respective values determined from spontaneous emission [150] and double resonance spectroscopy measurements [151]. Nonetheless, a more detailed theory of gas laser pressure broadening by Gyorffy, Borenstein, and Lamb [152] is consistent with the analysis of Szoke and Javan. Other theories of collision broadening have been developed by Fork and Pollack and by Smith that rely on the use of a single lineshape parameter that is crudely [87, 149, 153] or precisely [154] equivalent to the soft collisional parameter. Unfortunately, the inelastic collision rates appearing in the rate equation analyses of Section IV are not obviously separable from the lineshape measurements, although Gyorffy et al. [152] suggest that the separation may be feasible. Analogous difficulties are enountered in trying to extract depolarization collision rates from the two lineshape parameters. Recent advances in the theory of collisional broadening by Berman and Lamb [155] may prove helpful in settling the separability issues.

The three direct methods for lifetime determination mentioned earlier have the advantage that the lifetimes and inelastic collision rates can be determined relatively unambiguously in the frequency or time domain. When a sinusoidally varying source of excitation is applied to an atomic system, a phase shift is incurred between the modulated emission and the source. This shift is directly related to the level lifetime and forms the basis for the electron-excitation phase-shift method [141]. The usual considerations of cascade, collisional, and radiation trapping effects apply here [45], as well as an additional constraint imposed by the necessity of obtaining a reference transition with a small or known phase shift. The method has been applied successfully to many ultraviolet transitions in order to obtain a large number of Ne I-, II-, and III-level lifetimes [156]. Limiting resolutions of greater than a single nanosecond have been achieved.

One of the most reliable direct lifetime measurement techniques is the pulsed electron-beam multichannel delayed-coincidence method of Bennett

et al. [45, 157]. In this technique, direct electron impact excitation of particular states is achieved with a nearly monoenergetic pulsed electron beam. If
the beam energy is adjusted to precisely the threshold energy required for the
excitation of a specific level, no cascading from higher levels will occur. When
the electron beam is terminated, the excited-state population will then decay
exponentially with a single time constant (Fig. 15). Although ideal threshold
excitation of a particular level often can not be achieved, the effects of cascade
contributions are frequently separable. The delayed-coincidence method has
already been reviewed in great detail [45] and will not be discussed further.
A number of neutral neon 2s and 2p lifetimes have been determined with this
technique [157].

Monoenergetic electron pulses have the undesirable feature of appreciably
exciting most of the levels that lie below the level of interest. This feature
can sometimes lead to complications due to collisional transfer and radiation
trapping effects. In addition, even quasimonoenergetic electron pulses (of high
intensity) are difficult to generate. Pulses of monochromatic radiation, however,
are capable of producing extremely selective perturbations in the populations of
levels that are independently excited (as in a gas discharge). Here again, cascade,

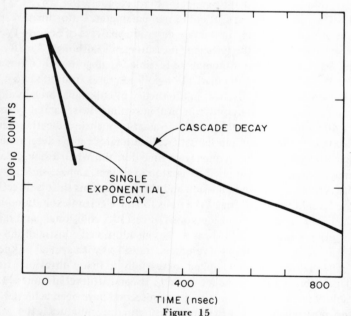

**Figure 15**
Delayed-coincidence counting data illustrating the difference between single exponential
and cascade decay [156].

collisional, and radiation trapping effects are sources of potential error, but in this case they are relatively easy to eliminate. High-intensity monochromatic perturbation techniques were first used with Q-switched $CO_2$ lasers in induced fluorescence [142] and transient gain [143] measurements (20 nanoseconds resolution). Somewhat later, Arrathoon and Sealer explored the principles and possibilities of ultrafast (subnanosecond) monochromatic-perturbation fluorescence measurements in discrete energy-level systems [31]. In an auxiliary experiment, they used a fast intracavity acoustooptic diffractor to deflect 6328-Å pulses through an external helium-neon test cell. From time-resolved spontaneous emission relaxation measurements, they were able to determine the relaxation rates of the Ne $3s_2$ and $2p_4$ levels. Since the pressures and currents in the test cell could be independently controlled, inelastic collisional cross sections and radiative decay rates could readily be extracted (Fig. 16). The ultimate temporal resolution of this experiment was limited by the fall time of the optical pulse and this time was extended to the subnanosecond region by mode-locked cavity dumping techniques. (In these measurements, some care must be taken

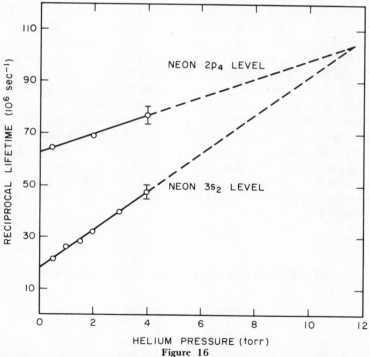

**Figure 16**

Variation with helium pressure of the Ne $3s_2$ and $2p_4$ destruction frequencies [31]. The measurements are based on monochromatic-perturbation time-decay experiments.

to ensure that the discharge current and the excitation conditions are not substantially altered by the presence of the optical field [158], although such errors may often be avoided if the times are sufficiently rapid [31]. The use of polarized light, however, can introduce errors due to depolarizing collisional effects.) Application of monochromatic perturbation time decay techniques to visible gas laser transitions [31, 159] has just begun and these techniques may eventually serve as selective standards for other lifetime measurement methods. The advent of high-intensity tunable dye lasers suggests that the full potential of monochromatic perturbation methods has yet to be exploited.

Concerning transition probabilities, most experimental values have been determined from appropriately normalized absorption, dispersion, or emission experiments [72]. The methods depend on the measurement of upward [8, 160] or downward [8] branching ratios from a given level or on the establishment of local thermodynamic equilibrium (LTE) conditions [72]. Relatively recently, a differential emission technique termed laser differential spectrometry has become prevalent [161, 162]. The method basically relies on measuring the ratios of differential emission intensities from levels that are directly or indirectly perturbed by the laser field. Hansch and Toschek first used this method to determine relative transition probabilities for Ne 3s-2p transitions [161]. Simultaneously, Parks and Javan developed a related technique to study inelastic collisional transfer between the $2s_2$ and $2s_3$ levels of neon [105]. (This technique was later applied to the Ne $3s_2$ and $3s_3$ levels [106], and a vaguely analogous approach was applied to the study of inelastic collisional transfer between states in neutral helium [39].) A method similar to that of Hansch and Toschek was developed independently by Bychkova et al. [163], who also measured Ne 3s-2p relative transition probabilities. Measurements of Ne 1s-2p transition probabilities are tabulated in Ref. 72 and are based on dispersion and emission measurements. Most of the remaining Ne s-p transition probabilities are known only from approximate theoretical calculations [50]. The neon transition probabilities of most interest here are presented in Tables 2 and 3. By contrast, all the low-lying helium transition probabilities have been quite accurately calculated [72] and are presented in Tables 4 and 5.

## VI. Discharge Characteristics and Plasma-Optical Noise

### A. Discharge Lifetime Effects

Two of the principal factors limiting the lifetime of helium-neon discharges are cathode deterioration and gas cleanup. Cathode deterioration is accompanied by a gradual or abrupt decline in electron emission capabilities, while gas cleanup is characterized by a continuous reduction in the concentration of helium or neon

**Table 2**

Neon Transition Probabilities ($10^6$ sec$^{-1}$) and [Wavelengths (Å)] for Prominent Spectral Lines Connected to the 2p Levels

|  | $2p_1$ | $2p_2$ | $2p_3$ | $2p_4$ | $2p_5$ | $2p_6$ | $2p_7$ | $2p_8$ | $2p_9$ | $2p_{10}$ |
|---|---|---|---|---|---|---|---|---|---|---|
| $1s_2$ | 71.9 [5852.49] | 25.1 [6598.95] |  | 23.8 [6678.28] | 23.4 [6717.04] | 19.0 [6929.47] |  | 3.65 [7173.94] |  |  |
| $1s_3$ | 16.0 | 16.0 [6163.59] |  |  | 22.3 [6266.50] |  | 12.8 [6532.88] |  |  | 2.92 [7438.90] |
| $1s_4$ |  | 6.27 [6030.00] | 61.7 [6074.34] | 16.9 [6096.16] | 3.27 [6128.45] | 5.07 [6304.79] | 27.9 [6382.99] | 23.2 [6506.53] |  | 9.77 [7245.17] |
| $1s_5$ |  | 12.8 [5881.90] |  | 10.5 [5944.83] | 4.33 [5975.53] | 21.6 [6143.06] | 7.77 [6217.28] | 13.6 [6334.43] | 43.3 [6402.25] | 19.2 [7032.41] |
| $2s_2$ | 0.802 [15231] | 4.089 [11767] | 0.801 [11602] | 6.537 [11523] | 2.301 [11409] | 7.543 [10844] | 0.816 [10621] | 0.726 [10295] |  | 1.708 [8865] |
| $2s_3$ |  | 5.341 [11985] |  |  | 6.796 [11614] |  | 11.037 [10798] |  |  | 4.136 [8989] |
| $2s_4$ | 0.247 [17162] | 0.006 [12887] | 1.386 [12689] | 0.762 [12595] | 2.131 [12459] | 3.267 [11789] | 3.758 [11525] | 9.784 [11143] |  | 2.763 [9487] |
| $2s_5$ |  | 0.651 [13219] |  | 2.478 [12912] | 0.334 [12770] | 1.858 [12066] | 0.324 [11790] | 2.470 [11390] | 12.278 [11178] | 5.114 [9665] |
| $3s_2$ | 0.48 [7304.9] |  | 0.70 [6351.9] | 6.56 [6328.2] | 1.35 [6293.8] | 1.28 [6118.0] | 0.68 [6046.1] | 0.56 [5939.3] |  | 0.59 [5433.6] |
| $3s_3$ |  |  |  |  |  |  |  |  |  |  |
| $3s_4$ |  |  |  |  |  |  |  |  |  |  |
| $3s_5$ |  |  |  |  |  |  |  |  |  |  |

**Note:** Values are taken from Refs. 50, 73, 161, and 163.

**Table 3**

Neon Transition Probabilities ($10^6$ sec$^{-1}$) for Prominent Spectral Lines Connected to the 3p Levels

| | $3p_1$ | $3p_2$ | $3p_3$ | $3p_4$ | $3p_5$ | $3p_6$ | $3p_7$ | $3p_8$ | $3p_9$ | $3p_{10}$ |
|---|---|---|---|---|---|---|---|---|---|---|
| $1s_2$ | 7.3 [3520.47] | | | | | | | | | |
| $1s_3$ | | | | | | | | | | |
| $1s_4$ | | | 8.5 [3454.19] | | | | | | | |
| $1s_5$ | | | | | | | | | 9.9 [3472.57] | |
| $2s_2$ | 7.710 [21041] | 3.518 [23956] | 0.233 [25855] | 5.265 [23951] | 1.762 [24249] | 0.137 [28533] | 0.043 [28744] | 0.012 [29714] | | 0.036 [33511] |
| $2s_3$ | | 1.799 [23100] | | | 3.941 [23373] | | 0.066 [27521] | | | 0.062 [31860] |
| $2s_4$ | 0.667 [18210] | 0.042 [20354] | 7.021 [21708] | 0.260 [20350] | 0.002 [20565] | 1.731 [23565] | 4.573 [23709] | 3.527 [24365] | | 0.750 [26861] |
| $2s_5$ | | 0.661 [19577] | | 0.176 [19574] | 0.050 [19772] | 4.374 [22530] | 1.075 [22662] | 1.948 [23260] | 5.744 [23636] | 3.488 [25524] |
| $3s_2$ | 0.263 [42172] | 1.124 [33903] | 0.107 [30712] | 2.871 [33913] | 0.595 [33333] | 0.083 [27631] | 0.001 [27436] | 0.017 [26607] | | 0.184 [24156] |
| $3s_3$ | | 1.462 [34490] | | | 3.495 [33900] | | 0.172 [27819] | | | 0.369 [24452] |
| $3s_4$ | 0.013 [61450] | 0.002 [45338] | 0.312 [39806] | 0.001 [45356] | 0.008 [44324] | 0.882 [34780] | 1.364 [34471] | 2.105 [33173] | 2.582 [33352] | 0.459 [29448] |
| $3s_5$ | | 0.026 [47147] | | 0.011 [47167] | 0.002 [46051] | 0.980 [35835] | 0.151 [35507] | 0.556 [34131] | | 1.140 [30201] |

Note: Values are taken from Refs. 50 and 73.

Table 4

Helium Transition Probabilities ($10^8$ sec$^{-1}$) and [Wavelengths (Å)] for Low-Lying Singlets (Ref. 73)

|  | 1¹S | 2¹S | 3¹S | 4¹S | 5¹S | 3¹D | 4¹D | 5¹D |
|---|---|---|---|---|---|---|---|---|
| 2¹P | 17.99 [584.334] | 0.01976 [20581.3] | 0.181 [7281.35] | 0.0655 [5047.74] | 0.0313 [4437.55] | 0.638 [6678.15] | 0.202 [4921.93] | 0.0907 [4387.93] |
| 3¹P | 5.66 [537.030] | 0.1338 [5015.68] | 0.00253 [74351] | 0.0459 [21132.0] | 0.0202 [13411.8] | $1.68 \times 10^{-6}$ [957600] | 0.0711 [19089.4] | 0.0331 [12968.4] |
| 4¹P | 2.46 [522.213] | 0.0717 [3964.73] | 0.0137 [15083.7] | $5.79 \times 10^{-4}$ [180950] | 0.0150 [46053] | 0.00277 [18555.6] | $5.70 \times 10^{-7}$ [$2.16 \times 10^6$] | 0.0153 [41216] |
| 5¹P | 1.28 [515.617] | 0.0376 [3613.64] | 0.00956 [11013.1] | 0.00302 [33299] |  | 0.00127 [12755.7] | 0.00166 [40053] |  |

Table 5

Helium Transition Probabilities ($10^8$ sec$^{-1}$) and [Wavelengths (Å)] for Low-Lying Triplets (Ref. 73)

|  | 2³S | 3³S | 4³S | 5³S | 3³D | 4³D | 5³D |
|---|---|---|---|---|---|---|---|
| 2³P | 0.1022 [10830] | 0.278 [7065.3] | 0.106 [4713.2] | 0.0430 [4120.8] | 0.706 [5875.7] | 0.251 [4471.5] | 0.117 [4026.2] |
| 3³P | 0.09478 [3888.65] | 0.0108 [42947] | 0.0652 [21120] | 0.0269 [12846] | $1.28 \times 10^{-4}$ [186200] | 0.0668 [17002] | 0.0343 [11969.1] |
| 4³P | 0.0505 [3187.74] | 0.00608 [12528] | 0.00227 [108800] | 0.0202 [46936] | 0.00597 [19543] | $4.15 \times 10^{-5}$ [439440] | 0.0129 [37026] |
| 5³P | 0.0293 [2945.10] | 0.00608 [9463.57] | 0.00128 [28542] |  | 0.00274 [12985] | 0.00333 [42430] |  |

or both. The available literature in the area of laser discharge lifetimes is relatively scarce and tends to be empirically oriented [164, 165]. Despite the lack of rigorous theories, intensive developmental efforts have already produced dc excited helium-neon laser discharge configurations capable of nearly two years of continuous operation [166]. In reliabiltiy and stability, these discharges far exceed any other sealed-off gas laser system.

Cathode destruction and gas cleanup are often inextricably related. One of the primary causes of cathode destruction is positive-ion bombardment. In a properly emitting hot cathode, the discharge current is primarily supplied by thermionic emission and the cathode potential fall is comparable to the ionization potential of the gas [167]. If the cathode is required to supply increasingly large amounts of current, the cathode fall will increase until secondary processes, such as positive-ion bombardment, induce the necessary emission [167]. When the bombardment becomes too severe, cathode destruction and sputtering will occur. Sputtering results in the deposition of layers of cathode material on the cool tube surfaces, which tends to trap or getter gas molecules. As the pressure decreases, the sputtering rate increases (quite rapidly [166]) and the destructive cycle accelerates. Eventually, either the cathode fails or the laser output drops to an unacceptable value. The destructive cycle may also be initiated by the presence of spuriously introduced impurities that "poison" the cathode and reduce primary emission. (This type of impurity-induced effect can usually be eliminated by the inclusion of barium getters in the discharge tube and by the preparation of relatively clean system components.) Impurities also adversely affect population inversion [25, 41, 165, 168] and may be inherently associated with fused silica tubes [165].

Some typical hot cathode emitters are tungsten and barium-strontium oxide. The emitters are generally formed as filaments and in the case of (Ba, Sr)O are impregnated in a nickel mesh base. A heating current is passed through the mesh. (Nickel can also serve as an anode material, but usually in a disc or cylindrical configuration.) On rare occasions, when more than 150 mA are required, specialized cathode designs are employed [167]. At the low-current extreme, cold cathodes are freqeuntly used in small-bore (1-3 mm) helium-neon lasers operating at currents below 20 or 30 mA. The present favorites in cold-cathode materials are aluminum, tantalum, or zirconium hollow cylinders with a thin layer of oxide on the inner emitting surface. In the proper operating regime, these cathodes exhibit lifetime characteristics that are superior to those of hot cathodes. More specifically, the lifetimes of aluminum cold cathodes in selected helium-neon discharges have been demonstrated by Hochuli et al. [166] to be 3,000 to 18,000 hr. As with hot cathodes, any initial gas cleanup results in accelerated cathode sputtering, which precipitates a destructive cycle. Although the initial cleanup can be minimized by attempting to saturate the discharge walls with helium and neon before sealing off the tube, some wall adsorption or diffusion (permeation) is inevitable.

In an rf-excited system, the internal cathode is replaced with external electrodes. The consequent eliminaton of potential cathode sputtering suggests that an improvement in discharge lifetime characteristics will occur. Actually, increased gas losses in these systems results in shorter discharge lifetimes. Turner et al. [164] have studied the relative cleanup rates of helium and neon in rf-excited discharges. They found that there is a large initial cleanup rate of neon, which levels off fairly quickly. The helium pressure, however, decreases continuously at approximately a constant rate. These discharges have lifetimes that are only in the hundreds of hours. Apparently, there is an irreversible and accelerated helium diffusive loss in the vicinity of the rf electrodes [164]. Other work has shown that the initiation of a discharge partially reverses neon wall losses, possibly through desorption [165]. By comparison, the primary cause of failure for dc-excited discharges appears to be neon cleanup [113]. In practice, the effects of gas cleanup on laser operation can be minimized by forming the discharge vessel with a material that has a relatively low permeation rate (Corning 7052) and by overfilling the tube (perhaps by 40% above the optimum pressure) with helium and neon. These effects can also be reduced by including a relatively large gas reservoir and eliminating local hot spots.

The 6328-Å voltage-current-power (V-I-P) characteristics of a typical overfilled discharge is indicated in Fig. 17. Also indicated in this figure are two V-I-P characteristics illustrating helium and neon cleanup. Since almost all the voltage drop in this relatively long, hot-cathode discharge occurs in the positive column, the tube voltage is roughly proportional to the axial electric field and is also crudely proportional to the electron temperature (at constant pressure). As the neon cleans up, the plasma becomes almost entirely dominated by helium and the electron temperature increases. For currents in excess of 20 mA, the applied voltage and the electron temperature appear to vary by less than ±10%. These characteristics are in essential agreement with the ambipolar diffusion theory predictions of Section III. The data presented in Fig. 17 also show that the laser power output is a particularly sensitive function of neon partial pressure. In dc-excited helium-neon discharges, neon cleanup is among the most common causes of laser failure [113]. This type of cleanup is particularly easy to recognize visually and results in apparent discharge color changes from cameo pink to whitish blue.

## B. Plasma-Induced Laser Noise

The spectral purity and amplitude stability of an ideal helium-neon laser is ultimately limited by spontaneous emission noise [169, 170]. In reality, certain externally controllable factors such as mode-interference [171], transition competition [40, 108, 109], plasma effects [172], and environmental disturbances [173] (thermal, mechanical, etc.) usually determine the attainable purity and stability. Of the external noise sources, environmental disturbances and plasma effects are the most difficult to minimize. Plasma effects include all discharge-induced perturbations that alter the level populations, while environmental disturbances include all external processes that alter the passive optical resonator characteristics. Since plasma noise affects the population inversion, it is relatively easy to perceive that this noise will produce laser amplitude fluctuations, provided the frequency of the noise falls below the value set by the transient response of the laser ($\cong 1$ MHz). Moreover, since plasma-induced perturbations of the level populations may also affect the refractive index at a particular wavelength, it is not difficult to imagine that the resulting index changes will shift the optical cavity modes and produce laser frequency fluctuations. Indeed, due to pushing and pulling contributions alone [41, 174-176], plasma-induced laser amplitude fluctuations will invariably be accompanied by laser frequency fluctuations. Even in the absence of all perturbations, dispersive effects can produce a lensing action which alters the diffraction losses of the optical resonator [128, 177]. A variety of relatively static, plasma-dependent, processes may alter the shape and absolute frequency of the atomic lineshape itself [178]. However, the primary topics of interest here will involve dynamic, rather than static, changes in plasma properties. In particular, the correspondence between plasma noise and laser amplitude and frequency effects will be considered.

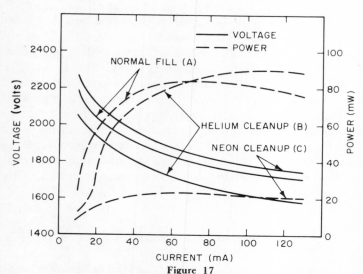

**Figure 17**

Voltage-current-power characteristics of a typical hot-cathode 100-cm by 6-mm cylindrical discharge. The curves indicate the effects of gas cleanup: Curve (A) represents a normal overfill at $p_{he} = 0.7$ Torr and $p_{ne} = 0.1$ Torr; curve (B) is at $p_{he} = 0.5$ Torr and $p_{ne} = 0.1$ Torr; and curve (C) is at $p_{he} = 0.7$ Torr and $p_{ne} = 0.02$ Torr.

The first detailed observations of excess amplitude noise in the output of a gas laser were made by Bolwijn, Alkemade, and Boschloo [179]. At frequencies below 10 kHz, a measured amplitude-to-shot noise ratio of nearly $10^8$ was reported. The experiments were conducted on a dc-excited multimode helium-neon laser operating at 1.15 μm. Bolwijn et al. originally attributed the observed amplitude fluctuations to excess photon noise, as predicted from the wave-interaction statistics of thermal sources. Later theories showed that these statistics were inapplicable to nonthermal sources (lasers), although the statistics did resemble

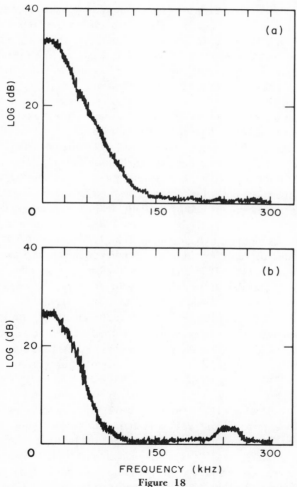

**Figure 18**
Spectral dependence of (a) excess laser amplitude noise, and (b) excess discharge current noise for dc excitation conditions [172].

those produced by several oscillating laser modes in the presence of background Gaussian noise [171]. Immediately following the observations of Bolwijn et al., the excess laser amplitude noise was tentatively identified by Bellisio, Freed, and Haus [172] as due to discharge current fluctuations. Using a single-mode 6328-Å helium-neon laser for their measurements, Bellisio et al. observed both laser output noise spectra and discharge current spectra. Some of their results, for conditions of dc excitation, are presented in Fig. 18. The low-frequency discharge current and laser noise are approximately 30 db above shot noise levels. For frequencies above 50 or 60 kHz, both excess noise factors decrease rather sharply. Apparently, there is a strong correlation between discharge current fluctuations and laser fluctuations. This interpretation was later established, almost conclusively, by Prescott and van der Ziel in cross-correlation measurements [180]. Further experiments by Bolwijn also suggested that the observed low-frequency excess laser noise (below 100 kHz) was primarily induced by the modulating effects of discharge current fluctuations [181].

The presence of excess noise in the discharge current spectrum is not an altogether unexpected phenomenon. This noise is related to various instabilities in the gas discharge and such effects have been studied for several decades [182, 183]. Suzuki [184] has somewhat arbitrarily classified discharge noise in helium-neon lasers into two components: current noise and traveling-wave striation noise. Current noise contributes to the smoothly varying background portion of the noise spectrum, whereas striations produce more or less discrete spectral spikes that are accompanied by spatially distinct traveling waves. (Standing-wave striations are relatively noise-free.) Moving striations in helium-neon lasers were first reported by Garscadden et al. [185], who observed that the striations modulated the laser output. (Other studies of moving striations in helium-neon discharges [186, 187] and various low-pressure glow discharges [188, 189] indicate that the physical processes involved are relatively complex.) Numerous attempts have been made to eliminate or suppress discharge current and striation noise. Met [190] has proposed an equivalent circuit for dc-excited helium-neon discharges that allows establishing stability criteria that are related to the external loading circuitry. (Equivalent circuits have also been derived by Prescott and van der Ziel to explain discharge noise spectra and resonance effects [180].) Somewhat earlier, Bellisio et al. had suggested the importance of external loading circuitry in the control of discharge current fluctuations [172]. Moving-striation noise, however, appears to be less amenable to control by external circuitry than discharge current noise does [185]. Fortunately, striation noise is usually unimportant [184]. Other attempts at eliminating plasma fluctuations by using feedback schemes [191, 192], altering physical design characteristics [193, 194], or judiciously applying magnetic fields [172, 195] have not always proved reliable or practical.

One of the best ways of reducing plasma noise involves the appropriate use of rf excitation [169, 172, 183]. Excess discharge noise is known to be nearly negligible for modulation frequencies above 1 MHz [172, 181]; consequently, rf excitation at some tens of megahertz might be expected to produce much less discharge noise than dc excitation. Indeed, this is almost always the case [196], although dc-excited 6328-Å lasers of the type used in frequency stability experiments have achieved shot noise limited outputs with long-term amplitude stabilities of greater than 1% [169]. In practice, certain difficulties associated with rf-excited discharges (relatively rapid cleanup rates, lack of discharge uniformity, impedance matching problems, and rf radiation effects) often necessitate dc excitation. Some commercial helium-neon lasers actually use a mixture of rf and dc excitation to achieve quiet operation.

Several qualitative efforts based on various analyses of the laser output response to discharge current modulation have been undertaken to predict the spectral distribution of amplitude fluctuations [80, 197-199]. Experiments that Kubo et al. performed indicate that the effect of dc discharge current modulation of the 6328-Å of 1.15-µm laser amplitude decreases sharply at frequencies above the relevant metastable-state relaxation rates [199]. (The triplets typically decay in 10 to 50 µsec and the singlets decay in 1 to 5 µsec [133].) Bolwijn suggested that the spectral noise intensity of the helium metastable levels could be expected to have a frequency response of the form [197]

$$S_{\Delta N_m}(f) = \frac{K_1 S_{\Delta N_e}(f)}{1 + (2\pi f \tau)^2} \tag{56}$$

as predicted from a simple two-level system. Here $S_{\Delta N_e}(f)$ is the spectral noise intensity of the electron number density, f is the modulating frequency, $\tau$ is the metastable-state lifetime, and $K_1$ is a proportionality factor that includes the slope of the metastable-state population vs electron number density curve. (The factor $K_1$ implicitly suggests that the discharge current fluctuations will grow less and less important as the metastable-level populations saturate with increasing current or number density. However, when the lower-laser level is included in the system response, the effect of low-frequency current fluctuation on the laser amplitude evidently becomes a minimum at the maximum of the power-current curve.) Bolwijn extended this analysis to describe current-induced laser output fluctuations, not only in terms of metastable-state population fluctuations, but also in terms of passive and active resonator characteristics [197] (cavity Q, saturation parameter, gain, etc.). The calculations were based on a surprisingly straightforward extension of Lamb's amplitude equations to form a Langevin noise equation. Other investigators have attempted to describe the spectral noise intensity in terms of rate equations involving only the passive optical resonator characteristics (cavity Q) and the level populations [80,

198, 199]. The differences in the two approaches are often not physically discernible because both the active and passive resonator characteristics usually determine photon buildup times that are far shorter than metastable-state relaxation times. (Photon buildup has also been analyzed in cavity dumping experiments [200, 201].

The effects of discharge current modulation on laser frequency stability were first examined by Bennett et al. [174]. These investigators induced antisymmetric frequency deviations about the center frequency of the 3.39-$\mu$m transition by modulating the inversion density. Boyne, Birky, and Schweitzer [176] subsequently observed antisymmetric pushing and pulling effects about the center frequency of the 1.15-$\mu$m transition; however, in contrast to the experiments of Bennett et al., the modulation-induced frequency deviations did not go to zero at the center of the Doppler broadened line. The antisymmetric frequency deviations appeared to be superimposed on a background deviation that was essentially independent of oscillation position within the atomic lineshape. Boyne et al. attributed this background shift to a combination of dispersive effects induced by the plasma electrons and other nearby neon lines ("principally the $2p_7$-$2s_4$ 1.15282 micron absorption line") [176]. They supported this interpretation with a variety of optical pumping schemes. (Optical modulation and cross-modulation of helium-neon level populations has been used to induce various other effects [100, 202].) Later experimetns by Arrathoon and Siegman suggested that the current-induced background shift might be caused by fluctuations in the He $2^3$ S population [203]. (The fluctuations induce changes in the absorption of the He $2^3$ S-$2^3$P 1.08-$\mu$m transition, which in turn affects the refractive index at 1.15 $\mu$m.) These researchers also observed background shift at 6328 Å that were approximately an order of magnitude larger than the 1.15-$\mu$m shifts [203]. At higher average discharge currents, where the metastable populations saturate, the dispersive shifts for both wavelengths were observed to decrease (Fig. 19). The 6328-Å shifts [O(MHz/mA)] were attributed to dispersive effects induced by the neon metastable level populations (particularly the 6334-Å and the 6402-Å transitions) and were actually large enough to obscure minor pushing and pulling contributions. Subsequent calculations of population perturbations and dispersive effects at 6328 Å and 1.15 $\mu$m tended to support these theories [21], while independent experiments later upheld the 6328-Å results [204].

The preceding experiments clearly indicate that plasma-induced population fluctuations can substantially affect both the laser amplitude and oscillation frequency. Barring oscillations, plasma-optical noise apparently depends on both the current and the partial pressures in the discharge. However, this noise is usually not excessive and helium-neon lasers are almost invariably regarded as appreciably quieter than other types of gas lasers. In general, the amplitude fluctuations can be substantially reduced by choosing sufficiently low pressures and high helium-to-neon ratios to broaden the power-current curve significantly. Moreover, the

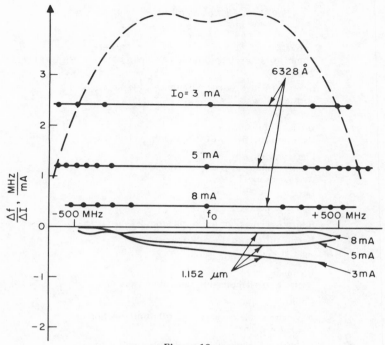

**Figure 19**

Current-induced shifts of the laser oscillation frequency at 6328 Å and 1.15 μm [203].

frequency fluctuations can be reduced by operating the discharge at or slightly above the maximum of the power-current curve. Although the qualitative features of these noise effects have been identified, development of quantitative theories is only beginning. Here again, any accurate quantitative theory must ultimately depend on a precise description of the excited state populations.

## Acknowledgments

The author would like to express his appreciation to E. I. Gordon for reviewing Sections II and VI of this chapter. He would also like to thank E. F. Labuda, A. D. White, and P. W. Smith for helpful comments on Sections III, IV, and V, respectively.

## List of Symbols

| | |
|---|---|
| $a$ | Number of ion pairs produced per electron per cm per Torr per volt |
| $a_0$ | Bohr radius |
| $A$ | Inverse effective radiative lifetime of the Ne $3s_2$ level |
| $B$ | Constant |
| $C, C_0, C_1, C_2, C_3$ | Constants |
| $d$ | Discharge tube diameter |
| $D_a, D_b, D_e$ | Diffusion coefficient of species a, b, and electrons |
| $e$ | Electron charge |
| $E$ | Electric field; also energy of atomic level |
| $\bar{E}$ | Average energy |
| $E_1, E_2$ | Energy of levels 1 and 2 |
| $E_i$ | Ionization energy |
| $E_h$ | Ionization energy of hydrogen atom |
| $E_n$ | Energy difference ($E_2 - E_1$) |
| $E_t$ | Threshold excitation energy |
| $f$ | Frequency |
| $f_1, f_2$ | Ratios of partial pressure to total pressure |
| $f_c$ | Collision frequency |
| $f(E)$ | Normalized relative energy distribution function |
| $f_{ik}$ | Oscillator strength |
| $f(v)$ | Normalized relative velocity distribution function |
| $g_1, g_2$ | Degeneracy of levels 1 and 2 |
| $G$ | Laser small signal gain |
| $G_{opt}$ | Maximum small signal gain |
| $I$ | Current |
| $J_0(\chi_i)$ | Zero-order Bessel function of the first kind of argument $\chi_i$ |
| $J_1$ | First-order Bessel function of the first kind |
| $k$ | Boltzmann constant |
| $K, K_0, K_1, K_2, K_3$ | Constants |
| $\ell$ | Discharge length |
| $m$ | Reduced mass |
| $m_1, m_2$ | Mass of species 1 and 2 |
| $N_1, N_2$ | Number density of levels 1 and 2 |
| $N_a, N_b, N_c$ | Number density of species a, b, and c |
| $N_e$ | Number density of free electrons |
| $N_{he}$ | Helium ground-state number density |
| $N_m$ | Number density of a metastable level |
| $N_{ne}$ | Neon ground-state number density |
| $N_0$ | Ground-state number density |
| $p$ | Pressure |
| $pd$ | Pressure-diameter product of discharge tube |

| | |
|---|---|
| $P_c$ | Number of electron-atom collisions per electron per cm per Torr |
| $P_i$ | Number of electron-atom ionizations per electron per cm per Torr |
| $Q_1$ | Collision cross section for collisions of the first kind |
| $Q_2$ | Collision cross section for collisions of the second kind |
| $Q_{10}$ | Maximum value of excitation cross section |
| $r$ | Arbitrary radius |
| $R$ | Tube radius |
| $R_c$ | Collision rate density |
| $R_i$ | Ionization rate density |
| $S_{\Delta N_m}(f)$ | Spectral noise intensity of the helium metastable levels |
| $T$ | Temperature |
| $T_a, T_b$ | Temperature of species a and b |
| $T_e$ | Electron temperature |
| $v$ | Velocity |
| $\bar{v}$ | Average velocity |
| $v_d$ | Axial drift velocity |
| $\bar{V}_e$ | Average random thermal velocity of the electrons |
| $z_a, z_b, z_c$ | Electron-ion production for species a, b, and c |
| $Z_1, Z_2$ | Rate of first- and second-kind collisions |
| $Z$ | Rate of depletion of the population of an initial state |
| $Z_r$ | Forward resonant transfer rate |
| $Z_r'$ | Reverse resonant transfer rate |
| $\alpha, \alpha_m$ | Excited state production rate coefficients |
| $\beta$ | Sum of two-body inelastic depletion processes |
| $\Gamma_a, \Gamma_b, \Gamma_e$ | Product of number density times drift velocity of atomic species a and b and electrons |
| $\lambda_e$ | Electron mean free path |
| $\Lambda_i$ | Characteristic diffusion length of an infinite cylinder |
| $\mu$ | Mobility |
| $\mu_a, \mu_b$ | Mobility of species a and b in a mixture of gases |
| $\mu_{aa}$ | Mobility of gas a within itself |
| $\mu_{ab}$ | Mobility of gas a in gas b |
| $\sigma(E)$ | Energy-dependent cross section |
| $\tau$ | Metastable state lifetime |

# References

1. A. Javan, W. R. Bennett, Jr., and D. R. Herriott, *Phys. Rev. Letters*, **6**, 106 (1961).
2. A. L. Schawlow and C. H. Townes, *Phys. Rev.*, **112**, 1940 (1958).
3. J. P. Gordon, H. J. Zeiger, and C. H. Townes, *Phys. Rev.*, **99**, 1264 (1955); **95**, 282 (1954).
4. R. C. Tolman, *Phys. Rev.*, **23**, 693 (1924).
5. A. Einstein, *Z. Physik*, **18**, 121 (1917).
6. W. Schottky, *Z. Physik*, **31**, 163 (1925).
7. I. Langmuir and L. Tonks, *Phys. Rev.*, **28**, 104 (1926); **34**, 874 (1929).
8. R. Ladenburg, *Rev. Mod. Phys.*, **5**, 243 (1933); see also A. C. G. Mitchell and M. W. Zemansky, *Resonance Radiation and Excited Atoms*, Cambridge Univ. Press, New York, 1934, p. 118.
9. V. A. Fabrikant, *Tr. Vses. Elektrotekhn. Inst.*, **41**, 254 (1940).
10. A. Javan, *Phys. Rev. Letters*, **3**, 87 (1959).
11. A. Javan, in *Quantum Electronics* (C. H. Townes, ed.), Columbia Univ. Press, New York, 1960, p. 564.
12. J. H. Sanders, *Phys. Rev. Letters*, **3**, 86 (1959).
13. A. D. White and J. D. Rigden, *Proc. IRE*, **50**, 1697 (1962).
14. J. Franck and H. Hertz, *Verhandl. deut. Physik, Ges.*, **16**, 512 (1914).
15. Maier-Leibnitz, *Z. Physik*, **95**, 518 (1935).
16. H. S. W. Massey and E. H. S. Burhop, *Electronic and Ionic Impact Phenomena*, Clarendon Press, Oxford, 1952; for a particularly cogent treatment of the general physics of atomic collisions, see Ref. 63; for an excellent treatise on ionized particle collisions, see L. Spitzer, Jr., *Physics of Fully Ionized Gases*, Wiley-Interscience, New York, 1967.
17. E. W. McDaniel, *Collision Phenomena in Ionized Gases* Wiley, New York, 1964.
18. A von Engel, *Ionized Gases*, Clarendon Press, Oxford, 1965.
19. O. Klein and S. Rosseland, *Z. Physik*, **4**, 46 (1921); see also B. Yavorsky, *J. Phys. USSR*, **10**, 476 (1946).
20. R. Arrathoon, *Phys. Rev.*, **4**, 203 (1971).
21. R. Arrathoon, *J. Appl. Phys.*, **40**, 2875 (1969).
22. C. Kenty, *J. Appl. Phys.*, **21**, 1309 (1950).
23. E. E. Benton, E. E. Ferguson, F. A. Matsen, and W. W. Robertson, *Phys. Rev.*, **128**, 206 (1962); A. L. Schmeltikopf and F. C. Fehsenfeld, *J. Chem. Phys.*, **53**, 3173 (1970).
24. F. T. Arecchi, in *Quantum Electronics and Coherent Light* (P. A. Miles, ed.), Academic Press, New York, 1964, p. 182.
25. S. A. Gonchukov, G. A. Ermakov, G. A. Mikhnenko, and E. D. Protsenko, *Opt. and Spectr.*, **20**, 601 (1966).
26. E. F. Labuda and E. I. Gordon, *J. Appl. Phys.*, **35**, 1647 (1964).
27. C. E. Moore, *Atomic Energy Levels*, Vol. 1, Government Printing Office, Washington, D. C., 1949, pp. 5 and 77.
28. C. K. N. Patel, *Lasers*, Vol. 2, (Marcel Dekker, New York, 1968), p. 1.
29. T. Holstein, *Phys. Rev.*, **72**, 1212 (1947); **83**, 1159 (1951).
30. A. Szöke and A. Javan, *Phys. Rev.*, **145**, 137 (1966).
31. R. Arrathoon and D. A. Sealer, *Phys. Rev.*, **4**, 815 (1971).
32. E. I. Gordon and A. D. White, *Appl. Phys. Letters*, **3**, 199 (1963).
33. G. Herzberg, *Atomic Spectra and Atomic Structure*, 2nd ed., Dover, New York, 1944, p. 71; see also C. G. B. Garrett, *Gas Lasers*, McGraw-Hill, New York, 1967, p. 8.
34. E. U. Condon and G. H. Shortley, *The Theory of Atomic Spectra*, Cambridge Univ. Press, Cambridge, 1951; for an excellent introductory treatment, see H. E. White, *Introduction to Atomic Spectra*, McGraw-Hill, New York, 1934; see also F. K. Richtmyer, E. H. Kennard, and J. N. Cooper, *Introduction to Modern Physics*, 6th ed., McGraw-Hill, New York, 1969).

35. G. F. Koster and H. Statz, *J. Appl. Phys.*, **32**, 2054 (1961).
36. R. A. McFarlane, W. L. Faust, C. K. N. Patel, and C. G. B. Garrett, *Quantum Electronics III*, (P. Grivet and N. Bloembergen, eds.), Columbia Univ. Press, New York, 1964, pp. 573-586.
37. G. Racah, *Phys. Rev.*, **61**, 537 (1942); see also A. R. Edmonds, *Angular Momentum in Quantum Mechanics*, Princeton Univ. Press, Princeton, 1960.
38. E. P. Wigner, *Gott. Nachr.*, 375 (1927); for a more recent interpretation, see Ref. 16.
39. R. L. Abrams and G. J. Wolga, *Phys. Rev. Letters*, **19**, 1411 (1967).
40. A. L. Bloom, W. E. Bell, and R. C. Rempel, *Appl. Opt.*, **2**, 317 (1963).
41. W. R. Bennett, Jr., *Appl. Opt., Suppl.*, **1**, 24 (1962).
42. C. K. N. Patel, *J. Appl. Phys.*, **33**, 3194 (1962).
43. J. T. Massey, A. G. Schulz, B. F. Hochheimer, and S. M. Cannon, *J. Appl. Phys.*, **36**, 658 (1965).
44. A. D. White and E. I. Gordon, *Appl. Phys. Letters*, **3**, 197 (1963).
45. W. R. Bennett, Jr., *Appl. Opt., Suppl.*, **2**, 3 (1965).
46. L. Allen and D. G. C. Jones, *Principles of Gas Lasers* Plenum, New York, 1967, p. 73.
47. W. S. C. Chang, *Principles of Quantum Electronics*, Addison-Wesley, Reading, Massachusetts, 1969), p. 341.
48. D. L. Perry, *IEEE J. Quantum Electron.*, **QE-7**, 102 (1971).
49. R. N. Zitter, *J. Appl. Phys.*, **35**, 4070 (1964).
50. P. W. Murphy, *J. Opt. Soc. Am.*, **58**, 1200 (1968).
51. H. A. Boot and D. M. Clunie, *Nature*, **197**, 173 (1963); H. A. Boot, D. M. Clunie, and R. S. A. Thorn, *Nature*, **198**, 773 (1963).
52. K. Toyoda and C. Yamanaka, *IEEE J. Quantum Electron.*, **QE-1**, 281 (1965); S. Kobayashi, H. Okamoto, and M. Kamiyama, *Ibid*, **QE-1**, 222 (1965); N. Suzuki, *Japan. J. Appl. Phys.*, **3**, 705 (1964).
53. G. G. Petrash and I. N. Knyazev, *Soviet Phys. JETP*, **18**, 571 (1964).
54. H. G. Heard and J. Peterson, *Proc. IEEE*, **52**, 1258 (1964); H. G. Heard, *ibid*, **53**, 173 (1965).
55. D. M. Clunie, R. S. A. Thorn, and K. E. Trezise, *Phys. Letters*, **14**, 28 (1965); D. A. Leonard, R. A. Neal, and E. T. Gerry, *Appl. Phys. Letters*, **7**, 175 (1965).
56. A. V. Phelps and J. P. Molnar, *Phys. Rev.*, **89**, 1202 (1953).
57. A. V. Phelps, *Phys. Rev.*, **99**, 1307 (1955).
58. H. S. W. Massey, in *Handbuch der Physik*, (S. Flugge, ed.), Vol. 36, Springer-Verlag, Berlin, 1956, p. 307.
59. R. A. Gerber, G. F. Sauter, and H. J. Oskam, Physica, **32**, 2173 (1966); D. B. Rees, C. B. Leffert, and D. J. Rose, *J. Appl. Phys.*, **40**, 1884 (1969); A. F. Kuckes, R. W. Motley, E. Hinnov, and J. G. Hirschberg, *Phys. Rev. Letters*, **6**, 337 (1961); C. B. Collins, H. S. Hicks, and W. E. Wells, *Phys. Rev.*, **A2**, 797 (1970).
60. S. C. Brown, *Introduction to Electrical Discharges in Gases*, Wiley, New York, 1966; S. C. Brown, *Basic Data of Plasma Physics*, Wiley, New York, 1967.
61. M. J. Druyvesteyn and F. M. Penning, *Rev. Mod. Phys.*, **12**, 87 (1940).
62. G. Francis, in *Handbuch der Physik*, (S. Flugge, ed.), Vol. 22, Springer-Verlag, Berlin, 1956, p. 53; W. B. Thompson, *An Introduction to Plasma Physics*, Addison-Wesley, Reading, Massachusetts, 1962.
63. J. B. Hasted, *Physics of Atomic Collisions*, Butterworths, London, 1964.
64. Ya. B. Zel'dovich and Yu. P. Raizer, *Physics of Shock Waves and High-Temperature Hydrodynamic Phenomena*, Academic, New York, 1966.
65. E. H. Kennard, *Kinetic Theory of Gases*, Mc-Graw-Hill, New York, 1938.
66. J. Y. Wada and H. Heil, *IEEE J. Quantum Electron.*, **QE-1**, 327 (1965).
67. M. J. Seaton, in *Atomic and Molecular Processes* (D. R. Bates, ed.), Academic Press, New York, 1962).
68. S. J. B. Corrigan and A. von Engel, *Proc. Phys. Soc. (London)*, **72**, 786 (1958).
69. R. Dorrestein, *Physica*, **9**, 447 (1942); S. N. Salinger and J. E. Rowe, *J. Appl. Phys.*,

**39,** 4299 (1968); J. Olmsted III, A. S. Newton, and K. Street, Jr., *J. Chem. Phys.,* **42,** 2321 (1965); see also Refs. 15 and 16.
70. D. Rapp and P. Englander-Golden, *J. Chem. Phys.,* **43,** 1464 (1965).
71. D. R. Long and R. Geballe, *Bull. Am. Phys. Soc.,* **12,** 918 (1967); L. Vriens, *Phys. Letters,* **8,** 260 (1964).
72. W. L. Wiese, M. W. Smith, and B. M. Glennon, *Atomic Transition Probabilities (Hydrogen Through Neon)* Vol. 1, National Bureau of Standards, Washington, D.C., 1966, pp. 9 and 126.
73. M. A. Biondi and S. C. Brown, *Phys. Rev.,* **75,** 1700 (1949); A. V. Phelps and S. C. Brown, *Phys. Rev.,* **86,** 102 (1952).
74. von H. B. Dorgelo, H. Alting, and C. J. Boers, *Physica,* **2,** 959 (1953).
75. R. T. Young, *J. Appl. Phys.,* **36,** 2324 (1964).
76. Yu. M. Kagan and V. M. Milenin, *Soviet Phys.–Tech. Phys.,* **10,** 1470 (1966).
77. E. F. Labuda, *Average Electron Energies and Densities in He-Ne Laser Discharges,* Ph.D. dissertation, Polytechnic Institute of Brooklyn, New York, 1967.
78. F. T. Arecchi, *Quantum Electronics III* (P. Grivet and N. Bloembergen, eds.), Columbia Univ. Press, New York, 1964, pp. 547-560.
79. S. Asami, *Japan. J. Appl. Phys.,* **5,** 1075 (1966).
80. K. Kawabe, U. Kubo, and Y. Inuishi, *Japan. J. Appl. Phys.,* **5,** 1254 (1966); K. Kawabe and Y. Inuishi, *Oyo Buturi,* **33,** 735 (1964).
81. E. O. Schulz du Bois, *Bell System Tech. J.,* **43,** 625 (1964); J. S. Wright and E. O. Schulz de Bois, Solid-State Maser Research, Rep. No. 5, Contract No. DA-36-039-sc-85357, 20 September 1961 (ASTIA No. Ad 265838).
82. E. I. Gordon, A. D. White, and J. D. Rigden, *Proceedings of the Symposium on Optical Masers,* Polytechnic Press, New York, 1963, pp. 309-318.
83. J. P. Gordon, unpublished memorandum; a brief discussion of this paper is given by A. L. Bloom, in *Gas Lasers,* Wiley, New York, 1968, pp. 36, 37.
84. I. Tobias, *J. Appl. Phys.,* **34,** 3200 (1963).
85. R. Karplus and J. Schwinger, *Phys. Rev.,* **73,** 1020 (1948); see also A. M. Portis, *ibid,* **91,** 1071 (1953).
86. W. W. Rigrod, *J. Appl. Phys.,* **34,** 2602 (1963); **36,** 2487 (1965).
87. P. W. Smith, *J. Appl. Phys.,* **37,** 2089 (1966); *IEEE J. Quantum Electron.,* **QE-2,** 62 (1966).
88. D. F. Hotz, *Appl. Opt.,* **4,** 527 (1965).
89. W. E. Lamb, Jr., *Phys. Rev.,* **134,** 1429 (1964).
90. D. J. Close, *Phys. Rev.,* **153,** 360 (9167).
91. L. F. Vellikok, A. E. Fotiadi, and S. A. Fridrikhov, *Soviet Phys.–Tech. Phys.,* **12,** 811 (1967); A. E. Fotiadi and S. A. Fridrikhov, *Soviet Phys.–Tech. Phys.,* **12,** 406, (1967).
92. E. Spiller, *Z. Physik,* **182,** 487 (1965).
93. Yu. M. Kagan, R. I. Lyagushchenko, and A. D. Khakhaev, *Opt. and Spectr.,* **14,** 317 (1963); Yu. M. Kagan, L. A. Luizova, R. I. Lyagushchenko, and A. D. Khakhaev, *ibid,* **15,** 241 (1963); Yu. M. Kagan, and R. I. Lyagushchenko, *ibid,* **17,** 90 (1964).
94. S. E. Frish and V. F. Revald, *Opt. and Spectr.,* **15,** 395 (1963); V. F. Revald, *ibid,* **18,** 318 (1965).
95. M. Ohi, *Japan. J. Appl. Phys.,* **5,** 1084 (1966).
96. T. Sakurai, T. Ohta, and T. Ogawa, *IEEE J. Quantum Electron.,* **QE-4,** 65 (1968).
97. G. Herziger, W. Holzapfel, and W. Seelig, *Z. Physik,* **200,** 103 (1967); **189,** 385 (1966).
98. V. M. Kaslin, G. G. Petrash, and A. S. Khaikin, *Opt. and Spectr.,* **23,** 14 (1967); A. S. Khaikin, *Soviet Phys. JETP,* **24,** 25 (1967).
99. R. Arrathoon, *J. Appl. Phys.,* **42,** 5175 (1971).
100. V. N. Lisitsyn and V. P. Chebotaev, **20,** 409 (1966).
101. Yu. Z. Ionikh and S. E. Frish, *Opt. and Spectr.,* **25,** 345 (1968).
102. P. K. Tien, D. MacNair, and H. L. Hodges, *Phys. Rev. Letters,* **12,** 30 (1964).
103. E. G. Gnevysheva, V. S. Krivchenkova, V. N. Tikhonov, I. P. Shibaev, and A. D.

Khakhaev, *Opt. and Spectr.*, **22**, 296 (1966).

104.  I. M. Beterov and V. P. Chabotaev, *Opt. and Spectr.*, **23**, 476 (1967).
105.  J. H. Parks and A. Javan, *Phys. Rev.*, **139**, 1351 (1965).
106.  R. A. Lilly and J. R. Holmes, *J. Opt. Soc. Am.*, **58**, 1406 (1968).
107.  R. A. McFarlane, W. R. Bennett, Jr., and W. E. Lamb, Jr., *Appl. Phys. Letters*, **2**, 189 (1963).
108.  A. L. Bloom, *Appl. Phys. Letters*, **2**, 101 (1963).
109.  J. D. Rigden and A. D. White, in *Quantum Electronics III* (P. Grivet and N. Bloombergen, eds.), Columbia Univ. Press, New York, 1964, pp. 499-505; A. D. White and J. D. Rigden, *Appl. Phys. Letters*, **2**, 211 (1963).
110.  P. W. Smith, *IEEE J. Quantum Electron.*, **QE-2**, 77 (1966).
111.  G. K. Moeller and T. K. McCubbin, Jr., *Appl. Opt.*, **4**, 1412 (1965).
112.  K. D. Mielenz and K. F. Nefflen, *Appl. Opt.*, **4**, 565 (1965).
113.  R. L. Field, Jr., *Rev. Sci. Instr.*, **38**, 1720 (1967).
114.  A. D. White, E. I. Gordon, and J. D. Rigden, *Appl. Phys. Letters*, **2**, 91 (1963); J. A. White, *ibid*, **3**, 107 (1963).
115.  A. D. White, *Proc. IEEE*, **51**, 1669 (1963).
116.  I. M. Belousova, O. B. Denilov, and V. M. Kiselev, *Soviet Phys.–Tech. Phys.*, **13**, 363 (1968).
117.  D. M. Clunie and N. H. Rock, *Phys. Letters*, **13**, 213 (1964); L. E. S. Matthias, and N. H. Rock, *Appl. Opt.*, **4**, 133 (1965).
118.  N. George, *Proc. IEEE*, **51**, 1152 (1963).
119.  F. P. Carlson, *IEEE J. Quantum Electron.*, **QE-4**, 98 (1968).
120.  R. G. Buser, J. Kainz, and J. Sullivan, *Appl. Opt.*, **2**, 861 (1963).
121.  S. A. Ahmed, R. C. Kocher, and H. J. Gorritsen, *Proc. IEEE*, **52**, 1356 (1964).
122.  M. A. Biondi, *Phys. Rev.*, **83**, 653 (1951); **88**, 660 (1952).
123.  P. A. Miller, J. T. Verdeyen, and B. E. Cherrington, *Phys. Rev.*, **A4**, 692 (1971).
124.  A. A. Kruithof and F. M. Penning, *Physica*, **4**, 450 (1937).
125.  W. P. Jesse and J. Sadauskis, *Phys. Rev.*, **100**, 1755 (1955); W. P. Sholette and E. E. Muschlitz, Jr., *J. Chem. Phys.*, **36**, 3368 (1962).
126.  C. R. Jones and W. W. Robertson, *J. Chem. Phys.*, **49**, 4240, 4241 (1968).
127.  C. E. Webb, A. R. Turner-Smith, and J. M. Green, *J. Phys. B: Atomic and Molecular Phys.*, **3**, L135 (1970).
128.  L. A. Schlie and J. T. Verdeyen, *IEEE J. Quantum Electron.*, **QE-5**, 21 (1969).
129.  E. Ebbinghaus, *Ann. Physik*, **7**, 267 (1930).
130.  J. R. Dixon and F. A. Grant, *Phys. Rev.*, **107**, 118 (1957).
131.  A. V. Phelps, *Phys. Rev.*, **114**, 1011 (1959).
132.  A. L. Schmeltekopf and H. P. Broida, *J. Chem. Phys.*, **39**, 1261 (1963); for a more recent discussion, cf. E. E. Ferguson, F. C. Fehsenfeld, and A. L. Schmeltekopf, in *Advances in Atomic and Molecular Physics* (D. R. Bates and I. Estermann, eds.), Academic Press, New York, 1969, Vol. 5, p. 1.
133.  J. W. Poukey, J. B. Gerardo, and M. A. Gusinow, *Phys. Rev.*, **179**, 211 (1969).
134.  G. E. Veatch and H. J. Oskam, *Phys. Rev.*, **A2**, 1422 (1970).
135.  V. P. Chebotaev and L. S. Vasilenko, *Opt. and Spectr.*, **20**, 505 (1966); I. M. Beterov and V. P. Chebotaev, *ibid.*, **20**, 597 (1966).
136.  M. Jaccaud, A. Erbeia, and J. Janin, *Compt. Rend.*, **268**, 222 (1969); S. Valignat, A. Erbeia, and J. Janin, *Phys. Letters*, **31**, 224 (1970).
137.  C. R. Jones, F. E. Niles, and W. W. Robertson, *J. Appl. Phys.*, **40**, 3967 (1969).
138.  A. Lurio, R. L. de Zafra, and R. J. Goshen, *Phys. Rev.*, **134**, 1198 (1964); A. Lurio and R. Novick, *ibid*, **134**, 608 (1964).
139.  S. Bashkin, *Appl. Opt.*, **7**, 2341 (1968).
140.  A. Szöke and A. Javan, *Phys. Rev. Letters*, **10**, 521 (1963).
141.  G. M. Lawrence, *J. Quant. Spectr. and Radiation Transfer*, **5**, 359 (1965); G. M. Lawrence and B. D. Savage, *Phys. Rev.*, **141**, 67 (1966).
142.  L. O. Hocker, M. A. Kovacs, C. K. Rhodes, G. W. Flynn, and A. Javan, *Phys. Rev. Letters*, **17**, 233 (1966); G. W. Flynn, M. A. Kovacs, C. K. Rhodes, and A. Javan, *Appl.*

*Phys. Letters,* **8**, 63 (1966).
143. P. K. Cheo, *J. Appl. Phys.,* **38**, 3563 (1967); P. K. Cheo and R. L. Abrams, *Appl. Phys. Letters,* **14**, 47 (1969).
144. B. Decamps and M. Dumont, *IEEE J. Quantum Electron.,* QE-4, 916 (1968).
145. Th. Hansch and P. Toschek, *Phys. Letters,* **22**, 150 (1966).
146. G. E. Assousa, L. Brown, and W. K. Ford, Jr., *J. Opt. Soc. Am.,* **60**, 1311 (1970).
147. P. H. Lee and M. L. Skolnick, *Appl. Phys. Letters,* **10**, 303 (1967); V. N. Lisitsyn and P. Chebotaev, *Soviet Phys. JETP,* **27**, 227 (1968).
148. R. G. Breene, Jr., *Rev. Mod. Phys.,* **29**, 94 (1957); R. G. Breene, Jr., in *Handbuch der der Physik* (S. Flugge, ed.), Vol. 27, Springer-Verlag, Berlin, 1964, p. 1; J. Cooper, Rep. Progr. Phys., **29**, 35 (1966).
149. R. H. Cordover and P. A. Bonczyk, *Phys. Rev.,* **188**, 696 (1969); a discussion of Ref. 87 is included here.
150. W. R. Bennett, Jr., V. P. Chebotaev, and J. W. Knutson, Jr., *Phys. Rev. Letters,* **18**, 688 (1967).
151. T. O. Carroll, *IEEE J. Quantum Electron.,* QE-6, 516 (1970).
152. B. L. Gyorffy, M. Borenstein, and W. E. Lamb Jr., *Phys. Rev.,* **169**, 340 (1968).
153. R. L. Fork and M. A. Pollack, *Phys. Rev.,* **139**, 1408 (1965).
154. P. W. Smith and Th. Hansch, *Phys. Rev. Letters,* **26**, 740 (1971); the correspondence between terms in this article and Ref. 149 appears in the third footnote.
155. P. R. Berman and W. E. Lamb, Jr., *Phys. Rev.,* **187**, 221 (1969); A2, 2435, (1970).
156. J. E. Hesser, *Phys. Rev.,* **174**, 68 (1968).
157. J. Z. Klose, *Phys. Rev.,* **141**, 181 (1966); W. R. Bennett, Jr. and P. W. Kindlmann, *ibid,* **149**, 38 (1966).
158. G. Schiffner and F. Seifert, *Proc. IEEE,* **53**, 1657 (1965); A. Garscadden and S. L. Adams, *ibid,* **54**, 427 (1966); see also A. Garscadden, P. Bletzinger, and E. M. Friar, *J. Appl. Phys.,* **35**, 3432 (1964).
159. M. B. Klein and D. Maydan, *Appl. Phys. Letters,* **16**, 509 (1970).
160. R. Arrathoon, *J. Opt. Soc. Am.,* **61**, 332 (1971).
161. Th. Hansch and P. Toschek, *Phys. Letters,* **20**, 273 (1966).
162. L. S. Vasilenko and V. P. Chebotaev, *J. Appl. Spectr.,* **6**, 353 (1967).
163. T. V. Bychkova, V. G. Kirpilenko, S. G. Rautian, and A. S. Khaikin, *Opt. and Spectr.,* **22**, 371 (1967).
164. R. Turner, K. M. Baird, M. J. Taylor, and C. J. Van der Hoeven, *Rev. Sci. Instr.,* **35**, 996 (1964); R. Turner and C. J. Van der Hoeven, *ibid,* **36**, 1003 (1965).
165. J. V. Martinez, *J. Appl. Phys.,* **37**, 4477 (1966).
166. U. Hochuli and P. Haldemann, *Rev. Sci. Instr.,* **36**, 1493 (1965); U. Hochuli, P. Haldemann, and D. Hardwick, *IEEE J. Quantum Electron.,* QE-3, 612 (1967).
167. D. MacNair, *IEEE J. Quantum Electron.,* QE-5, 460 (1969).
168. J. K. Powers and B. W. Harned, *Proc. IEEE,* **51**, 605 (1963).
169. C. Freed and H. A. Haus, *Appl. Phys. Letters,* **6**, 85 (1965).
170. A. E. Siegman, B. Daino, and K. R. Manes, *IEEE J. Quantum Electron.,* QE-3, 180 (1967); A. E. Siegman and R. Arrathoon, *Phys. Rev. Letters,* **20**, 901 (1968).
171. H. Hodara, *Proc. IEEE,* **53**, 696 (1965); H. Hodara and N. George, *IEEE J. Quantum Electron.,* QE-2, 337 (1966).
172. J. A. Bellisio, C. Freed, and H. A. Haus, *Appl. Phys. Letters,* **4**, 5 (1964).
173. T. S. Jaseja, A. Javan, J. Murray, and C. H. Townes, *Phys. Rev.,* **133**, 1221 (1964); T. S. Jaseja, A. Javan, and C. H. Townes, *Phys. Rev. Letters,* **10**, 165 (1963).
174. W. R. Bennett, Jr., *Phys. Rev,.* **126**, 580 (1962); W. R. Bennett, Jr., S. F. Jacobs, J. T. LaTourrette, and P. Rabinowitz, *Appl. Phys. Letters,* **5**, 56 (1964).
175. C. S. Liu, B. E. Cherrinston, and J. T. Verdeyen, *J. Appl. Phys.,* **40**, 3556 (1969).
176. H. S. Boyne, M. M. Birky, and W. G. Schweitzer, Jr., *Appl. Phys. Letters,* **7**, 62 (1965).
177. A. D. White, *Proc. IEEE,* **52**, 721 (1964); A. L. Bloom and D. L. Hardwick, *Phys. Letters,* **20**, 373 (1966); I. Tobias and W. M. Strouse, *Appl. Phys. Letters,* **10**, 342 (1967).

178. A. D. White, *IEEE J. Quantum Electron.*, **QE-1**, 349 (1965); A. L. Bloom and D. L. Wright, *Appl. Opt.*, **5**, 1528 (1966); F. J. Mayer, *IEEE J. Quantum Electron.*, **QE-3**, 690 (1967); J. L. Hall, *ibid,* **QE-4**, 638 (1968); S. P. Koutsoyannis and K. Karamcheti, *ibid,* **QE-4**, 912 (1968); T. P. Sosnowski and W. B. Johnson, *ibid,* **QE-5**, 151 (1969).
179. P. T. Bolwijn, C. Th. J. Alkemade, and G. A. Boschloo, *Phys. Letters,* **4**, 59 (1963).
180. L. J. Prescott and A. van der Ziel, *Appl. Phys. Letters,* **5**, 48 (1964); L. J. Prescott and A. van der Ziel, *IEEE J. Quantum Electron.*, **QE-2**, 173 (1966).
181. P. T. Bolwijn, *Phys. Letters,* **13**, 311 (1964).
182. F. W. Crawford and G. S. Kino, *Proc. IRE,* **49**, 1767 (1961).
183. S. F. Paik, R. N. Wallace, and H. C. McClees, *Phys. Rev. Letters,* **10**, 78 (1963).
184. T. Suzuki, *Japan. J. Appl. Phys.,* **9**, 309 (1970).
185. A. Garscadden, P. Bletzinger, and E. M. Friar, *J. Appl. Phys.,* **35**, 3432 (1964).
186. A. Garscadden, *Appl. Phys. Letters,* **8**, 85 (1966).
187. G. Forgo and M. J. O. Strutt, *Electron., Letters,* **3**, 423 (1967).
188. A W. Cooper, *J. Appl. Phys.,* **35**, 2877 (1964).
189. D. A. Lee, P. Bletzinger, and A. Garscadden, *J. Appl. Phys.,* **37**, 377 (1966).
190. V. Met, *Proc. IEEE,* **52**, 1357 (1964).
191. G. Forgo and M. J. O. Strutt, *IEEE J. Quantum Electron.*, **QE-3**, 417 (1967); G. Forgo and M. J. O. Strutt, *Electron. Letters,* **3**, 547 (1967).
192. T. Suzuki, *Japan. J. Appl. Phys.,* **7**, 788 (1968).
193. T. Suzuki, *IEEE J. Quantum Electron.*, **QE-5**, 132 (1969).
194. A. Waksberg and J. Wood, *Rev. Sci. Instr.,* **40**, 1306 (1969).
195. N. Konjevic and K. R. Hearne, *Electron. Letters,* **2**, 461 (1966).
196. R. T. Young, Jr. and R. T. Maupin, *J. Appl. Phys.,* **40**, 3881 (1969).
197. P. T. Bolwijn, *Phys. Letters,* **24**, 285 (1967).
198. S. Saito and S. Uehara, *Proc. IEEE,* **58**, 598 (1970).
199. U. Kubo, K. Kawabe, and Y. Inuishi, *Japan. J. Appl. Phys.,* **5**, 731 (1966).
200. R. N. Zitter, W. H. Steir, and R. Rosenberg, *IEEE J. Quantum Electron.*, **QE-3**, 614 (1967).
201. D. Maydan, *J. Appl. Phys.,* **41**, 1552 (1970).
202. B. Pariser and T. C. Marshall, *Proc. IEEE,* **52**, 1740 (1964); J. F. Delpech, *Electron. Letters,* **1**, 168 (1965); V. N. Lisitsyn and V. P. Chebotaev, *Opt. and Spectr.,* **20**, 603 (1966).
203. R. Arrathoon and A. E. Siegman, *Appl. Phys. Letters,* **13**, 197 (1968).
204. P. A. Miller, J. T. Verdeyen, and B. E. Cherrington, *IEEE J. Quantum Electron.*, **QE-5**, 473 (1969).

*Chapter 4*

# Optical Parametric Oscillators

*R. G. Smith*

Bell Laboratories, Incorporated
Murray Hill, New Jersey

# I.  Introduction

Since Maiman [1] first demonstrated laser action over a decade ago, it has been recognized that tunability of coherent optical sources would be desirable. From the time of this first achievement, literally scores of materials have been made to "lase" at discrete frequencies, and many techniques for achieving tunable coherent optical radiation have been investigated. This chapter is concerned with one type of tunable generator of coherent optical radiation—the optical parametric oscillator. Other tunable sources include the semiconductor laser [2], the dye laser [3], and forms of stimulated Raman oscillators [4-6].

## A.  History

The first proposals for tunable optical parametric oscillators were independently made by Giordmaine and Kleinman [7], Kingston [8], Kroll [9], and Akhmanov and Khokhlov [10] following the domonstration of the existence of optical nonlinearities by Franken et al. [11]. Shortly thereafter, Giordmaine

[12] and Maker et al. [13] independently demonstrated the concept of phase matching. In 1965, Giordmaine and Miller [14] achieved the first operation of an optical parametric oscillator, and since that time, considerable effort has been expended in understanding and improving device performance. At the time of this writing optical parametric oscillators have been made to tune from the ultraviolet through the full visible region of the spectrum and into the infrared as far as 3.6 $\mu$m, with operation at selected bands out to 10 $\mu$m. Oscillators have been constructed that have thresholds as low as 3 mW, and others have produced several hundred kilowatts of power; efficiencies approaching 50% have been achieved. With spectral narrowing techniques, linewidths of 0.001 cm$^{-1}$ have been achieved, and even lower values appear possible. Device performance is now at a level at which applications such as high-resolution spectroscopy and selective excitation of chemical reactions can be pursued.

In the evolution of the optical parametric oscillator and other nonlinear optical devices, much of the credit must go to the crystal growers who have synthesized and developed a vast number of nonlinear materials. Boyd et al. [15] in 1964 introduced the first of these new nonlinear materials, lithium niobate; it was with this material that the first oscillator was constructed. Other new materials such as barium sodium niobate, lithium iodate and proustite have also proved useful in making oscillators. At the present time, a substantial effort is under way to develop other materials, especially those that might be useful in constructing infrared oscillators.

## B. Scope

It is the goal of this chapter to give a reasonably thorough discussion of the various aspects of optical parametric oscillators. The bulk of the chaper is presented in six main sections, II through VII. Section II deals with the theory of optical parametric gain and applies this theory to determining the threshold of parametric oscillators; both plane wave and Gaussian mode interactions are considered. Section III considers the optical parametric oscillator above threshold and examines optimum coupling in particular. Section IV treats the tuning characteristics of optical parametric oscillators and also the factors determining their linewidth. Section V deals with spontaneous parametric emission. Nonlinear optical materials and their properties are covered in Section VI. Although some experimental work is presented throughout this chapter, Section VII deals with experimental results, placing emphasis on those results of particular significance. Section VIII concludes the chapter with a brief discussion of other nonlinear effects that are related to the subject of optical parametric oscillators but strictly do not fall under it.

As far as references are concerned, an attempt has been made to include the majority of relevant papers, but the bibliography is not necessarily complete. At the end of some sections, references to additional work not cited in the text are given. Throughout the text most formulas are in terms of dimensionless quantities; where reference to a particular unit system is required formulas are given in both mks and cgs units. General reviews of optical parametric oscillators can be found in Refs. 16-19. Other references to the general field of nonlinear parametric interactions can be found in Refs. 20-25.

## II.  Optical Parametric Gain

In any oscillator, some form of gain is required to overcome losses and produce oscillation. Gain is provided in a laser by population inversion between atomic or molecular levels. Gain is produced in a parametric oscillator by the interaction between electromagnetic fields in a nonlinear medium.

When an electromagnetic field propagates through a *linear* medium, its propagation characteristics are not influenced by its own intensity nor by the presence of other electromagnetic fields. However, different electromagnetic waves can interact when propagating through a nonlinear medium, with the result that their propagation constants become intensity-dependent. In particular, the propagation constant of one field can be influenced by the presence of other fields.

In the parametric amplification process, a strong, high-frequency electromagnetic wave of frequency $\omega_p$ interacts via the nonlinear response of the medium with two lower-frequency electromagnetic waves of frequencies $\omega_s$ and $\omega_i$ to produce amplification at these two lower frequencies. $\omega_p$ is called the pump frequency, $\omega_s$ the signal frequency, and $\omega_i$ the idler frequency. The three frequencies are connected by the relation

$$\omega_p = \omega_s + \omega_i \tag{1}$$

which, from a quantum standpoint, implies energy conservation. Other parametric interactions can also take place in the nonlinear medium but they are not specifically considered here because (1) they involve waves that are not electromagnetic (e.g., Raman scattering); (2) they involve more than three waves (e.g., four-frequency parametric amplification satisfying the frequency condition $2\omega_p = \omega_s + \omega_i$); or (3) they do not produce gain (e.g., sum frequency generation $\omega_i - \omega_s = \omega_p$). From a physical point of view, neglecting all parametric processes not described by Eq. (1) is justified because the interaction described by Eq. (2) can be phase-matched.* The phase-matched condition leads to a

---

*For a discussion of phase matching, see Section II,B.

cumulative interaction effect, whereas the other interactions will not in general be phase-matched and hence will be weak. In almost all situations, this assumption is valid. There are, however, some special cases where two or more parametric processes can be phase-matched simultaneously, and in such circumstances all processes must be considered in a self-consistent manner [26-28].

## A.  Parametric Interaction of Plane Waves

Consider three electromagnetic waves, the pump, signal, and idler, propagating in the z direction, whose frequencies satisfy Eq. (1). Let the form of the signal be

$$\underline{E}_s = \frac{1}{2}\underline{\mathcal{E}}_s(z)\,\exp[i(k_s z - \omega_s t + \varphi_s)] + \text{complex conjugate} \qquad (2)$$

where $\underline{\mathcal{E}}_s(z)$ is a slowly varying complex Fourier amplitude of the vector electric field, $\varphi_s$ is the initial phase of the wave, $k_s$ is the propagation constant given by

$$k_s = \frac{\omega_s n_s}{c} \qquad (3)$$

$n_s$ is the index of refraction at $\omega_s$, and c is the speed of light. The pump and idler waves have a similar form. The medium in which these waves propagate is assumed to possess a nonlinearity that gives rise to a nonlinear polarization $\mathcal{P}^{NL}$ of the form

$$\mathcal{P}_j^{NL} = \sum_{k,\ell} \chi_{jk\ell}^{(2)} \mathcal{E}_k \mathcal{E}_\ell \quad \text{(cgs units)}$$

$$\mathcal{P}_j^{NL} = \epsilon_0 \sum_{k,\ell} \chi_{jk\ell}^{(2)} \mathcal{E}_k \mathcal{E}_\ell \quad \text{(mks units)} \qquad (4)$$

where the subscripts refer to the Cartesian components of the various fields and $\epsilon_0$ is the permittivity of free space.* The nonlinear susceptibility $\chi_{jk\ell}^{(2)}$ is a tensor characterizing the second-order nonlinearity of the material, which is responsible for the parametric interaction of interest. This tensor is subject to the symmetry condition of the nonlinear material and may have several components that are zero. In many instances, it may be subject to further symmetry conditions [29].

Physically, the gain mechanism produced by the nonlinear interaction can be

---

*Some authors do not include the factor $\epsilon_0$ when using mks units.

viewed as follows: The signal and pump fields mix via the nonlinear response of the medium to generate a polarization wave with frequency $\omega_i = \omega_p - \omega_s$, propagating as $\exp[i(k_p - k_s)z]$. This polarization wave in turn generates an electromagnetic field $\delta\mathcal{E}_i$ at the frequency $\omega_i$. This idler field then mixes with the pump to produce a polarization at $\omega_s = \omega_p - \omega_i$, which generates an incremental field $\delta\mathcal{E}_s$. Provided that the fields are phased properly, the incremental signal and idler fields will add constructively to the existing fields, resulting in growth. It will be shown later that it is extremely important to maintain the proper phase relation between the three fields while they are interacting in the nonlinear medium.

Mathematically, the parametric interaction is handled by substituting the total electromagnetic field into Eq. (4) and selecting the nonlinear polarization terms at the frequencies $\pm\omega_p$, $\pm\omega_s$, $\pm\omega_i$. These polarization terms are then inserted into Maxwell's equations, where the total polarization at a given frequency is $\mathcal{P} = \mathcal{P}_{linear} + \mathcal{P}^{NL}$. If second derivatives of the slowly varying Fourier coefficients are neglected (i.e., $k\partial\mathcal{E}/\partial z \gg \partial^2\mathcal{E}/\partial z^2$), the following coupled differential equations result*,†

$$\frac{d\mathcal{E}_s(z)}{dz} = i\,\frac{(4\pi)\chi_{eff}}{2c}\,\frac{\omega_s}{n_s}\,\mathcal{E}_p(z)\mathcal{E}_i^*(z)\,\exp[i(\Delta kz + \varphi)] \tag{5a}$$

$$\frac{d\mathcal{E}_i(z)}{dz} = i\,\frac{(4\pi)\chi_{eff}}{2c}\,\frac{\omega_i}{n_i}\,\mathcal{E}_p(z)\mathcal{E}_s^*(z)\,\exp[i(\Delta kz + \varphi)] \tag{5b}$$

$$\frac{d\mathcal{E}_p(z)}{dz} = i\,\frac{(4\pi)\chi_{eff}}{2c}\,\frac{\omega_p}{n_p}\,\mathcal{E}_s(z)\mathcal{E}_i(z)\,\exp[-i(\Delta kz + \varphi)] \tag{5c}$$

where $\chi_{eff}$ is the effective nonlinear susceptibility coupling the three fields. A further discussion of the effective nonlinear susceptibility will be given in Section VI,A,1. The factor of $4\pi$ in parentheses in Eqs. (5) is absent in mks units. The quantity $\Delta k$ is the momentum mismatch between the waves, defined as

$$\Delta k = k_p - k_s - k_i \tag{6}$$

and $\varphi$ is the initial phase difference between the three fields,

---

*More exactly, these equations include factors of $\cos^2 \rho$, where $\rho$ is the double refraction angle. Since $\rho$ is small, in most all cases $\cos \rho \approx 1$ and this factor has been dropped for simplicity. The more exact form may be found in Ref. 25.

†Equations (5) are written in terms of the scalar amplitude of the fields. This is made possible by the definition of the effective nonlinear susceptibility. (See Section VI,A,1.)

$$\varphi = \varphi_p - \varphi_s - \varphi_i \tag{7}$$

and is a constant. Any change in the relative phase among the three fields as they propagate is accounted for by the fact that the $\mathcal{E}$'s are complex. The exact solution to these equations has been given for a general set of initial conditions by Armstrong et al. [25]. One limiting case that demonstrates the essential features of parametric amplification can be found by assuming that the signal and idler fields are small and the pump field is constant over the interaction region (i.e., neglecting pump depletion). Equation (5a) and the conjugate of (5b) can then be solved as a pair of coupled linear differential equations.

In terms of the plane wave power densities at the signal and idler, $S_s$ and $S_i$, the solutions are [30],

$$S_s(z) = \frac{S_0}{\Gamma^2} \left\{ [\Gamma \cosh(\Gamma z) + \Gamma_0 r \sin \varphi \sinh(\Gamma z)]^2 \right.$$

$$\left. + \left(\frac{\Delta k}{2} - \Gamma_0 r \cos \varphi\right)^2 \sinh^2(\Gamma z) \right\} \tag{8a}$$

$$S_i(z) = \frac{\omega_i}{\omega_s} \cdot \frac{S_0}{\Gamma^2} \left\{ [\Gamma r \cosh(\Gamma z) + \Gamma_0 \sin \varphi \sinh(\Gamma z)]^2 \right.$$

$$\left. + \left(\Gamma_0 \cos \varphi - \frac{\Delta k}{2} r\right)^2 \sinh^2(\Gamma z) \right\} \tag{8b}$$

where

$$\Gamma_0^2 = \pi K S_p \tag{9}$$

$$K = \begin{cases} \dfrac{32\pi^2 \omega_s \omega_i \chi_{eff}^2}{n_p n_s n_i c^3} & \text{(cgs; dimensions in sec erg}^{-1}) \\[4mm] \dfrac{\omega_s \omega_i \chi_{eff}^2 Z_0}{2\pi c^2 n_p n_s n_i} & \text{(mks; dimensions in watt}^{-1}) \end{cases} \tag{10}$$

$$\Gamma^2 = \Gamma_0^2 - \left(\frac{\Delta k}{2}\right)^2 \tag{11}$$

$$S_0 = S_s(z = 0) = \begin{cases} \dfrac{cn_s}{8\pi} |\mathcal{E}_s(0)|^2 & \text{(cgs)} \\[3mm] \dfrac{n_s |\mathcal{E}_s(0)|^2}{2Z_0} & \text{(mks)} \end{cases} \tag{12}$$

and

$$r^2 = \frac{\omega_s}{\omega_i} \frac{S_i(z = 0)}{S_0} \tag{13}$$

$\Gamma_0$ is the maximum gain constant, $\Gamma$ is the reduced gain constant, $S_0$ is the power density of the signal incident upon the nonlinear crystal at $z = 0$, $S_p$ is the pump density, $r^2$ is the ratio of the incident power density at the idler to the incident power density at the signal, normalized to the ratio of their frequencies, i.e., the ratio of the photon densities, and $Z_0 = (\mu_0/\epsilon_0)^{1/2}$ = impedance of free space $\cong 377$ ohms. When cgs units are used, the dimension of $\Gamma_0$ is cm$^{-1}$ when $S_p$ is expressed in erg sec$^{-1}$ cm$^{-2}$; and when mks units are used, $\Gamma_0$ is in m$^{-1}$ when $S_p$ is expressed in W/m$^2$.

When all three fields are initially present in a crystal of length $\ell$, there exists a value of the initial relative phase $\varphi$ for which maximum growth or gain of the signal and idler results. This optimum phase is given by

$$\cos \varphi_{opt} = -\frac{\Delta k}{2\Gamma} \frac{\sinh(\Gamma\ell)}{[1 + (\Gamma_0^2/\Gamma^2)\sinh^2(\Gamma\ell)]^{1/2}} \tag{14}$$

and the parametric gains at the signal and idler for this phase become

$$G_s = \frac{S_s(\ell)}{S_0} = \left\{\left[1 + \frac{\Gamma_0^2}{\Gamma^2}\sinh^2(\Gamma\ell)\right]^{1/2} + r\frac{\Gamma_0}{\Gamma}\sinh(\Gamma\ell)\right\}^2 \tag{15a}$$

$$G_i = \frac{S_i(\ell)}{S_i(0)} = \frac{1}{r^2}\left\{r\left[1 + \frac{\Gamma_0^2}{\Gamma^2}\sinh^2(\Gamma\ell)\right]^{1/2} + \frac{\Gamma_0}{\Gamma}\sinh(\Gamma\ell)\right\}^2 \tag{15b}$$

In the limiting case where the incident idler is small or zero ($r = 0$), the signal gain is given by

$$G_s(r = 0) = \frac{S_s(\ell)}{S_s(0)} \approx 1 + \frac{\Gamma_0^2}{\Gamma^2}\sinh^2(\Gamma\ell) \tag{16}$$

When $\Delta k = 0$, Eq. (16) takes on the more familiar form

$$G_s(r = 0, \Delta k = 0) = \cosh^2(\Gamma_0 \ell) \tag{17}$$

In the limit of small gain, $\Gamma_0 \ell \ll 1$, and for arbitrary momentum mismatch, Eq. (16) becomes

$$\lim_{\Gamma_0 \ell \ll 1} G_s(r = 0) \cong 1 + (\Gamma_0 \ell)^2 \frac{\sin^2(\Delta k \ell/2)}{(\Delta k \ell/2)^2} \tag{18}$$

The logarithmic gain for the case $r = 0$, Eq. (16), is plotted in Fig. 1 as a function of the momentum mismatch $\Delta k \ell$, normalized to the gain at $\Delta k \ell = 0$, Eq. (17). When $r = 0$, the idler gain is infinite and hence meaningless.

In the limit of equal photon fluxes at the signal and idler ($r = 1$) and for the optimum phase, the signal and idler gains are equal, ($r = 1$ in Eqs. (15)). In the limit $\Delta k = 0$,

$$G_s(r = 1, \Delta k = 0) = \exp[2\Gamma_0 \ell] \tag{19}$$

In the limit of small gain, $\Gamma_0 \ell \ll 1$, and for arbitrary momentum mismatch, Eq. (15a) becomes

$$\lim_{\Gamma_0 \ell \ll 1} G_s(r = 1) \cong 1 + (2\Gamma_0 \ell) \frac{\sin(\Delta k \ell/2)}{(\Delta k \ell/2)} \tag{20}$$

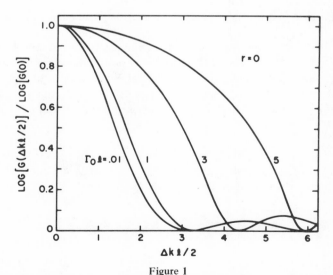

**Figure 1**

Logarithm of the signal gain with no idler initially present ($r = 0$) as a function of the momentum mismatch $\Delta k \ell/2$ for several values of the gain constant $\Gamma_0 \ell$ [30].

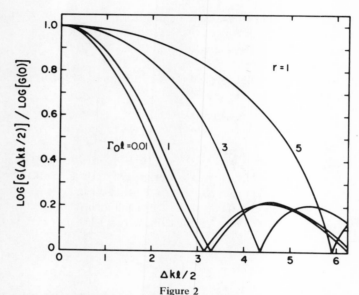

**Figure 2**

   Logarithm of the signal gain with equal numbers of signal and idler photons initially present ($r = 1$) as a function of the momentum mismatch $\Delta k \ell /2$ for several values of the gain constant $\Gamma_0 \ell$ [30].

The normalized logarithmic gain for $r = 1$, Eq. (15a), is plotted in Fig. 2. From both plots it is seen that the gain is maximum at $\Delta k \ell = 0$ and small for $\Delta k \ell \geqslant 2\pi$.

   Physically, the reduction in gain with increasing $|\Delta k|$ results from the fact that the electromagnetic fields and their nonlinear polarization source terms get out of phase as they propagate through the crystal. When $\Delta k = 0$, the waves propagate synchronously and maximum gain results; the interaction is then referred to as *phase-matched*. In vector form, phase matching requires

$$\underline{k}_p = \underline{k}_s + \underline{k}_i \tag{21}$$

Equations (1) and (21) are statements of energy and momentum conservation and are commonly referred to as the Tien-Suhl relations [31, 32].

## B. Phase Matching

   Parametric gain for the coupled waves is seen to be critically dependent on the amount of the momentum mismatch between the three uncoupled waves. In a medium without dispersion, the index of refraction is independent of frequency and all waves propagate with the same velocity; hence $\Delta k = 0$. In practice, dispersion is not zero and $\Delta k$ may be large, which in turn makes the parametric gain small. Several schemes have been realized for compensating for the effects of dispersion. These schemes include the use of birefringence, noncollinear interactions, guided waves, phase reflections at boundaries, and contributions to the index of refraction due to free electrons in a magnetic field.

## 1. Compensation for Dispersion by Use of Birefringence

Many materials possessing the required nonlinearity for parametric amplification are birefringent. In such materials, the index of refraction for a wave at a given frequency is a function of the direction of propagation in the crystal as well as its sense of polarization. In uniaxial crystals, the index of refraction $n_{extr}$ for an extraordinary wave propagating at an angle $\theta$ to the optic axis is given by

$$\frac{1}{n_{extr}^2} = \frac{\cos^2\theta}{n_0^2} + \frac{\sin^2\theta}{n_e^2} \tag{22}$$

where $n_0$ and $n_e$ are the ordinary and extraordinary indices of refraction.* The index $n_{extr}$ is thus bounded by $n_0$ and $n_e$. If the signal and idler are both ordinary rays with indices of refraction $n_s$ and $n_i$, then the index of refraction for the pump wave required to achieve collinear phase matching is

$$n_3' = \frac{\omega_s}{\omega_p} n_s + \frac{\omega_i}{\omega_p} n_i \tag{23}$$

If the pump is an extraordinary wave, then phase matching can be achieved for some angle $\theta_m$ if $n_3'$ lies between $n_0(\omega_p)$ and $n_e(\omega_p)$. The angle $\theta_m$ is referred to as the phase-matching angle. Propagation with $\Delta k = 0$ then results when all three waves travel collinearly at an angle $\theta_m$ to the optic axis. The case $\theta_m = 90°$ is referred to as noncritical phase matching.

In negative uniaxial crystals ($n_e < n_0$), phase matching can in principle be achieved for an extraordinary pump with either one or both of the signal and idler being ordinary rays. The case when both the signal and idler are ordinary rays is referred to as Type I, or parallel, phase matching; when either (but not both) is an extraordinary ray the case is referred to as Type II, or orthogonal, phase matching [34]. In positive uniaxial crystals, the pump must be an ordinary ray and either the signal or the idler or both may be extraordinary rays giving rise to Type II or Type I phase matching respectively. It should be

---

*See, for example, Born and Wolf [33] for a discussion of the optics of crystals.

noted that Type II phase matching requires more birefringence to compensate for dispersion than Type I phase matching does. For a given phase matching direction (if such a direction in fact exists), the effective nonlinear suscepti-bility $\chi_{eff}$ is determined by crystal symmetry and the direction of propagation within the crystal. Expressions for $\chi_{eff}$ for uniaxial crystals are given in Section VI,A,1.

Phase matching in biaxial crystals is also possible but the relations are more complicated. Hobden [35] has considered phase matching in biaxial crystals.

### 2. Noncollinear Phase Matching

When $|\underline{k}_s| + |\underline{k}_i| > |\underline{k}_p|$, it is possible to find some angle between the signal and idler k vectors for which vector momentum conservation and hence phase matching is achieved, Eq. (21). When beams of finite cross-sectional area are used, this type of phase matching has the disadvantage that the interaction volume is decreased compared with a collinear interaction. Noncollinear phase matching has been used in an experimental oscillator [36].

### 3. Phase Matching Using Guided Waves

It is well known that the phase velocity of a guided wave can differ signifi-cantly from the velocity of a plane wave in the same medium. In some guided wave structures, it is possible to find combinations of modes in which the phase-matching conditions are satisfied. Guided wave structures to achieve phase matching are of particular interest for use with some semiconductors that have large nonlinearities but are not birefringent. It also is relevant to the emerging area of integrated optics. Discussions of phase matching in guided wave structures are found in Refs. 25 and 37-45. Phase matching can also be achieved in guided-wave structures by introducing a periodicity into the structure that modifies either the propagation constants of the waves [46-49] or the sign or magnitude of the nonlinearity of the medium [50]. Modification of the propagation con-stant can be achieved by varying the height of the guiding region, for example. If the period of the variation is d, then $|k_p - k_s - k_i| = 2\pi M/d$, where "M is an integer" is the condition that must be satisfied to achieve phase matching. Phase matching in periodic guides can be viewed as the interaction of space harmonics of the waves involved.

### 4. Free-Carrier Magnetooptical Effects

Another technique for achieving phase matching is to use the contribution to the index of refraction of free electrons in a magnetic field. In the far infrared, in particular, these contributions can sufficiently modify the index of refraction to permit phase matching. Van Tran and Patel have used these magneto-plasma effects to obtain difference frequency mixing in the infrared using InSb, a cubic material [51].

## 5. Other Techniques for Phase Matching

Several other techniques for obtaining phase matching have been investigated, including phase reversals at material boundaries [25, 37], anomalous dispersion [52, 53], electric-field-induced birefringence [54, 55], and stress-induced birefringence [55, 56]. In the latter case, it was found not feasible to induce sufficient birefringence to permit phase matching by either electric field or stress for those III–IV semiconductors that possess no natural birefringence [55].

Although there are numerous methods for obtaining phase matching, all oscillators constructed to date have used birefringence to compensate for dispersion in collinear or noncollinear interactions.

## C. Measurement of Parametric Gain

Parametric gain is usually measured by combining a weak signal beam at frequency $\omega_s$ and a strong pump beam at $\omega_p$ in the nonlinear crystal. When pump depletion is negligible, the signal and idler power densities at the exit plane of a crystal of length $\ell$ can be found from Eqs. (8) with $r = 0$,

$$S_s(\ell) = S_0 \left[ 1 + (\Gamma_0 \ell)^2 \frac{\sinh^2(\Gamma \ell)}{(\Gamma \ell)^2} \right] \tag{24a}$$

$$S_i(\ell) = \frac{\omega_i}{\omega_s} S_0 (\Gamma_0 \ell)^2 \frac{\sinh^2(\Gamma \ell)}{(\Gamma \ell)^2} \tag{24b}$$

where $\Gamma_0$ and $\Gamma$ are defined by Eqs. (9) and (11). For small gain, i.e., $\Gamma_0 \ll 1$, these equations reduce to

$$S_s(\ell) \cong S_0 \left[ 1 + (\Gamma_0 \ell)^2 \frac{\sin^2(\Delta k \ell/2)}{(\Delta k \ell/2)^2} \right] \tag{25a}$$

$$S_i(\ell) \cong \frac{\omega_i}{\omega_s} S_0 (\Gamma_0 \ell)^2 \frac{\sin^2(\Delta k \ell/2)}{(\Delta k \ell/2)^2}, \qquad \Gamma_0 \ell \ll 1 \tag{25b}$$

In the small gain limit, the parametric gain expression depends on momentum mismatch $\Delta k \ell$ in exactly the same manner as second harmonic generation (i.e., with a $\sin^2(\Delta k \ell/2)/(\Delta k \ell/2)^2$ dependence).

Measurement of the parametric gain can be either direct or indirect. In a direct measurement, the increase in the injected signal is measured; in the indirect method, the generated idler is measured. Both techniques are equivalent. In a direct gain measurement, the signal power is measured at the input and exit faces of the nonlinear medium; the ratio of these two quantities is the signal gain given in Eq. (16). In practice, measurement of the signal beam at the exit face of the crystal, both in the presence and absence of the pump beam, is an easier measurement to make since corrections need not be made for surface reflection. For large gains, where the change in signal level is easily measured, the direct gain method is preferable. On the other hand, when the gain is small ($\Gamma_0 \ell \ll 1$, $G_s \approx 1$), it is easier to measure the generated idler wave $S_i(\ell)$. In this case,

$$\frac{S_i(\ell)}{S_s(\ell)} = \frac{\omega_i}{\omega_s} \cdot \frac{(\Gamma_0 \ell)^2 \sin^2(\Delta k \ell/2)/(\Delta k \ell/2)^2}{1 + (\Gamma_0 \ell)^2 \sin^2(\Delta k \ell/2)/(\Delta k \ell/2)^2}$$

$$\approx \frac{\omega_i}{\omega_s} (\Gamma_0 \ell)^2 \frac{\sin^2 \Delta k \ell/2}{(\Delta k \ell/2)^2} \tag{26}$$

and hence

$$G_s(k\ell) \approx 1 + \frac{\omega_s}{\omega_i} \frac{S_i(\ell)}{S_s(\ell)} \tag{27}$$

The indirect measurement thus requires only reasonably accurate measurement of the idler power to obtain a good measurement of the gain. Although gain measurements are not absolutely necessary for constructing an optical parametric oscillator, they can provide a good measure of the actual gain a real crystal provides in contrast to the gain calculated for an ideal crystal. Phrased in another way, it is possible to find the actual value of K, in Eq. (10), and hence $\Gamma_0^2$.

### 1. Gain Measurements with Beams of Finite Cross-Sectional Area

In practice, gain measurements are made with beams of finite cross-sectional areas. The expressions presented up to this point have applied to plane waves and need modification to be useful in interpreting actual measurements. In the small gain limit, the idler power density is given by Eq. (25b). If Eq. (9) is used for $\Gamma_0^2$, Eq. (26) becomes, for $\Delta k = 0$,

$$S_i(r, z = \ell) \approx \frac{\omega_i \, \ell^2 \pi K}{\omega_s} \, S_p(r) S_0(r) \tag{28}$$

where the transverse variation of the beams is indicated by their dependence on $r$. The respective powers are:

$$P_s = \int S_0(r) \, dA$$

$$P_p = \int S_p(r) \, dA \tag{29}$$

$$P_i(\ell) = \int S_i(r, \ell) \, dA$$

Integrating Eq. (28) over the transverse plane and rewriting in terms of the powers gives

$$\frac{P_i(\ell)}{P_s} \approx \frac{\omega_i \ell^2 \pi K P_p}{\omega_s} \left[ \frac{\int S_p(r) S_s(r) dA}{\int S_p(r) dA \int S_s(r) dA} \right] \tag{30}$$

The term in brackets is merely a geometrical factor.

Three limiting cases are of interest.

*a. Signal Beam Much Smaller Than the Pump Beam.* In this case the factor in brackets becomes $S_p(0)/\int S_p(r) \, dA = S_p(0)/P_p$, where $S_p(0)$ is the pump power density at the location of the signal beam. Hence,

$$\frac{P_i(\ell)}{P_s} = \frac{\omega_i \ell^2 \pi K}{\omega_s} \, S_p(0) \tag{31}$$

A knowledge of the pump power density at the location of the signal beam along with the measured signal and idler powers determines K.

*b. Pump Beam Much Smaller Than Signal Beam.* In this case only a portion of the signal beam is amplified. The expression in brackets becomes $S_s(0)/P_s$ and

$$\frac{P_i(\ell)}{P_s} = \frac{\omega_i \ell^2 \pi K P_p}{\omega_s} \cdot \frac{S_s(0)}{P_s} \tag{32}$$

where $S_s(0)$ is the signal power density at the point at which it interacts with the pump.

*c. Gaussian Signal and Pump Beams.* Let the signal and pump be Gaussian beams with profiles $S_s(r) = S_{so} \exp(-2r^2/w_s^2)$, and $S_p(r) = S_{po} \exp(-2r^2/w_p^2)$, where $w_s$ and $w_p$ are the respective beam radii.* Assuming no beam spread (near field limit), Eq. (30) becomes

$$\frac{P_i(\ell)}{P_s} \approx \frac{\omega_i}{\omega_s} \, 2KP_p \, \frac{\ell^2}{w_s^2 + w_p^2} \tag{33}$$

Equation (33) applies when the beams are collinear and coaxial. Note that the idler generated in this case has a beam radius given by

$$\frac{1}{w_i^2} = \frac{1}{w_p^2} + \frac{1}{w_s^2} \tag{34}$$

Equation (33) can be used in either of the two limits previously considered ($w_s^2 \ll w_p^2$ or $w_p^2 \ll w_s^2$). This expression is the most useful, since gain measurements are usually made with laser sources whose lowest order mode is a Gaussian.

Equation (33) can be illustrated by the following example. Consider a pump at a wavelength of 5,145 Å and a power of 1 W mixing with a signal at a wavelength of 11,523 Å. The corresponding idler wavelength, $\lambda_i = 9,295$ Å. Let the pump and signal beams be focused into a crystal of barium sodium niobate, $Ba_2NaNb_5O_{15}$, of length 1 cm, and take the beam radii of the pump and signal to be $w_p = w_s = 10^{-2}$ cm. Further assume that the beams are collinear and that noncritical phase matching is achieved (as it can in this case). The pertinent parameters for $Ba_2NaNb_5O_{15}$ are $\chi_{eff} = 2d_{15} = 29.2 \times 10^{-12}$ m/V and $n_p \approx n_s \approx n_i \approx 2.26$ (see Section VI for a discussion of materials). From Eq. (10), $K = 1.63 \times 10^{-7}$ W$^{-1}$, and hence

$$\frac{P_i(\ell = 1 \text{ cm})}{P_s} = 2 \times 10^{-3}$$

For $P_s = 1$ mW, this corresponds to a generated idler power of 2 $\mu$W. Generation of idler powers of smaller than the above value would indicate a lower effective nonlinear coefficient or shorter effective crystal length.

Direct measurement of parametric gain has been reported by Akhmanov et al. [58, 59], Patel [60], and Colles and Smith [61], and indirect measurements by Wang and Racette [62], and Boyd and Ashkin [63]. Boyd and Ashkin used a cw argon-ion laser as the pump source and Patel used a Q-switched $CO_2$ laser; in the other experiments, pulsed solid state sources were used as the pump. The ex-

---

*See Kogelnik [57] for a discussion of Gaussian modes.

periments that Akhmanov et al. reported are interesting in that they used an attenuated portion of their laser as the signal beam while pumping the parametric amplification process with the second harmonic of the laser. Since the signal and idler are simultaneously injected along with the pump in this experiment ($\omega_s = \omega_i = \omega_p/2$), the magnitude of the gain is critically dependent on the relative phase between the pump and the signal and idler fields. Without a relative phase shift between fields in going from the second harmonic generation crystal to the parametric amplification crystal, parametrically induced attenuation would be expected. In the first of their experiments [58], they argued that a relative phase shift was introduced by the filters used. This phase shift permitted amplification. In the second experiment [59], a noncollinear geometry was used, with the signal and idler degenerate in frequency but nondegenerate spatially.

## D.  Parametric Oscillator Threshold Conditions

Parametric interaction is capable of providing gain as discussed above. To achieve oscillation, some form of feedback is required. In optical parametric oscillators, this is accomplished by enclosing the nonlinear material in an optical resonator similar to that used in a laser. Although there are many configurations that optical parametric oscillators take, there are basically two types. In one, feedback is provided for both the signal and idler; this type is called the doubly resonant oscillator, or DRO. In the second class, feedback is provided for either the signal or idler but not both; this type of oscillator is referred to as a singly resonant oscillator, or SRO. Fundamental differences between these two types are discussed later.

In either form of oscillator, DRO or SRO, there is a threshold condition defined by the requirement that the round-trip gain experienced by the resonated wave or waves equal the round-trip loss or losses. Below threshold there is a small amount of spontaneous parametric emission (see Section V); however, above threshold the signal and idler fields experience a *net* round-trip gain and can grow to the point that the magnitudes of the fields are comparable to the magnitude of the pump, and useful output can be obtained.

For the DRO, the threshold condition is found from Eqs. (15) by requiring that the gains at the signal and idler compensate for the losses at the respective frequencies. If we let the *round-trip power losses* at the signal and idler be $\alpha_s$ and $\alpha_i$, the threshold condition for plane waves with the pump making a single pass in one direction through the crystal is given by

$$(\Gamma_0 \ell)^2 \, \frac{\sinh^2(\Gamma \ell)}{(\Gamma \ell)^2} = \frac{\alpha_s \alpha_i}{[(1 - \alpha_s)^{1/2} + (1 - \alpha_i)^{1/2}]^2} \qquad \text{(DRO)} \qquad (35)$$

From small losses at both the signal and idler, Eq. (35) becomes

$$(\Gamma_0 \ell)^2 \; \frac{\sin^2(\Delta k \ell/2)}{(\Delta k \ell/2)^2} \approx \frac{\alpha_s \alpha_i}{4} \qquad \text{(DRO)} \tag{36}$$

For the SRO, threshold is determined by requiring that the gain at the signal (assuming that the idler is the nonresonant wave) equal the round-trip loss $\alpha_s$. With the pump making a single pass through the nonlinear crystal, the threshold condition is

$$(\Gamma_0 \ell)^2 \; \frac{\sinh^2(\Gamma \ell)}{(\Gamma \ell)^2} = \frac{\alpha_s}{1 - \alpha_s} \qquad \text{(SRO)} \tag{37}$$

For small losses at the resonant signal, the threshold relation becomes

$$(\Gamma_0 \ell)^2 \; \frac{\sin^2(\Delta k \ell/2)}{(\Delta k \ell/2)^2} \approx \alpha_s \qquad \text{(SRO)} \tag{38}$$

The pump power density required to achieve threshold can be found from Eqs. (9), (10), and (35) or (37). In the limit of small losses, the threshold pump power densities are given for the DRO by

$$S_p \Big|^{th} = \frac{\alpha_s \alpha_i}{4 \pi K \ell^2} \left[ \frac{\sin^2(\Delta k \ell/2)}{(\Delta k \ell/2)^2} \right]^{-1} \qquad \text{(DRO)} \tag{39}$$

and for the SRO by

$$S_p \Big|^{th} = \frac{\alpha_s}{\pi K \ell^2} \left[ \frac{\sin^2(\Delta k \ell/2)}{(\Delta k \ell/2)^2} \right]^{-1} \qquad \text{(SRO)} \tag{40}$$

It is seen from these expressions that the pump power density required to achieve threshold is inversely proportional to the square of the crystal length, inversely proportional to K and hence the square of the nonlinear coefficient, and directly proportional to the product of the three indices of refraction. The increase in threshold pump power density resulting from momentum mismatch is clearly evident. If Eqs. (39) and (40) are compared, it is also seen that the threshold pump power density for the SRO is a factor $4/\alpha_i$ greater than for a DRO with the same loss at the signal.

### E.  Threshold for Gaussian Beams

The threshold conditions given above for the DRO and the SRO are for plane waves and are expressed in terms of the pump power *density* required to produce oscillation. The theory of optical parametric oscillator threshold for finite beams with Gaussian spatial dependence has been considered by Kingston and McWhorter [64], Boyd and Ashkin [63], Boyd and Kleinman [65], Ammann and Montgomery [66], Boyd and Nash [67], Asby [68], Aslaksen [69], and Kuizenga [70]. Several of these authors have considered the effects of diffraction and double refraction and evaluate the dependence of the parametric gain on the degree of focusing of the beams involved. Their results for those cases considered are described below.

## 1. Symmetric Doubly Resonant Oscillator (DRO)

Boyd and Kleinman [65] (BK), consider the parametric interaction of an extraordinary pump wave with ordinary signal and idler waves (i.e., Type I phase matching in a negative uniaxial crystal). The pump, signal, and idler beams are assumed to be $TEM_{00}$ Gaussian modes with circular symmetry characterized by their minimum beam radii $w_{op}$, $w_{os}$, $w_{oi}$ respectively. The signal and idler are both assumed to be resonant modes of the parametric oscillator cavity, Fig. 3, and the pump is assumed to make a single pass through the nonlinear crystal. BK find that with the beam radii for the signal and idler cavity modes $w_{os}$ and $w_{oi}$, the optimum spot size for the pump is given by

$$\frac{1}{w_{op}^2} = \frac{1}{w_{os}^2} + \frac{1}{w_{oi}^2} \tag{41}$$

In terms of the confocal parameter b, defined by $b_j = k_j w_{oj}^2$, where $k_j$ = the propagation constant of the jth wave in the crystal $= \omega_j n_j / c$, this condition reduces to $b_p = b_s = b_i$ when the signal and idler modes have the same confocal parameter. BK also find that the optimum interaction occurs when the beam

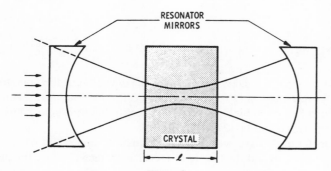

RESONATOR
MIRRORS

CRYSTAL

$\ell$

**Figure 3**
Schematic representation of the symmetric cavity resonator [66].

waists are all located in the center of the crystal. They define the degree of focusing of the beams by a parameter $\xi$, given by

$$\xi = \frac{\ell}{b} \tag{42}$$

The effect of beam walkoff due to double refraction is characterized by a parameter B, defined by

$$B = \frac{\rho(\ell k_0)^{\frac{1}{2}}(n_p/n_0)^{\frac{1}{2}}}{2} \tag{43}$$

where $k_0$ and $n_0$ are the propagation constant and index of refraction at degeneracy, i.e., $\omega_s = \omega_i = \omega_0 = \omega_p/2$, and $\rho$ is the double refraction angle for the extraordinary pump beam. In specific terms, the double refraction angle is given by

$$\tan \rho = \frac{1}{2} \sin 2\theta_m \frac{n_0^2(\omega_p) - n_0^2(\omega_p)}{n_e^2(\omega_p)\cos^2\theta_m + n_0^2(\omega_p)\sin^2\theta_m} \tag{44}$$

where $\theta_m$ is the phase matching angle and $n_e(\omega_p)$ and $n_0(\omega_p)$ are the extraordinary and ordinary indices of refraction at the pump. To a good approximation, Eq. (44) can be written

$$\tan \rho \approx \rho \approx \frac{\Delta n}{n} \sin 2\theta_m \tag{45}$$

where $\Delta n = n_0(\omega_p) - n_e(\omega_p)$ and $n = [n_e(\omega_p) + n_0(\omega_p)]/2$.

For such a symmetric cavity, the threshold pump power for the DRO with $\Delta k = 0$ is given by

$$P_p^{th} = \frac{\alpha_s \alpha_i}{4K(\ell k_0)(1 - \delta^2)} \cdot \frac{1}{\overline{h}_m(\xi, B)} \tag{46}$$

where $\delta = (\omega_s - \omega_0)/\omega_0$ and is a measure of the deviation of the operating frequency from degeneracy, and as before, $\alpha_s$ and $\alpha_i$ are the round-trip signal and idler losses, and K is given by Eq. (10). (For $\Delta k \neq 0$, the threshold is higher by the factor $[\sin^2(\Delta k\ell/2)/(\Delta k\ell/2)^2]^{-1}$.)

The parameter $\overline{h}_m(\xi, B)$ is a dimensionless quantity dependent on the double refraction parameter B and the degree of focusing characterized by the parameter $\xi$. It has been calculated by BK for a wide range of values of B as a function of $\xi$, and their calculations are summarized in Fig. 4.* A number of important properties of $\bar{h}_m(\xi, B)$ can be obtained by examining Fig. 4. (1) There exists an optimum degree of focusing for any value of the double refraction parameter B. (2) For B = 0 (no double refraction), $\bar{h}_m(\xi, 0)$ obtains a maximum value of 1.07 for $\xi = 2.84$, corresponding to a focus whose near field (given by b) is roughly one-third as long as the crystal. (3) For B >> 1 and near the maximum, $\bar{h}_m(\xi, B)$ is relatively insensitive to $\xi$. (4) For B > 0, the maximum value obtained by $\bar{h}_m(\xi, B)$ is a rapidly decreasing function of B. Finally it should be noted that for B = 0 the threshold power for optimum focusing conditions varies inversely as the first, not second, power of the crystal length.

In determining the calculated threshold for a particular DRO configuration, one would proceed as follows: First, from the crystal length, indices of refraction, and phase-matching angle, $\rho$ and then B can be evaluated for a given pump frequency. Next, the confocal parameter of the cavity can be determined from resonator theory, Ref. 57. (*Note:* The confocal parameter of a beam in a material of index n is nb where b is the value in vacuum.) Further, if the pump beam is assumed to be focused into the oscillator cavity with $b_p = b_{cavity}$ and with a waist located at the cavity waist, $\bar{h}(\xi, B)$ is determined from Fig. 4 and the threshold is given by Eq. (46).

Two approximations to $\bar{h}(\xi, B)$ are useful.

a. For B = 0, $\xi \ll 1$ (near field limit),

$$\bar{h}(\xi, B) \approx \xi \tag{47}$$

in which case

$$P_p^{th} \cong \frac{\alpha_s \alpha_i}{4K(1 - \delta^2)} \frac{w_0^2}{\varrho^2} \tag{48}$$

where $w_0$ is the minimum beam radius of the cavity corresponding to the degenerate frequency. This approximation is valid to $\approx 10\%$ for $\xi < 0.4$ and to better than 30% for $\xi \leqslant 1$.

b. For any B, the maximum value of $\bar{h}_m(\xi, B) \equiv \bar{h}_{mm}(B)$ is approximately given by

---

*For given values of B and $\xi$, the parametric gain (and hence the oscillator threshold) is also a function of the momentum mismatch $\Delta k$. Because of additional phase shifts introduced into the signal, idler, and pump waves due to focusing, the maximum gain does not in general occur for $\Delta k = 0$. In evaluating the maximum gain and hence minimum threshold condition, Boyd and Kleinman determine the optimum $\Delta k$, and for this value the parameter $\bar{h}_m(\xi, B)$ is defined. For details see Ref. 65.

$$\overline{h}_{mm}(B) \cong \frac{\overline{h}_{mm}(0)}{1+(4B^2/\pi)\overline{h}_{mm}(0)} \tag{49}$$

where $\overline{h}_{mm}(0) = 1.07$. In the limit $B \gg 1$,

$$\overline{h}_{mm}(B) \approx \frac{\pi}{4B^2} \tag{50}$$

For this case, it can be seen from Eqs. (43), (46), and (50) that $P_p^{th}$ is independent of crystal length.

Boyd and Kleinman also show that their analysis is equally valid for Type I phase matching in positive uniaxial crystals. No attempt has been made to

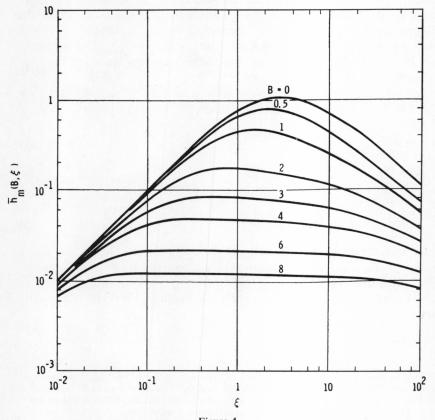

**Figure 4**

Plot of $h_m$ for the symmetric doubly resonant oscillator as a function of the focusing parameter $\xi$ for several values of the double refraction parameter B [66].

analyze Gaussian mode interactions for a Type II interaction in which one but not both of the signal and idler modes is an extraordinary ray.

## 2. Hemispherical Doubly Resonant Oscillator

It is not convenient in many experimental conditions to use a symmetrical cavity configuration, and instead a cavity in which the waist lies at or near one end of the crystal is used (near-hemispherical). Such a cavity configuration is shown in Fig. 5. Ammann and Montgomery [66] have analyzed this case in a manner similar to Boyd and Kleinman for arbitrary B; Boyd and Nash [67] have analyzed the same problem for the special case B = 0. Again defining $\xi = \ell/b$, locating the pump waist at the crystal face, and setting $b_p = b_s = b_i$ we find the threshold for this resonator configuration by Eq. (46), where $\bar{h}_m(\xi, B)$ is now found from Fig. 6. The primary differences between the symmetrical and unsymmetrical cases occur in the region of moderate to tight focusing; for loose focusing, $\xi < 0.1$, the two cases are essentially identical.

For a given value of B, maximum value of $\bar{h}_m(\xi, B)$, $\bar{h}_{mm}(B)$ is shown in Fig. 7 for the symmetric and hemispherical configurations. For B = 0 and the same crystal length and losses, the minimum parametric oscillator threshold is twice as high for the unsymmetric resonator as for the symmetric one. For increasing B, the difference between the two cases becomes smaller.

## 3. Cylindrical Focusing for Doubly Resonant Oscillators

When double refraction is present, the walkoff of the extraordinary ray limits the degree of focusing of the interacting beams that can be effectively employed. This in turn results in the decrease of $\bar{h}_{mm}(B)$, which is the maximum value of

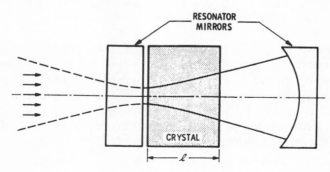

**Figure 5**
Schematic representation of the near-hemispherical cavity resonator [66].

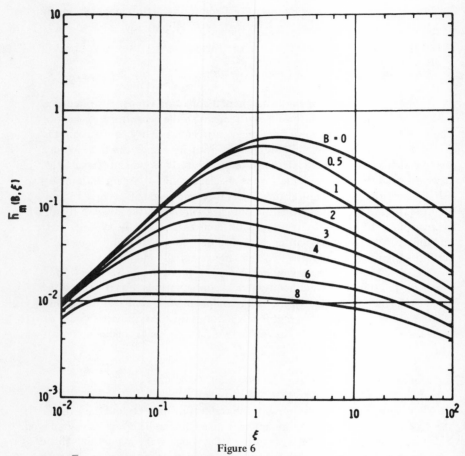

**Figure 6**

Plot of $\bar{h}_m$ for the hemispherical doubly resonant oscillator as a function of the focusing parameter $\xi$ for several values of the double refraction parameter B [66].

$h_m(\xi, B)$, shown in Fig. 7. Since the beam walkoff of the extraordinary ray is in only one direction, i.e., the plane containing the optic axis and the direction of propagation, an enhanced interaction can be obtained with tighter focusing of the beams in the other transverse dimension. Kuizenga [70] has considered this case in detail. In his analysis, following the technique of Boyd and Kleinman for a symmetric DRO, suitably modified to account for beams of elliptical cross section, he reaches the following conclusions:

1. In the direction perpendicular to the walkoff direction, the confocal parameter of the pump, signal, and idler should be equal.
2. For $B \neq 0$, the cross section of the signal and idler beams for optimum in-

teraction are elliptical; however, only a slight penalty in threshold (at most about 30%) is paid for using modes with circular symmetry.

3. For $B \neq 0$, the pump beam is less tightly focused in the direction of walk-off than in the orthogonal direction.

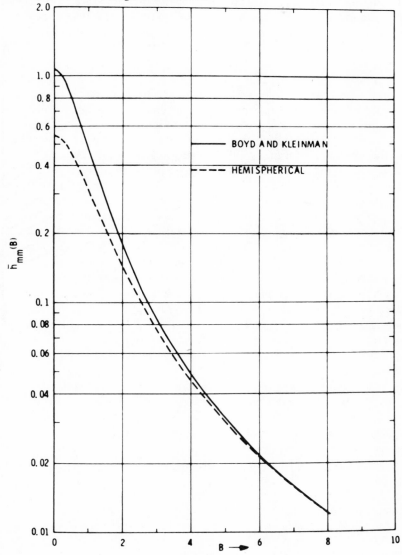

**Figure 7**

Plots of the maximum values of $\bar{h}_m$ for the symmetrical and hemispherical doubly resonant oscillator as a function of the double refraction parameter B [66].

4.  For any value of B, $\bar{h}_{mm}(B)_{elliptical} \approx (\bar{h}_{mm}(B)_{circular})^{1/2}$ and thus for B $\neq 0$ gives a lower oscillator threshold. For large B, $\bar{h}_{mm}(B)_{elliptical} \approx \pi/4B$ compared with $\pi/4B^2$ for circular beams.
5.  For elliptical focusing and large B, the oscillator threshold varies as $\ell^{-1/2}$ in contrast to the case of circular beams, where threshold is independent of the crystal length. This means that long crystals can be used to advantage in reducing threshold.

These results are particularly important for those cases for which beam walk-off is significant and for which long crystals are available. In a practical case, the signal and idler modes would be defined by spherical mirrors (at a small increase in threshold as mentioned above) and the pump beam would be appropriately focused by a combination of cylindrical and spherical optics. An example of the advantages of using cylindrical optics is given below. Details of the calculations and results can be found in Kuizenga's paper, Ref. 70.

To show the calculation of parametric oscillator thresholds and to show also the range of thresholds that might be encountered, three examples are now considered. For illustration, the pump wavelengths will be chosen to be the 1.064 $\mu$m fundamental of the $Nd^{3+}$ laser, the second harmonic of $Nd^{3+}$ at 0.532 $\mu$m and the fourth harmonic at 0.266 $\mu$m. The nonlinear crystals used for these pump wavelengths are $LiNbO_3$ ($\lambda_p = 1.064 \mu$m), $Ba_2NaNb_5O_{15}$ ($\lambda_p = 0.532 \mu$m), and ADP ($\lambda_p = 0.266 \mu$m). These examples correspond closely to oscillators that have been constructed. For simplicity in all cases, it is assumed that each of the crystals is 1 cm long, optimum focusing conditions in a symmetric cavity configuration are employed, operation is near degeneracy, and the round-trip signal and idler power losses are 1% for all cases. Deviations from these assumptions are easily taken into account by scaling the results of these calculations with the threshold formulas.

In the first example with $\lambda_p = 1.064 \mu$m and $\lambda_s = \lambda_i = \lambda_0 = 2.128 \mu$m for Type I phase matching, an examination of the refractive index date of $LiNbO_3$ (determined from original publications; see Section VI, or summaries by Singh [71] or Bechmann and Kurtz [72]) shows that noncritical phase matching near room temperature is not possible. From the published index data, the phase-matching angle, computed from Eq. (22) and the requirement that $n_{extr}(1.064 \mu m)$ = $n_0$ (2.128 $\mu$m) gives a phase matching angle $\theta_m \approx 43°$. For this case, where noncritical phase matching cannot be achieved, the effects of beam walkoff due to double refraction are important. From index data, the birefringence at the pump is $\Delta n = 0.084$, $n = 2.21$; and from Eq. (45) the walkoff angle is found to be $\rho \approx 0.038$ rad. From Eq. (43), the double refraction parameter B is found to be 4.7. From Eq. (49) or Fig. 4, for circular beams $\bar{h}_{mm}(B)$ is found to be 0.034; and for elliptical beams, $\bar{h}_{mm}(B) \approx 0.17$ from the approximate expression given above. From Fig. 4 it is also seen that the optimum focusing condition is also relatively insensitive to the degree of focusing for this large value of B. In practice, one would use a small value of $\xi$ (loose focusing) to reduce the pump power density. Along with $\bar{h}_{mm}(B)$ and the assumed losses, it is only necessary to determine K to obtain the threshold, and this in turn requires knowledge of $\chi_{eff}$. From Eq. (113), Section VI, $\chi_{eff} = 2d_{eff}$; and from Table 2 for Type I phase matching (OOE), and the crystal class 3m, $d_{eff} = d_{15} \sin(\theta_m + \rho) - d_{22} 3\varphi\cos(\theta + \rho)$. Also from Section VI, $d_{15}(\text{LiNbO}_3) = 5.2 \times 10^{-12}$ m/V and $d_{22}(\text{LiNbO}_3) = 3.1 \times 10^{-12}$ m/V. For the fixed phase matching angle $\theta_m$ and the walkoff angle $\rho$, the maximum value of $d_{eff}$ occurs for $\sin 3\varphi = -1$ ($\varphi$ is the angle defined in the plane perpendicular to the optic axis; see Fig. 39). The above values yield $d_{eff} = 5.87 \times 10^{-12}$ m/V and $\chi_{eff} = 11.7 \times 10^{-12}$ m/V. Finally, $k_0 = 2\pi n/\lambda_0$ and n = 2.21, giving $k_0\ell = 6.53 \times 10^4$. Substituting the appropriate values into Eq. (10) gives K = $6.68 \times 10^{-9}$ W$^{-1}$; and Eq. 46 gives as the threshold pump power $P_p^{th} = 1.7$ W for circular beams and $P_p^{th} = 0.34$ W for elliptical beams. The effect of double refraction, which manifests itself in limiting $\bar{h}_{mm}(B)$ to 0.034, is seen to produce an increase in threshold by a factor of approximately 30 compared with noncritical phase matching for circular beams and by a factor of approximately 6 for elliptical beams. This demonstrates the desirability of achieving noncritical phase matching where possible.

The second example considers an oscillator pumped at $\lambda_p = 0.532$ $\mu$m with $\text{Ba}_2\text{NaNb}_5\text{O}_{15}$ used. An examination of index of refraction data shows that for this pump wavelength and degenerate operation, $\lambda_0 = 1.064$ $\mu$m, noncritical phase matching can be achieved by increasing the temperature of the crystal to the neighborhood of 100°C. For noncritical phase matching (B = 0), $h_m = 1.07$ and circular modes are optimum. The other important parameters are $n_p = n_s = n_1 = 2.26$, and $\chi_{eff} = 2d_{15} = 29.2 \times 10^{-12}$ m/V. From Eq. (10), K = $1.55 \times 10^{-7}$ W$^{-1}$, $k_0\ell = 1.335 \times 10^5$, and $P_p^{th} = 1.1 \times 10^{-3}$ W. This value represents a reduction of approximately three orders of magnitude from the first case considered. Of this difference, a factor of approximately 30 results from beam walkoff, a factor of 6 from the differences in $\chi_{eff}$, and a factor of 8 from the difference in the wavelengths.

For the third oscillator using ADP (ammonium dihydrogen phosphate), noncritical phase matching can also be achieved at a temperature of approximately 50°C. The nonlinear coefficient is $\chi_{eff} = 2d_{36} = 1.15 \times 10^{-12}$ m/V, and the refractive indices are approximately 1.49. Again from Eq. (10), K = $3.35 \times 10^{-9}$ W$^{-1}$ and $P_p^{th} = 40$ mW. This threshold value is approximately 40 times greater than the second case considered. This value results from an increase of approximately 640 due to a smaller nonlinear coefficient counterbalanced by a decrease of 8 for wavelength and approximately 2 for the lower refractive index of ADP compared with $\text{Ba}_2\text{NaNb}_5\text{O}_{15}$. A summary of these threshold calculations is given in Table 1.

## Table 1

Calculated Threshold Pump Power Values for Several Doubly Resonant Optical
Parametric Oscillators under Optimum Focusing Conditions

| $\lambda_p(\mu m)$ | Material | B | $\bar{h}_{max}$ | $P_p^{th}$ |
|---|---|---|---|---|
| 1.064 | LiNbO$_3$ | 4.7 | 0.034 (circular) | 1.7 W |
|  |  |  | 0.17 (elliptical) | 0.34 W |
| 0.532 | Ba$_2$NaNb$_5$O$_{15}$ | 0 | 1.07 | 1.1 mW |
| 0.266 | ADP | 0 | 1.07 | 40 mW |

Typical thresholds observed with pulsed pump sources run considerably
above the values indicated in Table 1. This is primarily because optimal focusing
has not been used in most of these experiments. Ammann et al. [73], using a
repetitively Q-switched 1.064 $\mu m$ Nd: YAG laser as a pump, have measured a
pulsed threshold of 25 W with a LiNbO$_3$ crystal 3.5 mm long, in good agreement
with theory for their measured losses. Using a Ba$_2$NaNb$_5$O$_{15}$ crystal 5 mm long
and an argon laser as the pump, Smith [74] has obtained a threshold of 3 mW
in a hemispherical configuration corresponding to round-trip losses less than 1%
at the signal and idler, in good agreement with theory.

## 4.  Singly Resonant Oscillator (SRO)

In the DRO, both the signal and idler are resonant modes of the cavity and
in the above analyses are assumed to be lowest order TEM$_{00}$ Gaussian modes.
The problem of the SRO is more complicated since only one of the signal and
idler waves is resonant and thus specified as an eigenmode of the cavity. The
nonresonant mode is not so constrained and ultimately takes up a spatial configuration determined by the pump and the resonant mode. The uncertainty in
the specification of the nonresonant mode complicates the mathematics of the
problem considerably. Asby [68] has considered the SRO for the limiting case
of no double refraction (B = 0) and for a symmetric cavity configuration. In
the loose focusing or near field limit, the threshold is given by

$$P_p^{th} = \frac{\alpha_s}{2K} \left( \frac{w_s^2 + w_p^2}{\varrho^2} \right) \tag{51}$$

For tighter focusing, where diffraction becomes important, the optimum focusing conditions correspond to $b_p = b_s$, and $\xi = 2.8$. Details may be found in Ref.
[68].

### F.  Pump Characteristics

In the preceding discussions, the pump, signal, and idler have been assumed to be monochromatic waves. For some nonlinear devices a high degree of monochromaticity of the pump is not required. On the other hand, monochromaticity is important for parametric oscillators, except as discussed below.

For a DRO, both the signal and the idler are resonant modes of the parametric oscillator cavity. In the limit of low losses, these modes have high Q's, and the signal and idler frequencies are bandwidth-limited by these Q's. For the condition $\omega_p = \omega_s + \omega_i$ to be satisfied, the pump frequency must have a bandwidth less than the sum of the bandwidths of the signal and idler cavities to be effective in pumping the oscillator. If the bandwidth of the pumping radiation is broader than this value, then only a fraction of the pumping power will be effective in pumping the oscillator. If the pumping radiation consists of a number of longitudinal modes, then only one of these modes will be effective. An exception to this occurs if the longitudinal mode spacing of the pump modes equals or is some multiple of the spacing of either the signal or the idler cavity. In this case, a comb of pump modes, Fig. 8, can interact with a comb of idler modes to produce a single signal mode, or alternatively with a comb of signal modes to produce a single idler mode. Harris [75] has shown that the phases of the individual mode pairs adjust in such a way that the full multimode pump power is effective in pumping the oscillator. Byer et al. [76] have constructed an oscillator using this scheme. A second exception occurs when all three mode spacings are equal and the pump is mode-locked. In this case, the *peak* power in the mode-locked pulse is effective in pumping the oscillator (Harris [77]).

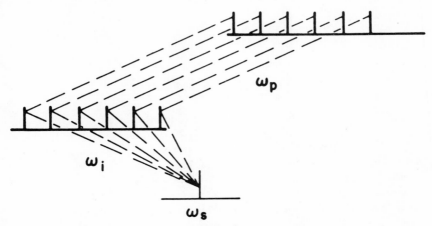

**Figure 8**
Mode diagram showing how a comb of pump modes can combine with a comb of idler modes to interact with a single signal mode [75].

For the SRO where either the signal or idler is nonresonant, the pump linewidth restrictions are much less severe and a multimode pump can be just as effective as a single-mode pump in driving the oscillator. This occurs because the nonresonant wave is not restricted by any cavity Q and is therefore free to adjust to any spectral content of the pump within reason. The full multifrequency pump power will be effective in pumping a *single* resonant mode provided phase matching is satisfied for each different pump frequency $\nu_{pj}$ and the corresponding nonresonant wave $\nu_{nr_j} = \nu_{pj} - \nu_{res}$. If for some pump frequency $\nu_{po}$ and nonresonant frequency $\nu_{nr_0}$, $\Delta k = 0$, then the momentum mismatch $\delta k$ as a function of the spread in pump frequency $\delta\nu_p$ is given by

$$\delta k = \left( \frac{\partial k_p}{\partial \nu_p} - \frac{\partial k_{nr}}{\partial \nu_{nr}} \right) \delta\nu_p \tag{52}$$

where $\delta\nu_p = \nu_p - \nu_{po} = \nu_{nr_0} - \nu_{nr}$. For the full pump linewidth $\Delta\nu_p$ to be effective in pumping the SRO, it is thus restricted by

$$\Delta\nu_p < \frac{\pi}{\ell} \left[ \frac{\partial k_p}{\partial \nu_p} - \frac{\partial k_{nr}}{\partial \nu_{nr}} \right]^{-1} \tag{53}$$

where $\ell$ is the crystal length, Young et al. [78]. Young and co-workers also point out that when the nonresonant wave is the higher frequency of the signal-idler pair, its dispersion is more nearly equal to that of the pump and permits the use of the maximum pump bandwidth. An example of the spectral content of the pump, resonant, and nonresonant waves is shown in Fig. 9.

## G. Transverse Modes

In most nonlinear interactions, it is desirable to use the lowest order $TEM_{00}$, or Gaussian, mode to pump or drive the interaction. This is primarily because this mode has the greatest power density for a given power level, contains no hot spots, and has the least beam spread. It has been demonstrated [64, 79, 80] both theoretically and experimentally that the lowest-order mode is most effective in generating optical harmonics. Similar arguments can be given for parametric oscillators although detailed theoretical results are not available. Experimentally, the use of the lowest-order mode for pumping an oscillator does permit the achievement of low-order operation of the oscillator, as seen in Fig. 10, where both the $TEM_{00}$ and $TEM_{10}$ modes of an oscillator are shown [81].

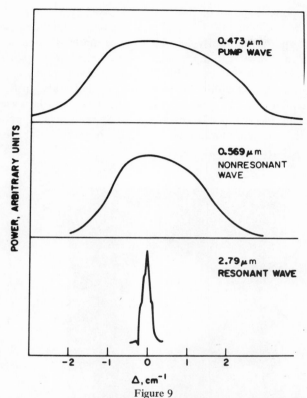

Figure 9

Spectra of the pump, resonant and nonresonant waves in a singly resonant oscillator [78].

## III. Operation of the Optical Parametric Oscillator
## Above Threshold: Output Power and Efficiency

In the preceding section, the conditions for the threshold of an optical parametric oscillator were presented. In this section, operation of the oscillator above threshold will be considered.

### A. Doubly Resonant Oscillator (DRO)

A schematic of the DRO is shown in Fig. 11. The nonlinear crystal of length $\ell$ is surrounded by mirrors $M_1$ and $M_2$. It is assumed that these mirrors are completely transparent to the pump radiation and reflecting at both the signal and idler. The pump power incident on the cavity is denoted by $P_p^{inc}$ and the pump power transmitted is denoted by $P_p^{tr}$. In addition, a reflected pump power $P_p^r$ is introduced to account for intensity-dependent reflections (discussed below). The quantities $P_s$ and $P_i$ refer to the total powers generated at the signal and idler. This generated power can be coupled out of the cavity, producing useful power output, or dissipated within the cavity in scattering or absorptive losses. The results presented below have been derived in the limit that the waves can be considered plane waves; it can be shown that these results also apply in the steady state to the case of Gaussian modes when the beam radius of the pump satisfies Eq. (41) [82].

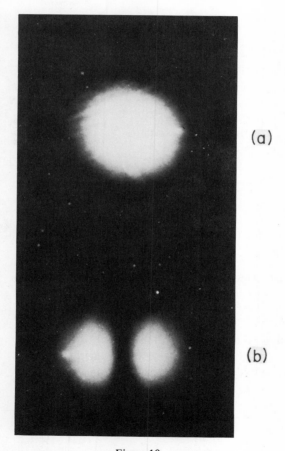

(a)

(b)

**Figure 10**
Transverse modes of the optical parametric oscillator: (a) $TEM_{00}$ mode, (b) $TEM_{10}$ mode [81].

NONLINEAR
CRYSTAL

Figure 11

Schematic diagram of the optical parametric oscillator showing the relevant waves. Note that $P_s$ and $P_i$ refer to the net signal and idler powers generated and not to the powers flowing in the cavity.

The results presented in this section are derived also under the assumption of small losses at the signal and idler (i.e., $\alpha_s$, $\alpha_i \ll 1$). The procedure for deriving Eqs. (56a) through (56d) is as follows: In the steady state and under the assumption of small losses, the amplitudes of the resonant signal and idler fields are nearly constant over the cavity length and hence over the length of the nonlinear crystal. Assuming these fields to be constant, Eq. (5c) for the pump field propagating in the $+z$ direction can be integrated directly. The resulting equation relates the pump field at the exit face of the nonlinear crystal, $z = \ell$, to its value at $z = 0$, with the amplitudes of the signal and idler fields (constant but unknown) and also the initial phase $\varphi$ as parameters. It is argued that the phase $\varphi$ takes on that value resulting in the maximum depletion of the pump (resulting also in the maximum gain) [83],*

$$\varphi = -\frac{\pi}{2} - \frac{\Delta k \ell}{2} \tag{54}$$

leaving the magnitudes of the signal and idler fields as unknowns. A second equation similar to Eq. (5c) can also be integrated directly to find the backward-generated pump wave resulting from the mixing of the backward-traveling signal and idler fields. By equating the energy lost by the pump (including the backward generated pump, $P_p^r$) to the total energy dissipated by the signal and idler fields, and using the Manley-Rowe relation ($P_s/\omega_s = P_i/\omega_i$ [84], one can determine the magnitudes of the signal, idler, and pump powers self-consistently in terms of the incident pump field.

---

*This value of $\varphi$ agrees in the limit of small gain with Eq. (14) derived for constant pump intensity; for large gain, they do not agree because of the different assumptions under which they are derived.

## 1. Doubly Resonant Oscillator with Power-Dependent Reflections

When the pump power is below threshold, the relations for the various fields are

$$P_p^{tr} = P_p^{inc}$$

$$P_p^{r} = 0 \tag{55}$$

$$P_s = P_i = 0$$

The pump is thus transmitted through the cavity, unattenuated, with no signal or idler generated, and with no reflected pump. Above threshold (i.e., for $P_p^{inc} > P_p^{th}$), the fields are given by

$$\frac{P_p^{tr}}{P_p^{inc}} = \frac{P_p^{th}}{P_p^{inc}} = \frac{1}{\Phi} \tag{56a}$$

$$\frac{P_p^{r}}{P_p^{inc}} = \frac{1}{\Phi} [\Phi^{\frac{1}{2}} - 1]^2 \tag{56b}$$

$$\frac{P^s}{P_p^{inc}} = 2 \frac{\omega_s}{\omega_p} \frac{1}{\Phi} [\Phi^{\frac{1}{2}} - 1] \tag{56c}$$

$$\frac{P_i}{P_p^{inc}} = 2 \frac{\omega_i}{\omega_p} \frac{1}{\Phi} [\Phi^{\frac{1}{2}} - 1] \tag{56d}$$

where

$$\Phi \equiv \frac{P_p^{inc}}{P_p^{th}} \tag{57}$$

The quantity $\Phi$ defined in Eq. (57) is referred to as the pumping ratio and is simply the ratio of the incident pump power to the pump power required to achieve threshold. Equations (56a) and (56b) and the sum of (56c) and (56d) are plotted in Fig. 12 as a function of $\Phi$. It is seen from Eq. (56a) that the transmitted pump power limits at the threshold value, i.e., $P_p^{tr} = P_p^{th}$, providing the basis for an optical limiter [85]. The internal efficiency $\eta^{int}$ defined as the fraction of the pump power going into the signal and idler fields is given by

$$\eta^{int} = \frac{P_s + P_i}{P_p^{inc}} = \frac{2}{\Phi} [\Phi^{\frac{1}{2}} - 1] \tag{58}$$

A plot of $\eta^{int}$ as a function of $\Phi$ is presented in Fig. 13, which shows that the maximum internal efficiency of 50% occurs when the oscillator is pumped at four times threshold. The reason for the decrease in efficiency when pumping at a level greater than four times threshold is that since the reflected pump power (56b) is proportional to the product of the signal and idler intensities, it increases more rapidly than either of these fields and thereby extracts an increasing fraction of the incident pump power. At maximum efficiency, one-half the pump power goes into the signal and idler, one-quarter is transmitted, and one-quarter is reflected.

The signal and idler powers coupled out of the oscillator are given by

$$P_s^{ext} = \frac{T_s}{T_s + L_s} P_s \tag{59a}$$

$$P_i^{ext} = \frac{T_i}{T_i + L_i} P_i \tag{59b}$$

where the T's are the total transmission values, the L's are the total round-trip losses and $\alpha = L + T$. The external efficiency is defined as the ratio of the power

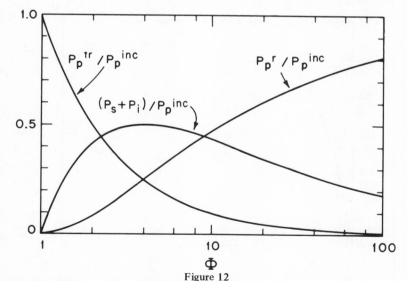

**Figure 12**

Transmitted pump, reflected pump and sum of signal and idler powers generated as a function of the pumping parameter $\Phi$ for the doubly resonant oscillator.

coupled out of the cavity to the incident pump power. These external efficiencies defined for the signal, idler, and total ouput powers are given by

$$\eta_s^{ext} = \frac{T_s}{T_s + L_s} \; \frac{\omega_s}{\omega_p} \; \eta^{int} \tag{60a}$$

$$\eta_i^{ext} = \frac{T_i}{T_i + L_i} \; \frac{\omega_i}{\omega_p} \; \eta^{int} \tag{60b}$$

$$\eta^{ext} = \left( \frac{\omega_s}{\omega_p} \frac{T_s}{T_s + L_s} + \frac{\omega_i}{\omega_p} \frac{T_i}{T_i + L_i} \right) \eta^{int} \tag{60c}$$

The frequency ratios are not present in these expressions if efficiency is defined on a photon basis.

Since $P_p^{th}$ depends on the product of the total losses at the signal and idler, increasing the transmission T in order to increase the fraction of the power coupled out of the cavity, $T/(T + L)$, also increases $P_p^{th}$. Hence there exists a transmission that optimizes the output power from the oscillator. Two cases are of interest: in one it is desired to optimize the power at either the signal or the idler and in the other it is desired to optimize the sum of the signal and the idler powers.

For the first case, the value of the transmission at the signal $T_s$ is varied to

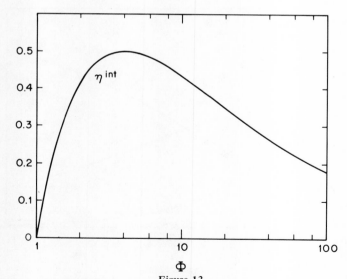

**Figure 13**
Internal efficiency of the doubly resonant oscillator as a function of $\Phi$.

optimize the external signal power with $T_i = 0$. In discussing optimum coupling, it is convenient to define the following quantities,

$$\Phi_0 = \Phi(T_s = 0) = \frac{P_p^{inc}}{P_p^{th}(T_s = 0)} \tag{61}$$

$$r = \frac{T_s}{L_s} \tag{62}$$

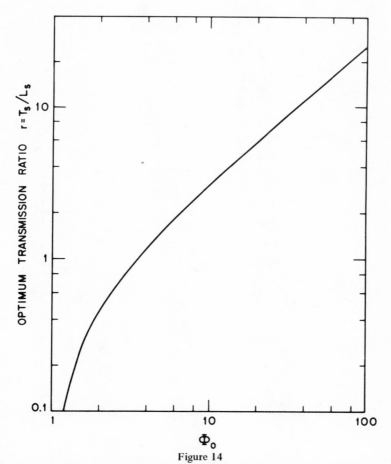

Figure 14

Optimum transmission ratio $r = T_s/L_s$, which maximizes the output power at the signal as a function of $\Phi_0 = \Phi(T_s = 0)$.

$\Phi_0$ is the ratio of the available pump power to the threshold power with $T_s = T_i = 0$; the quantity r is the ratio of the optimum transmission value to the unavoidable cavity losses. The value of r that optimizes the external signal efficiency is shown in Fig. 14 as a function of $\Phi_0$. In Fig. 15, the maximum external efficiency normalized to the frequency ratio $\omega_s/\omega_p$, along with the actual pumping ratio at $T = T_{opt} = rL$, is shown as a function of $\Phi_0$. For large $\Phi_0$, $r \approx \Phi_0/4$ and $(\omega_p/\omega_s)\eta_s^{ext}$ tends toward 0.5 and the pumping ratio approaches 4, which also optimizes the internal efficiency.

In the second case of interest, the transmissions at both the signal and the idler are varied to optimize the output power. For the special case of operation near degeneracy, $\omega_s \approx \omega_i$, and for $L_s = L_i$, defining

$$r = \frac{T_s}{L_s} = \frac{T_i}{L_i} \tag{63}$$

$$\Phi_0 = \frac{P_p^{inc}}{P_p^{th}(T = 0)} \tag{64}$$

the optimum value of r is given in Fig. 16 and the efficiency as well as the pumping ratio are given in Fig. 17, all as functions of $\Phi_0$.

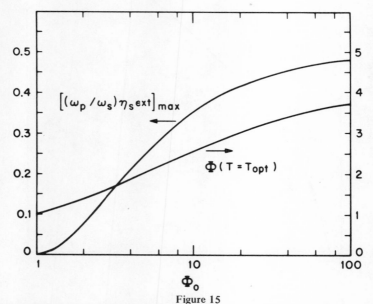

**Figure 15**

Maximum external efficiency for the signal and pumping ratio for $T = T_{opt}$ as a function of $\Phi_0$, for a doubly resonant oscillator.

## 2. Doubly Resonant Oscillator Without Power-Dependent Reflections

For the DRO configuration analyzed, the maximum conversion efficiency is 50%. This upper limit on the efficiency results from the rapid increase in the power-dependent, backward-generated pump wave. Bjorkholm [83] has analyzed the case in which there is no pump wave generated in the backward direction to limit the efficiency. Such a configuration can be realized in practice by using a ring cavity in which the signal and idler travel in only one direction because of the unidirectionality of the gain. An oscillator of this type has been operated by Byer et al. [86]. For this case, the relations analogous to Eq. (56) are:

$$\frac{P_p^{tr}}{P_p^{inc}} = 1 - \frac{4}{\Phi} [\Phi^{\frac{1}{2}} - 1] \tag{65a}$$

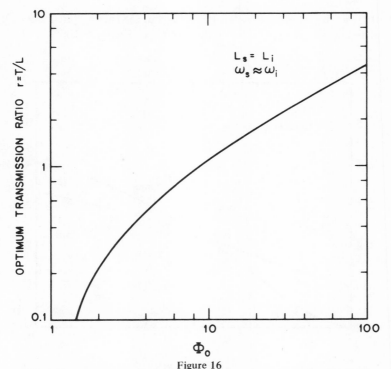

**Figure 16**

Optimum transmission ratio r, which optimizes the total power coupled out of the doubly resonant oscillator at the signal and idler for the case $\omega_s \approx \omega_i$, $L_s \approx L_i$ as a function of $\Phi_0$.

$$\frac{P_p^r}{P_p^{inc}} = 0 \tag{65b}$$

$$\frac{P_s}{P_p^{inc}} = \frac{\omega_s}{\omega_p} \frac{4}{\Phi} [\Phi^{1/2} - 1] \tag{65c}$$

$$\frac{P_i}{P_p^{inc}} = \frac{\omega_i}{\omega_p} \frac{4}{\Phi} [\Phi^{1/2} - 1] \tag{65d}$$

The transmitted pump power, Eq. (65a), and the internal efficiency are shown in Fig. 18 as a function of $\Phi$. It is seen that in this case the transmitted pump power goes to zero for $\Phi = 4$. The internal efficiency for this case is given by

$$\eta^{int} = \frac{P_s + P_i}{P_p^{inc}} = \frac{4}{\Phi} [\Phi^{1/2} - 1] \tag{66}$$

This efficiency is just twice the efficiency that Eq. (58) gives, which is shown in Fig. 13; and hence the upper limit to the internal efficiency is 100%.

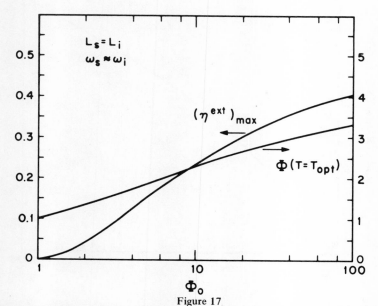

**Figure 17**

Maximum external efficiency and pumping ratio at optimum transmission as a function of $\Phi_0$ for a doubly resonant oscillator.

The external efficiencies are defined in a similar manner to Eqs. (60). Optimization of the output power or external efficiency is identical to that for the DRO with power-dependent reflections, hence the curves in Figs. 14 to 17 apply, except that the values for the efficiencies must be doubled.

### 3. Effects of Nonresonant Pump Reflections on the Doubly Resonant Oscillator

In the DRO considered in Section III,A,1 it was assumed that the mirrors of the oscillator cavity were transparent at the pump. If mirror $M_2$ is made to be reflecting at the pump as well as at the signal and idler, then the operation of the DRO is altered and can be improved [87]. In particular, if the phases of the reflection coefficients at mirror $M_2$ for the pump, signal, and idler are such that the reflected pump continues to amplify the signal and idler in the backward direction, then a reduction in threshold and an increase in efficiency result. Letting $R_p = r_p^2$ be the power reflectivity from $M_2$ for the pump, and $\varphi = \varphi_p - \varphi_s - \varphi_i$, where the $\varphi_j$'s are the phases of the respective reflection coefficients, the threshold pump power density becomes

$$S_p^{th}(r_p) = \frac{S_p^{th}(r_p = 0)}{1 + r_p^2 + 2r_p \cos(\varphi + \Delta k \ell)} \qquad (67)$$

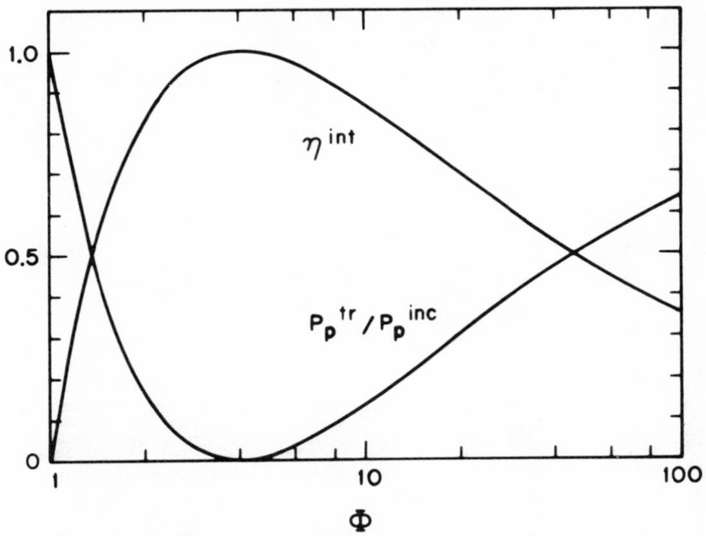

**Figure 18**
Transmitted pump and internal efficiency as a function of $\Phi$ for the doubly resonant oscillator without pump-power-dependent reflections.

where $S_p^{th}(r_p = 0)$ is given by Eq. (39). For Gaussian modes in the near-field approximation, Eq. (48) is modified by the same factor. For $(\varphi + \Delta k \ell) = 0$, the threshold can be reduced by a factor of four if $r_p = 1$. The total signal and idler powers generated are given by

$$\frac{P_s}{P_p^{inc}} = \frac{\omega_s}{\omega_p} \cdot \frac{2}{\Phi} [\Phi^{\frac{1}{2}} - 1] \frac{1 + r_p^2 + 2r_p \cos(\varphi + \Delta k \ell)}{1 + r_p \cos(\varphi + \Delta k \ell)} \tag{68a}$$

$$\frac{P_i}{P_p^{inc}} = \frac{\omega_i}{\omega_p} \frac{P_s}{P_p^{inc}} \tag{68b}$$

and the internal efficiency is given by

$$\eta^{int} = \frac{2}{\Phi} [\Phi^{\frac{1}{2}} - 1] \frac{1 + r_p^2 + 2r_p \cos(\varphi + \Delta k \ell)}{1 + r_p \cos(\varphi + \Delta k \ell)} \tag{69}$$

In the limit, $\varphi + \Delta k \ell = 0$ and $r_p = 1$, the expression for the internal efficiency is exactly the same as for the DRO without power-dependent reflections and has an upper limit of 100%. For any value of $r_p, \varphi$, and $\Delta k \ell$, optimization of the external efficiencies is the same as for the two cases presented in Section III,A,1 and III,A,2. Thus, nonresonant pump reflection can reduce the oscillator threshold by up to a factor of 4 and increase the internal efficiency to an upper limit of 100%. Some experimental evidence on the effects of pump reflections has been obtained [82, 88].

## B. Singly Resonant Oscillator (SRO)

### 1. Unidirectional Pump

The physical configuration of the SRO is the same as that shown in Fig. 11 except that mirrors $M_1$ and $M_2$ are reflecting at either the signal *or* the idler and are completely transparent at the other as well as at the pump. Since only the resonated wave propagates in the backward direction, there is no backward pump wave generated; hence $P_p^r = 0$. For arbitrary momentum mismatch and a single pass of the pump through the cavity, the other waves are given by [89].

$$\frac{P_p^{tr}}{P_p^{inc}} = \cos^2(\beta\ell) + \left(\frac{\Delta k}{2\beta}\right)^2 \sin^2(\beta\ell) \tag{70a}$$

$$\frac{P_s}{P_p^{inc}} = \frac{\omega_s}{\omega_p} \left[1 - \left(\frac{\Delta k}{2\beta}\right)^2\right] \sin^2(\beta\ell) \tag{70b}$$

$$\frac{P_i}{P_p^{inc}} = \frac{\omega_i}{\omega_p} \frac{P_s}{P_p^{inc}} \tag{70c}$$

where $\beta\ell$ is determined from the relation

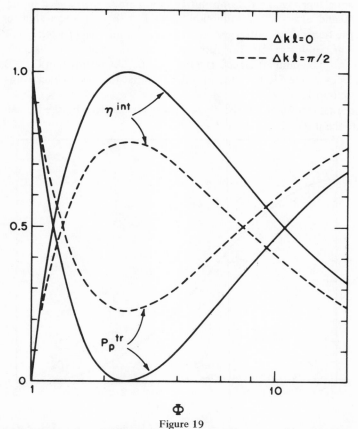

**Figure 19**

Transmitted pump power and internal efficiency for the singly resonant oscillator as a function of $\Phi$ for $\Delta k\ell = 0$, $\Delta k\ell = \pi/2$.

$$\frac{\sin^2(\beta\ell)}{(\beta\ell)^2} = \frac{P_p^{th}}{P_p^{inc}} \frac{\sin^2(\Delta k\ell/2)}{(\Delta k\ell/2)^2} \tag{71}$$

These relations are derived in a manner similar to the case of the DRO: It is assumed that the resonated wave is constant over the crystal length, and the coupled differential equations for the pump and nonresonant wave are solved. Employing energy conservation and the Manley-Rowe relations gives Eqs. (70) and (71). The internal efficiency is given by

$$\eta^{int} = \left[1 - \left(\frac{\Delta k}{2\beta}\right)^2\right] \sin^2(\beta\ell) \tag{72}$$

The internal efficiency and the transmitted pump power are plotted in Fig. 19 for $\Delta k\ell = 0$ and $\Delta k\ell = \pi/2$ as a function of $\Phi = P_p^{inc}/P_p^{th}$. It is seen that for $\Delta k\ell = 0$, the transmitted pump goes to zero and the internal efficiency is 100% when $\beta\ell = \pi/2$ or $\Phi = (\pi/2)^2$. For $\Delta k\ell = \pi/2$, the efficiency is less than 100%. A plot of the maximum efficiency as a function of $\Delta k\ell$ is shown in Fig. 20. The high efficiency of the SRO results from the fact that there is no backward-generated pump wave.

The external efficiency for the nonresonant wave is given by the frequency ratio times the internal efficiency

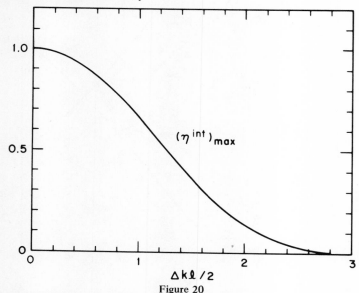

**Figure 20**

Maximum internal efficiency of the singly resonant oscillator as a function of the momentum mismatch $\Delta k\ell/2$.

$$\eta_{nonres}^{ext} = \frac{\omega_{nonres}}{\omega_p} \eta^{int} \tag{73}$$

and for the resonant wave by

$$\eta_{res}^{ext} = \frac{\omega_{res}}{\omega_p} \frac{T_r}{T_r + L_r} \eta^{int} \tag{74}$$

For the nonresonant wave, optimum external efficiency corresponds to the optimum internal efficiency and occurs for $\Phi = (\pi/2)^2$. On the other hand, the efficiency for the resonant wave depends upon the transmission of the mirrors. As before, if a parameter r is defined as the ratio of the mirror transmission $T_r$ to the total round-trip losses at the resonant wave, $L_r$,

$$r = \frac{T_r}{L_r} \tag{75}$$

and a pumping ratio is defined

$$\Phi_0 = \frac{P_p^{inc}}{P_p^{th}(T_r = 0)} \tag{76}$$

The value of r that maximizes the output power for the resonant wave is shown as a function of $\Phi_0$ in Fig. 21. In Fig. 22, the external efficiency of the resonated wave and the optimum threshold ratio $\Phi(T_r = $ optimum$)$ are shown. The photon efficiency is seen to tend asymptotically toward 100%, whereas the pumping ratio tends toward $(\pi/2)^2$.

## 2. Effects of Pump Reflections on the SRO

In the SRO considered in the last section, it was assumed that both mirrors were completely transmitting at the pump. If mirror $M_2$ is made reflecting at the pump, then the backward-traveling pump wave will be effective in pumping the oscillator. In contrast to the case of the DRO, the phase of the pump reflection coefficient is unimportant since only two of the three waves are reflected. If the power reflection coefficient of mirror $M_2$ is given by $r_p^2 = R_p$, the threshold for the SRO becomes

$$P_p^{th}(r_p^2) = \frac{P_p^{th}(r_p = 0)}{1 + r_p^2} \tag{77}$$

with a maximum reduction of a factor of two. When $r_p^2 \neq 0$, two internal efficiencies can be defined: the first relates to the efficiency of the forward-traveling, nonresonant wave; the second relates to the internal efficiency of the resonated wave. In the limit $r_p^2 = 1$ and $\Delta k = 0$, these two efficiencies are given by

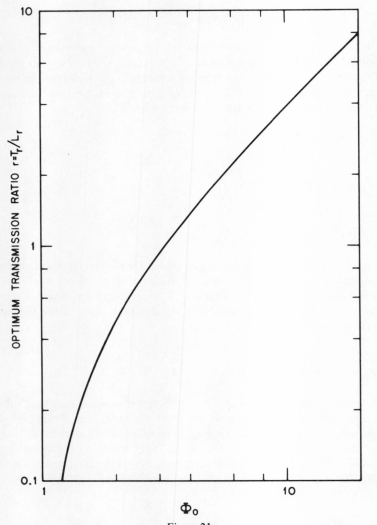

**Figure 21**
Optimum transmission ratio $r = T_r/L_r$, which maximizes the power coupled out for the resonant wave of the singly resonant oscillator ($\Delta k = 0$) as a function of $\Phi_0$.

$$\eta^{int}_{nores\text{-}forward} = \frac{\omega_{nr}}{\omega_p} \left[1 - \cos^2(\beta\ell)\right] \tag{78a}$$

$$\eta^{int}_{res} = \frac{\omega_r}{\omega_p} \left[1 - \cos^4(\beta\ell)\right] \tag{78b}$$

where $\beta\ell$ is determined from the relation

$$\frac{P^{th}_p(r^2_p = 1)}{P^{inc}_p} = \frac{1 + \cos^2(\beta\ell)}{2} \frac{\sin^2(\beta\ell)}{(\beta\ell)^2} \tag{79}$$

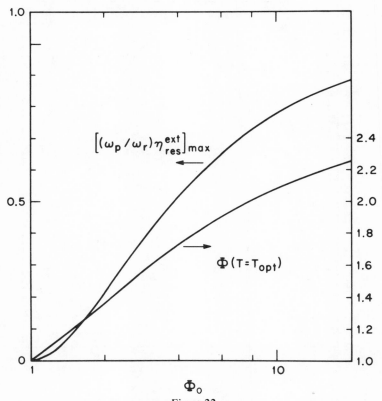

**Figure 22**
Maximum external efficiency for the resonant wave of the singly resonant oscillator and corresponding pumping ratio at optimum transmission as a function of $\Phi_0$.

The two efficiencies are plotted in Fig. 23 as a function of $P_p^{inc}/P_p^{th}$. The efficiency of the resonant wave is seen to be much broader than for the case where $r_p = 0$.

More complicated configurations involving reflections at the nonresonant wave at either $M_1$ or $M_2$ can further reduce the threshold and modify the performance [87].

### C.  Internal Parametric Oscillator

Another type of optical parametric oscillator configuration incorporates the oscillator within the cavity of the pump source. Such a configuration makes use

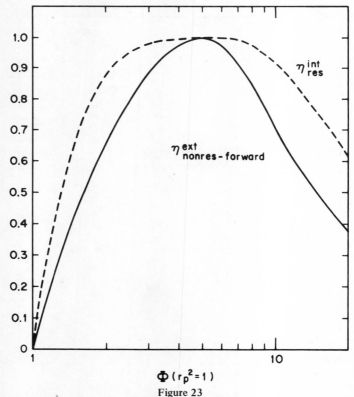

**Figure 23**

Internal efficiency of the resonant wave and external efficiency of the nonresonant forward traveling wave for the singly resonant oscillator when mirror $M_2$ has a pump reflection coefficient $r_p^2 = 1$.

of the high pump power levels present within the pump cavity. The analysis of this oscillator, first performed by Oshman and Harris [90], shows that there are at least three modes of operation. Above threshold, the first mode is characterized by limiting of the pump power density within the cavity at the level producing parametric oscillation. In this mode of operation, the internal efficiency can be 100%.

In the second mode of operation, the phase angle between the pump, and signal and idler fields shifts from the optimum value, resulting in decreased parametric coupling. This mode is characterized by a saturation of the laser gain at a value equal to the sum of the signal, idler, and pump cavity losses. Both the first and second modes are steady-state solutions.

The third mode of operation is non-steady-state, with the signal and idler emitted as a periodic train of pulses. The origin of this instability is the third-order nonlinearity associated with the gain of the pump source. Which of the three modes of operation occurs is determined by the losses of the laser and oscillator cavities, by the laser gain and the amount of nonlinear coupling, and by the initial conditions [81, 90].

The analysis of the internal optical parametric oscillator has been extended by Falk et al. [91] to include the rate equations for the pump laser. In particular, they analyze the case of Q-switched operation of the pump, finding multiple pulsing solutions analogous to those above for the case of non-Q-switched operations. Their experimental results verify their analysis in most respects.

Primary reasons for incorporating the optical parametric oscillator within the cavity of the pumping laser are the higher pump powers available and the possibility of achieving efficient operation. A discussion of experimental results is given in Section VII.

## IV. Tuning, Linewidth, and Frequency Control

### A. Tuning

As shown in Section II, parametric gain occurs for frequencies $\omega_s$ and $\omega_i$, where $\omega_s + \omega_i = \omega_p$. The gain is greatest for $\Delta k = k_p - k_s - k_i = 0$, and falls off as the magnitude of $\Delta k$ increases. A parametric oscillator will then tend to oscillate for those signal and idler frequencies for which $\Delta k = 0$. These frequencies are here referrred to as $\omega_{so}$ and $\omega_{io}$. By changing the pump frequency, the indices of refraction of the crystal, or the angle between the three waves for a non-collinear interaction, the frequencies $\omega_{so}$ and $\omega_{io}$ that satisfy the conservation equations can be varied. The indices of refraction of the crystal can be varied by changing the crystal temperature (temperature tuning), varying the direction of propagation with respect to the crystal axes (angle tuning), applying an external electric field, or stressing the crystal, or some combination of these techniques. The most common methods of tuning oscillators use temperature or angle tuning.

With any of these techniques, there will exist a relation between the signal frequency and the parameter(s) being varied. This relation defines the tuning curve for the oscillator. The tuning curve is conveniently characterized by a degeneracy parameter $\delta$, defined by

$$\delta = \frac{\omega_{so} - \omega_0}{\omega_0} = \frac{\omega_0 - \omega_{io}}{\omega_0} \tag{80}$$

where $\omega_0 = \omega_p/2$ is the degenerate frequency. The tuning curve is then a relation of the form

$$f(\delta, \zeta_1, \zeta_2, \ldots) = 0 \tag{81}$$

where $\zeta_1, \zeta_2, \ldots$ are independent variables such as temperature, and $f$ is some function of the dependent and independent variables. The tuning curve can be measured experimentally (see Section V) or it can be calculated provided that the explicit dependence of the indices of refraction on frequency and the independent variable(s) is known.

Consider the tuning characteristics of a collinear interaction with the pump frequency fixed, as a function of a single independent variable $\zeta$, which might be temperature, for example. Letting $\delta = 0$ at $\zeta = \zeta_0$ and expanding in a Taylor's series about this point gives

$$A'\delta^2 + B'\delta - C' = 0 \tag{82}$$

where

$$A' = \left[ \omega_0 \frac{\partial}{\partial \omega} + \frac{1}{2}\omega_0^2 \frac{\partial^2}{\partial \omega^2} + \omega_0(\zeta - \zeta_0) \frac{\partial^2}{\partial \zeta \partial \omega} \right] (n_s + n_i) \Bigg|_{\substack{\delta = 0 \\ \zeta = \zeta_0}} \tag{83a}$$

$$B' = \left[ 1 + \omega_0 \frac{\partial}{\partial \omega} + (\zeta - \zeta_0) \frac{\partial}{\partial \zeta} + \frac{1}{2!}(\zeta - \zeta_0)^2 \frac{\partial^2}{\partial \zeta^2} \right.$$
$$\left. + \omega_0(\zeta - \zeta_0) \frac{\partial^2}{\partial \zeta \partial \omega} \right] (n_s - n_i) \Bigg|_{\substack{\delta = 0 \\ \zeta = \zeta_0}} \tag{83b}$$

$$C' = \left[ (\zeta - \zeta_0) \frac{\partial}{\partial \zeta} + \frac{1}{2!} (\zeta - \zeta_0)^2 \frac{\partial^2}{\partial \zeta^2} \right] (2n_p - n_s - n_i) \Bigg|_{\substack{\delta = 0 \\ \zeta = \zeta_0}} \tag{83c}$$

where derivatives higher than the second, and powers of $\delta$ greater than 2 have not been included. For an interaction in which the signal and idler are the same type of wave, i.e., Type I phase matching, and hence indistinguishable at $\delta = 0$, $B' \equiv 0$ and the tuning curve has the form

$$\delta^2 = \frac{C'(\zeta)}{A'(\zeta)} \quad \text{(Type I)} \tag{84}$$

For Type II phase matching, where the signal and idler are distinguishable at $\delta = 0$, the tuning curve near $\delta = 0$ is approximately given by

$$\delta \approx \frac{C'(\zeta)}{B'(\zeta)}, \quad 0 \leqslant \delta \ll 1 \quad \text{(Type II)} \tag{85}$$

As seen from the above relations, it is generally true that the Type I interaction, Eq. (84), has a much more rapid rate of tuning near degeneracy than the Type II interaction, Eq. (85). In fact, for the Type I interaction, the rate of tuning, $d\delta/d\zeta$, becomes extremely large as $\delta \to 0$. Although providing for rapid tuning, the Type I interaction presents two important problems for operation near degeneracy. First of all, to operate at a particular frequency near degeneracy the independent parameter $\zeta$ must be adjusted very precisely. Secondly, operation near degeneracy results in a potentially large oscillation linewidth (as discussed below).

At any given operating point, the rate of change of the signal frequency with respect to the indepdent variable $\zeta$ for fixed $\omega_p$ is given by

$$\frac{d\omega_{so}}{d\zeta} = \frac{\partial(k_p - k_s - k_i)/\partial \zeta}{\partial(k_s - k_i)/\partial \omega} \tag{86}$$

where the partial derivatives are evaluated at the operating point. The quantity in the denominator is sometimes referred to as the dispersive constant b [92].

$$b = \frac{\partial}{\partial \omega} (k_s - k_i) \tag{87}$$

If the pump frequency is varied and all other independent variables held constant, then the rate of change of $\omega_{so}$ is given by

$$\frac{d\omega_{so}}{d\omega_p} = \frac{\partial(k_p - k_i)/\partial\omega}{\partial(k_s - k_i)/\partial\omega} = \frac{\partial(k_p - k_i)/\partial\omega}{b} \tag{88}$$

where the partial derivatives are evaluated at the respective frequencies. Kovrigin and Byer [93] have shown that this ratio can be positive or negative and of very great magnitude. Examples of tuning curves taken from oscillator experiments are shown in Figs. 24 – 26. Figure 24 shows the tuning curve of a DRO pumped at $\lambda_p \cong 5,290$ Å and tuned by varying the temperature. The rapid rate of tuning

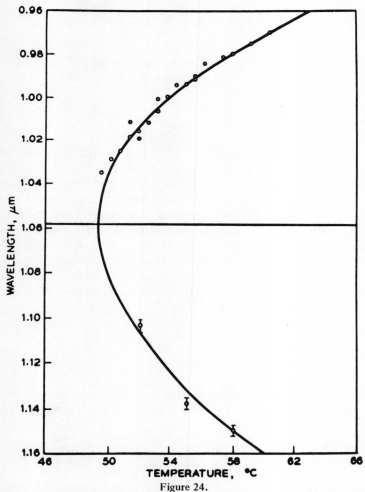

Figure 24.
Tuning curve for a doubly resonant oscillator using Type I phase matching as a function of temperature [14].

with temperature near degeneracy ($\lambda_s = \lambda_i = 10{,}580$ Å) is characteristic of Type I phase matching. Figure 25 shows a similar tuning curve taken for collinear Type I phase matching as a function of the angle the three waves make with respect to the crystal c axis. Again the rapid tuning with angle near degeneracy is seen. In Fig. 26, the tuning curve for a Type II interaction is shown. It is seen that the slope of the tuning curve varies only slightly in passing through the degenerate point.

### B. Operating Point

The wavelength of peak gain follows the tuning curve, Eq. (81). The operating point of the optical parametric oscillator, defined as the frequency at which oscillation actually takes place, may or may not coincide with the tuning curve. Since the behavior of the SRO and DRO are different in this respect, they will be discussed separately. First, however, the dependence of the threshold on the deviation of the operating point from $\omega_{so}$ is considered.

As shown in Section II, the gain is maximum and threshold minimum when $\Delta k = 0$, corresponding to the frequencies $\omega_{so}$, $\omega_{io}$ above. The inverse of the threshold power varies with $\Delta k$ as

$$\left(P_p^{th}\right)^{-1} \alpha \frac{\sin^2(\Delta k \ell/2)}{(\Delta k \ell/2)^2} \tag{89}$$

where $\ell$ is the crystal length. The momentum mismatch can be expressed in terms of the deviation of the signal frequency from $\omega_{so}$

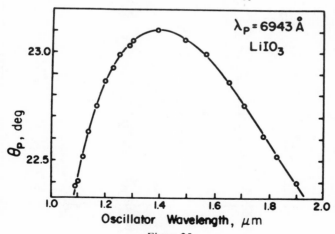

Figure 25
Tuning curve for a doubly resonant oscillator using Type I phase matching as a function of angle [185].

$$\Delta k = -b(\omega_s - \omega_{so}) - d(\omega_s - \omega_{so})^2 \tag{90}$$

where b is given by Eq. (87) and

$$d = \frac{1}{2} \frac{\partial^2}{\partial \omega^2}(k_s + k_i) \tag{91}$$

The parametric gain is appreciable roughly over the range $|\Delta k\ell| < \pi$; the frequency range for which this relation is satisfied is termed the bandwidth. When b $\gg$ d, the bandwidth is given by

$$\Delta \omega = \frac{2\pi}{b\ell} \tag{92}$$

This bandwidth is also the intrinsic linewidth of spontaneous parametric noise emission [92]. In terms of the bandwidth, Eq. (89) becomes

$$\left(P_p^{th}\right)^{-1} \alpha \ \frac{\sin^2\left[(\pi/\Delta\omega)(\omega_s - \omega_{so})\right]}{\left[(\pi/\Delta\omega)(\omega_s - \omega_{so})\right]^2} \tag{93}$$

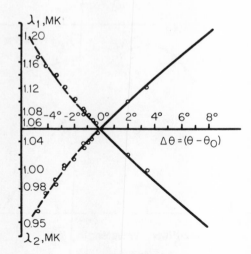

Figure 26

Tuning curve for a doubly resonant oscillator using Type II phase matching as a function of angle [245].

## 1. Operating Point of the SRO

For convenience, take the signal to be the resonant wave and the idler as non-resonant (i.e., perfectly transmitting mirrors) and assume that the pump is abruptly turned on at t = 0. All signal modes (and their corresponding idlers) that are above threshold will see net gain and grow in time. During the buildup time, the spectrum of the SRO will be broad. When the parametrically generated waves approach their steady-state values, they begin to deplete the pump, reducing the gain. Ultimately, only that mode or modes seeing the greatest gain, or alternatively having the lowest threshold, will oscillate. If it is assumed that all modes see the same loss and start from noise, only the mode nearest to $\omega_{so}$ will oscillate. Thus, ideally the SRO will, in the steady state, oscillate on that cavity mode nearest to $\omega_{so}$. The operating point is thus within ± one-half cavity mode spacing (c/2L spacing) of the frequency $\omega_{so}$ determined by the tuning curve. For most cavity configurations, this implies a deviation of at most a fraction of a wavenumber. As will be seen later, this is not so for the DRO.

In a detailed steady-state analysis of the SRO, Kreuzer [89] has shown that single-mode operation will occur for pumping levels below 4.61 times threshold. Above that value and below 11 times threshold, it is predicted, the SRO will oscillate on two modes and above 11 times threshold more than two modes can oscillate. Since maximum efficiency of the SRO occurs for pumping at $(\pi/2)^2$, or 2.46 times threshold, it is in principle possible to achieve high-efficiency, single-mode operation of the SRO.

For many applications of the parametric oscillator, such as high-resolution spectroscopy, a high degree of frequency control is needed. Small deviations in pump frequency or drifts in temperature, for example, can cause $\omega_{so}$, and hence the operating point, to wander. Several techniques for overcoming these limitations have been devised.

*a. Radiation Injection.* A technique applicable to *pulsed* SRO's is to inject into the cavity a cw wave at the signal frequency desired. The length of the oscillator cavity is adjusted so that it is resonant at the injected frequency. When the pump is applied, all signal modes for which there is net gain will grow from their initial values. For all but the desired mode, the buildup begins from spontaneous emission or quantum fluctuations, whereas the desired mode starts from the level of the injected radiation within the cavity. When the desired frequency is near $\omega_{so}$ and the injected power level is sufficiently high, it will be the first to build up to a high power level and will deplete the pump. If, however, this frequency is not the one for which maximum gain is obtained, modes with higher gain will continue to grow. In the steady state, the mode closest to $\omega_{so}$ will oscillate for all but extremely high values of the injected signal. Thus, radiation injection provides a means for controlling the frequency of a parametric oscillator in a transient state such as is obtained in a pulsed system. The level of the injected signal required to make the power at the desired frequency greater than at any other frequency is a function of the frequency deviation from $\omega_{so}$ and the required output power ratio. Since injection requires more than a single photon per mode, a laser source or a black body at an extremely high temperature is required to provide the injected signal. The details of the theory and experimental results on radiation injection are given by Bjorkholm and Danielmeyer [94].

*b. Control by Resonant Absorption.* Harris has proposed a technique for forcing an SRO to oscillate at a frequency characteristic of some strong absorption line [95]. The technique involves using two nonlinear crystals along with a resonant absorber within the cavity of an SRO, as shown in Fig. 27. The cavity is resonant at the signal, and the frequency of the absorber corresponds to the nonresonant idler. The two nonlinear crystals have their axes reversed in such a way that the parametric interaction in one tends to cancel the other, resulting in zero or a small net parametric gain. When the absorber is inserted within the cavity, it attenuates the idler and introduces phase shift in such a way that the gain cancellation of the two crystals is eliminated, permitting oscillation at the frequency of the resonant absorber. To date, this technique has not been experimentally verified.

*c. Intracavity Etalon.* As mentioned earlier, a pulsed SRO in the transient state tends to emit a broad-band output. Kreuzer [96] has shown that the use of a tilted etalon within the cavity that produces a frequency-sensitive loss can result in a single-frequency output at the longitudinal mode closest to the minimum loss point of the etalon. In Fig. 28a, the spectrum of an SRO without an etalon is seen to be extremely broad, representative of an oscillator in the transient state. In Fig. 28b, with a tilted plate etalon in the cavity, the spectrum of the oscillator output is narrowed considerably, and consists of a single

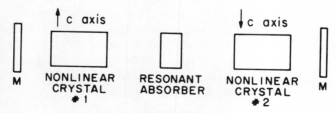

**Figure 27**
Schematic diagram of a technique for slaving the frequency of a singly resonant oscillator to an atomic absorption line [95].

longitudinal mode. Kreuzer found that by rotating the etalon the oscillating frequency could be varied with respect to $\omega_{so}$.

With either resonant absorption or an intracavity etalon, the oscillation will take place on the cavity mode nearest the absorption frequency or the pass band of the etalon. This frequency can be fine-tuned by varying the cavity length, thereby moving the cavity frequency in exact coincidence with the value desired.

*d. Interferometric Stabilization.* Another technique for producing line narrowing using a three-mirror cavity arrangement has been demonstrated by Pinard and Young [97]. A schematic diagram of this cavity arrangement is shown in Fig. 29. Two cavities, formed between mirrors $M_1$ and $M_3$, and $M_2$ and $M_3$, are coupled by the beam splitter S. The coupling of these two cavities produces a modulation of the Q of the cavity modes, as the tilted plate etalon does. Pumping an oscillator of this type at $\lambda_p = 0.532$ $\mu$m, Pinard and Young have achieved linewidths as narrow as 0.001 cm$^{-1}$. A complete discussion of techniques for obtaining single-frequency operation of lasers can be found in Ref. [98].

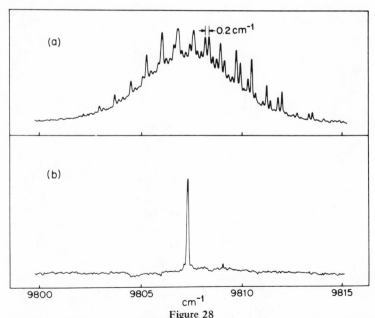

**Figure 28**

Spectral characteristics of a singly resonant oscillator (a) without and (b) with an intra-cavity etalon to provide mode selection [96].

## 2.  Operating Point of the DRO

Whereas the operating point of the SRO will in general lie within one-half cavity mode spacing of $\omega_{so}$ the same is not true of the DRO. This perhaps is the biggest problem associated with operating the DRO. The primary reason why determination of the actual operating point of the DRO is not as simple as for the SRO is that *both* the signal and idler must be resonant modes of the oscillator, whereas for the SRO only one must be. To see why this condition is so restrictive, assume that the pump frequency is fixed with a value $\omega_p$, and consider the resonant modes of the DRO cavity. The absolute frequencies of these modes are determined by the condition that on a round trip through the cavity the phase shift is some multiple of $2\pi$, i.e.,

$$\oint_{\substack{\text{round} \\ \text{trip}}} [k_z(\omega_m) + \varphi_m]\, dz = 2\pi m \tag{94}$$

where $k_z(\omega_m)$ is the value of the longitudinal k vector at the frequency $\omega_m$, the mth eigenfrequency, and $\varphi_m$ is the sum of the phase shifts due to reflection at the two mirrors (usually assumed equal to 0). The integral implicitly takes into account that the wave may propagate through many different media in passing through the cavity (e.g., the nonlinear crystal, air, or lenses). The eigenfrequencies of the cavity $\omega_m$ are then solutions to Eq. (94) and are sensitive in particular to the lengths of the various components making up the cavity. The intermode spacing between adjacent longitudinal modes is given by

$$\Delta\omega = \frac{\pi}{\sum_j \ell_j\, \partial k_j/\partial\omega} = \frac{\pi c}{\sum_j \ell_j\, (n_j + \omega\, \partial n_j/\partial\omega)} \tag{95}$$

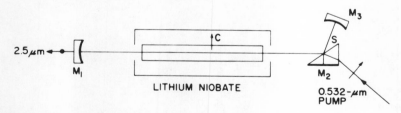

$M_1$ = 16-cm RADIUS
$M_2$ = FLAT
$M_3$ = 25-cm RADIUS

**Figure 29**
Schematic diagram of an SRO using a three-mirror cavity to provide mode selection [97].

where the summation is explicitly taken over all different elements of length $\ell_j$ in the cavity.

In the vicinity of both $\omega_{so}$ and $\omega_{io}$, there will be a number of cavity modes spaced by an amount given by Eq. (95). Note that the spacing of the modes near $\omega_{so}$ will not in general be equal to the spacing near $\omega_{io}$ because of dispersion in the indices of refraction. For the resonance conditions for the DRO to be satisfied, it is necessary that there be some cavity resonance near $\omega_{so}$, denoted $\omega_{sn}$, and another near $\omega_{io}$, denoted $\omega_{im}$, for which $\omega_{sn} + \omega_{im} = \omega_p$. Since the set of eigenfrequencies $\omega_n$ for the cavity as a whole is finite, it is not a priori clear that any pair will add up to $\omega_p$, the pump frequency, and more restrictively, that there exists a pair, one near $\omega_{so}$ and one near $\omega_{io}$, that do so. Thus determining the operating point of the DRO reduces to finding some pair of signal and idler modes whose eigenfrequencies add up to the given pump frequency, which in turn is some eigenfrequency of a separate cavity.

The problem can be seen more clearly by considering Fig. 30. In Fig. 30a, the resonant modes of the oscillator cavity are schematically indicated by vertical lines, with the degenerate frequency $\omega_0 = \omega_p/2$ shown dotted. For the modes displayed in this fashion, the frequency condition reduces to finding modes that are symmetrically displaced with respect to $\omega_0$. If the frequency,

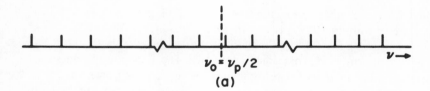

(a)

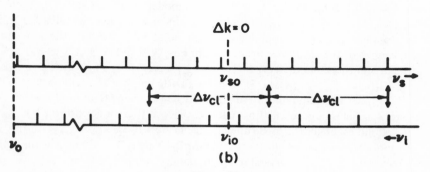

(b)

**Figure 30**
Schematic representation of resonant modes of a doubly resonant oscillator.

axis to the left of $\omega_0$ in Fig. (30a) is reflected through $\omega_0$ such that increasing idler frequencies run to the left ($v_i < v_s$ by assumption), then the condition $\omega_{sn} + \omega_{im} = \omega_p$ corresponds to signal and idler modes vertically disposed toward each other. In Fig. 30b, the frequencies $v_{so} = \omega_{so}/2\pi$ and $v_{io}$ are shown by the dotted line, indicating the condition $\Delta k = 0$. In this figure, three vertical coincidences of the signal and idler modes are shown by the arrows, each separated in frequency from the next by an amount $\Delta v_{cl}$, which is referred to as the *cluster spacing* [14, 99]. In terms of the mode separations $\Delta \omega_s$ and $\Delta \omega_i$, the cluster spacing is determined by the condition that $(M+1) \Delta \omega_s \cong M \Delta \omega_i$ for some integer M, and in terms of the cavity parameters is given by

$$\Delta \omega_{cl} = \frac{\pi}{\sum_j \ell_j \, \partial [k_j(\omega_s) - k_j(\omega_i)]/\partial \omega} \tag{96}$$

where the summation is again over all elements of the cavity. When the dominant dispersive element is the nonlinear crystal, which is usually the case, Eq. (96) reduces to

$$\Delta \omega_{cl} \approx \frac{\pi}{\ell \, \partial (k_s - k_i)/\partial \omega} = \frac{\pi}{b\ell} \tag{97}$$

where $\ell$ is the length of the nonlinear crystal and b is given by Eq. (87). In a comparison with Eq. (92), it is seen that $\Delta \omega_{cl} = \Delta \omega/2$.

In considering Fig. 30, it is first necessary to ask whether it is valid to assume that there are any mode coincidences as shown. The answer to this question depends on the number of signal or idler modes within one cluster spacing and the actual linewidth of a given resonant mode. When the number of modes in a cluster spacing, $M = \Delta \omega_{cl}/\Delta \omega_i$, is small compared with the finesse of the signal and idler resonances, then it is unlikely that a coincidence will occur near $\omega_{so}$. On the other hand, when M is much greater than the finesse, a coincidence, at least to within the linewidths of the individual modes, will likely occur. In the latter case, it is clear that the operating point will be somewhere within $\pm \Delta \omega_{cl}/2$ of $\omega_{so}$. Within this range, the actual operating point will depend on the absolute locations of the cavity resonances. From Eqs. (93) and (97), it is seen that the maximum threshold increase for $|\omega_s - \omega_{so}| = \Delta \omega_{cl}/2$ is a factor $[\sin^2(\pi/4)/(\pi/4)^2]^{-1} = \pi^2/8 = 1.23$. Thus for a DRO pumped at a level greater than 1.23 times the minimum threshold, and when the density of modes within a cluster spacing is large, oscillation will take place at that mode with the lowest threshold, generally the mode coincidence nearest to $\omega_{so}$.

A plot of the calculated cluster spacing for $Ba_2NaNb_5O_{15}$ is shown as the solid curve in Fig. 31 for a crystal of length 0.4 cm pumped at $\lambda_p = 5,145$ Å. Type I phase matching is assumed. Near degeneracy, the cluster spacing is seen to be large, decreasing to a few $cm^{-1}$ far from degeneracy. Thus the uncertainty in the actual operating frequency can be large. Note that the cluster spacing varies directly as the rate of tuning, Eqs. (86), (87), and (97).

Consider next how the DRO might tune as some independent variable such as temperature is varied. Assume for the moment that the indices of refraction at the signal and idler are temperature-independent but the index at the pump varies in some prescribed manner. Referring to Fig. 30 again, assume that the point $\Delta k = 0$ moves in some specified manner as the temperature is changed. Since it is assumed that the signal and idler indices are not to depend on temperature, the mode structure remains fixed. In this case the operating point will occur at whichever mode coincidence is closest to $(\omega_{so}, \omega_{io})$ and will jump a full $\Delta\omega_{cl}$ when it does change, resulting in discontinuous tuning. In the more realistic case where the signal and idler indices depend on temperature, the mode

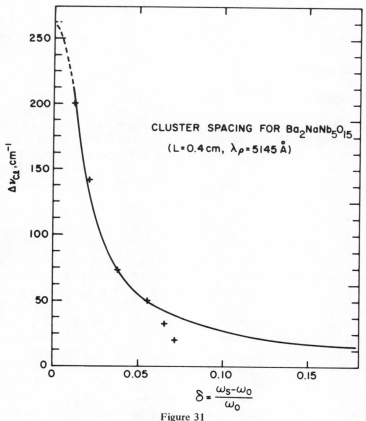

**Figure 31**

Calculated cluster spacing as a function of the degeneracy parameter for a 0.4-cm crystal of $Ba_2NaNb_5O_{15}$ pumped at 5145 Å.

coincidences will also change with temperature. This will result in an even more complicated variation in the operating point. In Fig. 24, the erratic tuning, especially near degeneracy, is clearly seen.

Since the operating point of the DRO is primarily determined by the condition $\omega_{sn} + \omega_{im} = \omega_p$, it is sensitive to any change in the pump frequency and also to any parameter that changes the location of the signal and idler resonant frequencies, such as cavity length. The change in pump frequency that will result in a shift in the operating point by one intermode spacing to the adjacent signal and idler modes is given by

$$\left| \delta\omega_p \right| = \Delta\omega_i - \Delta\omega_s = \frac{\Delta\omega_s \Delta\omega_i}{\Delta\omega_{cl}} \tag{98}$$

or

$$\frac{\left| \delta\omega_p \right|}{\Delta\omega_s} = \frac{\Delta\omega_i}{\Delta\omega_{cl}} \tag{99}$$

where $\Delta\omega_s$ and $\Delta\omega_i$ are the signal and idler intermode spacings. Thus when the cluster spacing is large, it takes only a very small pump frequency change to produce a shift in the operating point. Similarly, if the length of the air space in the cavity is varied, the absolute mode frequencies will change. The amount of length change required to shift the operating point one mode is given by

$$\left| \delta\ell \right| = \frac{\lambda_s}{2} \frac{\Delta\omega_s}{\Delta\omega_{cl}} \left[ \frac{\omega_i}{\omega_s} + \frac{\Delta\omega_s}{\Delta\omega_i} \right]^{-1} \tag{100}$$

Again, for $\Delta\omega_{cl} \gg \Delta\omega_s$, it is seen to take only a small fraction of a wavelength change in the cavity length to produce such a frequency shift. In fact, near degeneracy, a cavity length change of $\lambda_s/4$ or a pump frequency change of $\Delta\omega_i$ will result in a shift of the operating point by one cluster spacing, Eq. (97).

Thus under normal operating conditions, slight cavity-length variations and pump-frequency fluctuations will result in a signal-frequency wander with a total excursion of $\Delta\omega_{cl}$ and with an *average* frequency, or center of gravity, of $\omega_{so}$. Conversely, if a narrow linewidth is to be obtained for the output of the DRO the pump frequency must be stabilized to better than the value given by Eq. (98) and cavity-length variations held to tolerances better than given by Eq. (100). In addition to producing a broad spectral output, pump-frequency shifts and cavity-length changes also produce amplitude instabilities in the oscillator output resulting from mode hopping.

The dependence of both the linewidth and amplitude stability on pump frequency stability are shown in Figs. 32 and 33 for a cw DRO pumped at $\lambda_p$ = 5,145 Å, using a 4-mm crystal of $Ba_2NaNb_5O_{15}$ [74]. The experimental conditions are as follows:

    a. Frequency-stabilized, single-frequency pump with isolation between pump and oscillator.
    b. Unstabilized, single-frequency pump with isolation.
    c. Unstabilized, single-frequency pump without isolation.
    d. Multifrequency pump, without isolation.

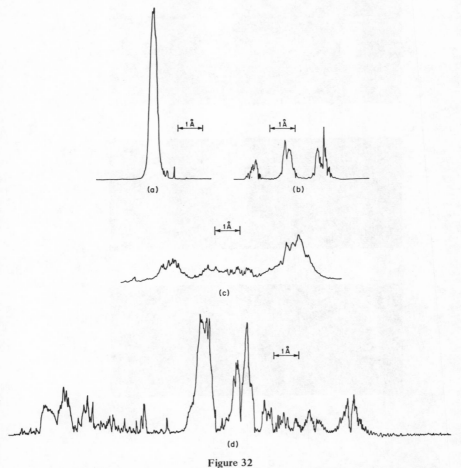

**Figure 32**
Spectral characteristics of the doubly resonant oscillator for different degrees of pump-frequency stability.

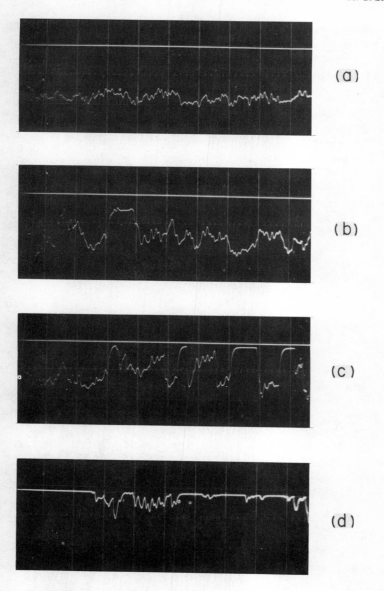

(a)

(b)

(c)

(d)

5 msec / div

**Figure 33**
Envelope of the output of a doubly resonant oscillator for different degrees of pump-frequency stability.

In Figure 32d the oscillator linewidth with the multifrequency pump is broad, a large fraction of the cluster spacing; in contrast, the linewidth is considerably less than 1 Å for a frequency-stabilized pump (a). Measurements with a scanning Fabry-Perot interferometer confirm that the emission shown in Fig. 32a is primarily in a single longitudinal mode of the oscillator cavity. The envelope of the oscillator output, Fig. 33, also shows considerable improvement for a stabilized pump. Much of the amplitude noise remaining in Fig. 33a was traced to mechanical resonances in the oscillator cavity that were excited by airborne acoustic disturbances. Weller et al. [100], using a streak camera to observe the evolution in time, have observed mode hopping in a cw DRO.

The dependence of the oscillator frequency on overall cavity length has been studied using the same cw DRO. For these experiments, the length of the cavity was varied by applying a voltage to a piezoelectric ceramic that held one of the mirrors of the oscillator. In the upper traces of Figs. 34a-c, the total oscillator output is displayed, while the lower traces show the output *after passing* through a spectrometer set at the wavelengths (a) 9,930 Å, (b) 9,950 Å, and (c) 9,980 Å. The operating wavelength is seen to be a rapid function of the cavity length (as discussed above). The cavity length modulation required to tune the full range shown was found to be 2,500 Å, or $\lambda_s/4$, as predicted by Eq. (100). The full bandwidth of operation taken for each crystal temperature is plotted by a cross in Fig. 31. The observed oscillation bandwidth is seen to be given by the cluster spacing within experimental error. One feature of these experiments not fully understood is the failure of the oscillator to oscillate for certain cavity spacings. This is presumably due to etalon effects resulting from reflections within the oscillator cavity and may explain the often erratic behavior of doubly resonant oscillators.

Finally, consider the possibility of obtaining oscillation at some specified and well-defined frequency $\omega_s'$. This condition can be obtained if first the phase matching conditions are such that $\omega_{so}$ is within $\Delta\omega_{cl}/2$ of $\omega_s'$. Next, the cavity length can be varied to obtain a mode coincidence at the signal mode nearest to $\omega_s'$. Finally, a third parameter such as the pump frequency can then be adjusted along with the cavity length to obtain oscillation exactly at the frequency $\omega_s'$ [63].

Instabilities in the doubly resonant oscillator have recently been investigated in some detail by Falk [101], who analyzes an oscillator with very general values for the mirror reflectivities. For high reflectivities at both the signal and idler (DRO), his analysis predicts the same results as discussed above. Particularly interesting is his discussion of the effects of small reflections at the nonresonant wave in an SRO, in which he concludes that power reflectivity coefficients as small as 1% for the nonresonant wave can cause significant mode hopping similar to those discussed above. Details may be found in Ref. [101].

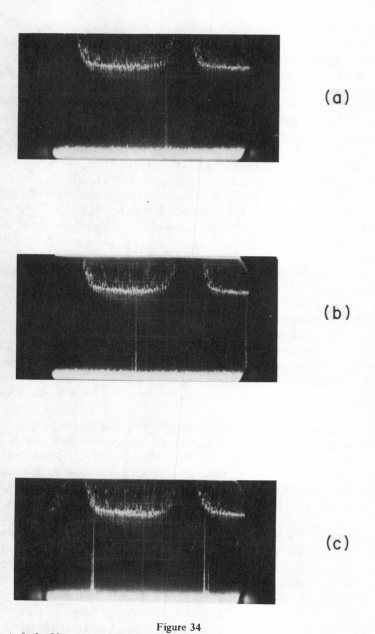

**Figure 34**
Output of a doubly resonant oscillator as the cavity length is varied. The upper trace displays
the total oscillator ouput; the lower trace gives the output after passing through a spectrometer set at (a) 9,930 Å, (b) 9,950 Å, and (c) 9,980 Å.

## V.  Spontaneous Parametric Emission

### *A.  General*

Above threshold, the emission from an optical parametric oscillator is stimulated by the presence of the signal and idler fields. Below threshold, and even
without a resonator to provide feedback, there is spontaneously emitted radiation at the signal and idler. This radiation is variously referred to as spontaneous
parametric emission, optical parametric noise, or parametric fluorescence. Viewed
quantum-mechanically, this effect results from the spontaneous annihilation of
a pump photon and the creation of a signal and an idler photon. The details of
the theory of this effect, and also of much experimental work, are found in the
references cited at the end of this section. The study of this effect is interesting
in itself but it also gives information useful in characterizing the behavior of
optical parametric oscillators. For example, spontaneous parametric emission is proportional to the parametric gain, and hence displays the
$\sin^2 (\Delta k \ell/2)/(\Delta k \ell/2)^2$ dependence. The peak of the spontaneous parametric
emission occurs when $\Delta k = 0$, and the locus of the wavelength of peak emission
versus some independent tuning parameter such as temperature allows the experimental determination of the tuning curve. Furthermore, measurement of
the linewidth of the parametric emission permits the measurement of the dispersion parameter b, which is important in determining the incremental tuning,
Eq. (86), as well as the cluster spacing, Eq. (97).

Also, since spontaneous parametric emission has a magnitude that depends
on the nonlinear coefficient of the material, it provides an alternative to optical
second harmonic generation (SHG) as a method for measuring this coefficient.
The spontaneous parametric emission *technique* is particularly convenient since
the amount of the emission turns out to be linearly proportional to the pump
power and is independent of the degree of focusing of the pump beam, in contrast to optical SHG [92].

### *B.  Collinear and Noncollinear Phase Matching*

The strongest spontaneous parametric emission occurs for signal and idler
waves that are phase matched, i.e., for which

$$\underline{k}_s + \underline{k}_i = \underline{k}_p \tag{21}$$

where energy conservation $\omega_s + \omega_i = \omega_p$ is assumed. Whereas in stimulated
emission the directions of $\underline{k}_s$ or $\underline{k}_i$ or both are determined by the properties of

the resonant cavity, in spontaneous emission all pairs of signal and idler waves satisfying the conservation equations will in general be excited. In other words, noncollinear phase-matched waves as well as collinear interactions are possible. Consider the case of a Type I phase-matched interaction in a negative uniaxial crystal (i.e., extraordinary pump, ordinary signal, and idler). Figure 35 shows the momentum vectors for a general noncollinear interaction. The signal wave makes an angle $\theta_s$ with respect to the direction of the pump and the idler an angle $\theta_i$. Conservation of momentum requires

$$k_s \cos \theta_s + k_i \cos \theta_i = k_p$$

$$k_s \sin \theta_s = k_i \sin \theta_i \tag{101}$$

and for small angles the latter equation becomes $k_s \theta_s \approx k_i \theta_i$. If we let $\omega_s(0)$ and $\omega_i(0)$ be the signal and idler frequencies satisfying these equations for $\theta_s = 0$,

$$\omega_s(\theta_s) - \omega_s(0) = \frac{(k_s k_p / 2k_i)}{\partial(k_s - k_i)/\partial\omega} \theta_s^2$$

$$= \frac{g}{b} \theta_s^2 \tag{102}$$

where b is the dispersion parameter defined in Eq. (87), $g = k_s k_p / 2k_i$, and the angle $\theta_s$ is measured internal to the crystal. These equations determine the frequency for which exact momentum conservation is achieved. In general, the magnitude of the component of the momentum mismatch along the direction of the pump beam is given by

$$|\Delta k| = g\theta_s^2 - b\left[\omega_s - \omega_s(0)\right] \tag{103}$$

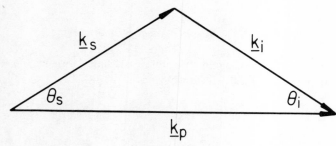

Figure 35
Signal, idler, and pump k vectors for a noncollinear interaction.

The parametric gain and hence the parametric noise is proportional to

$$\frac{\sin^2(\Delta k \ell/2)}{(\Delta k \ell/2)^2} \tag{104}$$

where $\ell$ is the length of the crystal. In a small solid angle located at an angle $\theta_s$ with respect to $\underline{k}_p$, the spectrum of the parametric noise emitted is proportional to

$$P^{spon} \propto \frac{\sin^2\{[\omega - \omega_s(\theta_s)]\,b\ell/2\}}{\{[\omega - \omega_s(\theta_s)]\,b\ell/2\}^2} \tag{105}$$

The dispersion parameter b can be determined in two ways. First, the locus of the peak emission frequency vs $\theta_s$ can be measured and b calculated from Eq. (103) since g can be quite accurately determined from approximate index data. The angular dependence of the emitted signal frequency for $LiNbO_3$ using the 4,800-Å line of the argon laser as the pump [102] is shown in Fig. 36. Alternatively, b can be determined by measuring the spectral width of the parametric emission into a small solid angle using Eq. (105). Care must be taken in measuring b in this way since the total observed spectral width is a function of the capture angle. Figure 37 shows the computed and measured spectral distribution for $LiNbO_3$ as a function of the acceptance angle [92].

An example of tuning curves measured as a function of temperature for KDP and ADP with $\lambda_p = 2573$ Å is shown in Fig. 38. It is seen that in the case of ADP the full visible range can be covered by varying the crystal temperature of 50°C [103].

### C. Magnitude of the Spontaneously Emitted Power

The magnitude of the spontaneous parametric noise emitted at the signal frequency $\omega_s$ into a solid angle $d\Omega_s$, measured within the crystal and in a frequency interval $d\nu_s$(Hz), is given by Kleinman [104]:

$$\frac{dP_s}{d\nu_s d\Omega_s} = \frac{32\pi P_p \hbar d^2 n_s \omega_s^4 \omega_i \ell^2}{n_p n_i c^5} \frac{\sin^2(\Delta k \ell/2)}{(\Delta k \ell/2)^2} \quad \text{(cgs)}$$

$$= \frac{Z_0 P_p \hbar d^2 n_s \omega_s^4 \omega_i \ell^2}{2\pi^2 n_p n_i c^4} \frac{\sin^2(\Delta k \ell/2)}{(\Delta k \ell/2)^2} \quad \text{(mks)} \tag{106}$$

where $\hbar$ = Planck's constant/$2\pi$, $P_p$ is the total pump power, $\ell$ is the crystal length, d is the effective nonlinear coefficient, and the n's are the indices of refraction at the respective frequencies.

The total power radiated into an acceptance angle $\theta_s$, $\Omega_s = \pi\theta_s^2$, integrated over all signal frequencies contained within the solid angle $\Omega_s$ (measured within the crystal), is given by Byer and Harris [92] as

$$P_s^{spon} = \frac{32\pi^2 P_p \hbar d^2 n_s \omega_s^4 \omega_i \ell \theta_s^2}{b n_p n_i c^5} \quad (cgs)$$

$$= \frac{Z_0 P_p \hbar d^2 n_s \omega_s^4 \omega_i \ell \theta_s^2}{2\pi b n_p n_i c^4} \tag{107}$$

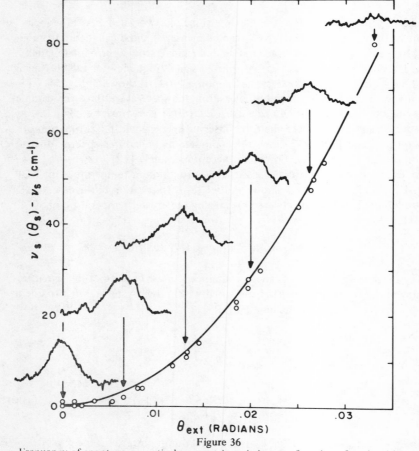

**Figure 36**

Frequency of spontaneous optical parametric emission as a function of angle with respect to the pump. Shown set in are the observed spectra. Solid curve is the theoretical angular dependence [102].

It can be seen that the spontaneous power is linearly proportional to the pumping power (valid in the small gain limit) and independent of the area of the beam. Hence the total parametric noise is insensitive to the degree of focusing of the pump beam and also insensitive (on the average) to fluctuations in the pump intensity. These proporties make it in many ways a superior technique to optical second harmonic generation for measuring the magnitude of the nonlinear coefficient since SHG is sensitive to the spatial and temporal characteristics of the fundamental.

Additional material on theoretical and experimental aspects of spontaneous optical parametric emission can be found in Refs. [105–125].

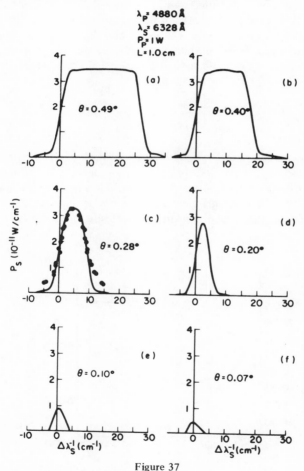

Figure 37

Theoretical spectral distribution of spontaneous parametric emission as a function of acceptance angle. Experimental results are shown for (c) [92].

## VI.  Materials

The key element in an optical parametric oscillator is the nonlinear material
that produces the coupling between the radiation fields. An intensive search has
been made in the past and continues for new and better nonlinear materials. In
the first part of this section, general material parameters as they relate to the
performance of optical parametric oscillators are examined. The second part is
a brief discussion of several nonlinear materials that either have been used in
optical parametric oscillators or appear promising for such applications. This
list is not complete; the reader interested in a more detailed discussion on nonlinear materials is referred to the works of Bechmann and Kurtz [72], Kurtz
[126], and Singh [71], and references cited therein. For more information
on the origin and physical mechanisms of the nonlinear process, the reader is
referred to the articles by Wemple and DiDomenico [127] and Ducuing and
Flytzanis [128].

### A.  General Properties

The requirements for materials to be useful in optical parametric oscillators
are basically the same as for optical second harmonic generation and optical
parametric up-conversion. Desirable properties include a large usable nonlinear
coefficient, ability to be phase-matched, transparency at the wavelengths of
interest, high optical quality, and resistance to optically induced damage.

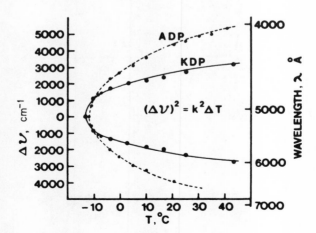

Figure 38
Tuning curves for KDP and ADP pumped at 2573 Å as a function of temperature [103].

## 1. Definition of $\chi_{eff}$

The second-order nonlinear susceptibility tensor is defined by the relation

$$\mathcal{P}_i^{NL}(\omega_3) = \chi_{ijk}^{(2)}(-\omega_3, \omega_1, \omega_2)\, \mathcal{E}_j(\omega_1)\mathcal{E}_k(\omega_2) \tag{108}$$

where $\mathcal{P}$ and $\mathcal{E}$ are the Fourier amplitudes of the polarization and electric field respectively, the subscripts refer to the Cartesian components of these quantities, and summation over repeated indices is assumed. The nonlinear susceptibility tensor representing a physical property of the system must conform to the symmetry of the crystal [129]; it is thus zero in all materials that possess a center of symmetry.* Hence materials useful for optical parametric effects must lack a center of symmetry. When the frequency dependence of $\chi^{(2)}$ is negligible, as it will be when all three frequencies are well below the ultraviolet absorption bands and well above the infrared bands, a second, approximate, symmetry condition, termed the Kleinman symmetry condition [29], applies. In this case $\chi_{ijk} = \chi_{jki}$, etc., for any permutation of the subscripts, and the maximum number of independent components of $\chi^{(2)}$ is reduced from 27 to 10; these remaining 10 components are still subject to crystal symmetry. Although the Kleinman symmetry condition has been recently shown not to hold for several crystals [130, 131], it is normally assumed valid in discussions of nonlinear coefficients, and the frequency dependence of the nonlinear coefficients is thus rarely used.

For optical second harmonic generation where $\omega_1 = \omega_2$ and $\omega_3 = 2\omega_1$, $\chi_{ijk}^{(2)}$ is symmetric in its last two subscripts. For this case it is customary to use the contracted notation for the last two subscripts, xx → 1, yy → 2, zz → 3, yz → 4, xz → 5, xy → 6, and to write Eq. (108) in matrix form

$$\begin{pmatrix} \mathcal{P}_x^{NL}(\omega_3) \\ \mathcal{P}_y^{NL}(\omega_3) \\ \mathcal{P}_z^{NL}(\omega_3) \end{pmatrix}_{\omega_3 = 2\omega_1} = \begin{pmatrix} d_{11} & d_{12} & d_{13} & d_{14} & d_{15} & d_{16} \\ d_{21} & d_{22} & d_{23} & d_{24} & d_{25} & d_{26} \\ d_{31} & d_{32} & d_{33} & d_{34} & d_{35} & d_{36} \end{pmatrix} \begin{pmatrix} \mathcal{E}_x^2(\omega_1) \\ \mathcal{E}_y^2(\omega_1) \\ \mathcal{E}_z^2(\omega_1) \\ 2\mathcal{E}_y(\omega_1)\mathcal{E}_z(\omega_1) \\ 2\mathcal{E}_x(\omega_1)\mathcal{E}_z(\omega_1) \\ 2\mathcal{E}_x(\omega_1)\mathcal{E}_y(\omega_1) \end{pmatrix} \tag{109}$$

---

*Weak nonlinear effects due to magnetic dipole or electric quadrupole interactions are not excluded by inversion symmetry but are of little practical importance.

The quantities $d_{ij}$ are the nonlinear coefficients of the medium. The corresponding relation when $\omega_1 \neq \omega_2$ is

$$
\begin{pmatrix} \mathcal{P}_x^{NL}(\omega_3) \\ \mathcal{P}_y^{NL}(\omega_3) \\ \mathcal{P}_z^{NL}(\omega_3) \end{pmatrix} = 2(d) \begin{pmatrix} \mathcal{E}_x(\omega_1)\mathcal{E}_x(\omega_2) \\ \mathcal{E}_y(\omega_1)\mathcal{E}_y(\omega_2) \\ \mathcal{E}_z(\omega_1)\mathcal{E}_z(\omega_2) \\ \mathcal{E}_y(\omega_1)\mathcal{E}_z(\omega_2) + \mathcal{E}_y(\omega_2)\mathcal{E}_z(\omega_1) \\ \mathcal{E}_x(\omega_1)\mathcal{E}_z(\omega_2) + \mathcal{E}_x(\omega_2)\mathcal{E}_z(\omega_1) \\ \mathcal{E}_x(\omega_1)\mathcal{E}_y(\omega_2) + \mathcal{E}_x(\omega_2)\mathcal{E}_y(\omega_1) \end{pmatrix}
$$

$$\omega_3 = \omega_1 + \omega_2$$

(110)

for which the matrix of d coefficients is the same as in Eq. (109). The factor of 2 occurs because of the definition of the nonlinear susceptibility in terms of the Fourier amplitudes; it does not occur in a formalism that defines the nonlinear coefficients in terms of real fields.[*] Equation (110) is the basic relation between polarization and electric fields useful for the analysis of optical parametric oscillators.

The effective nonlinear coefficient is defined in the following manner: Let the signal, idler, and pump have unit vectors $\hat{e}_s$, $\hat{e}_i$, $\hat{e}_p$, such that the vector fields are $\hat{e}_s\mathcal{E}_s(\omega_s)$, $\hat{e}_i\mathcal{E}_i(\omega_i)$, $\hat{e}_p\mathcal{E}_p(\omega_p)$. The effect of the nonlinear polarization on the signal generated by the mixture of the pump and idler is proportional to $\hat{e}_s \cdot \underline{\mathcal{P}}^{NL}(\omega_s)$. Substituting for the pump and idler fields on the right-hand side of (110), evaluating the nonlinear polarization, and performing the operation $\hat{e}_s \cdot \underline{\mathcal{P}}^{NL}(\omega_s)$ gives an effective nonlinear polarization proportional to the scalar field amplitudes and dependent on the three unit field vectors, given by

$$\mathcal{P}_{eff}^{NL}(\omega_s) = \hat{e}_s \cdot \underline{\mathcal{P}}^{NL}(\omega_s) \equiv \chi_{eff}\mathcal{E}_p\mathcal{E}_i^* \qquad (cgs)$$

$$\equiv (\epsilon_0)\chi_{eff}\mathcal{E}_p\mathcal{E}_i^* \quad (mks) \qquad (111)$$

This is the definition of the effective nonlinear susceptibility used in this chapter. In terms of the general form of the susceptibility tensor,

$$\chi_{eff} = 2\hat{e}_s \cdot \underline{\underline{\chi}} : \hat{e}_p\hat{e}_i \qquad (112)$$

---

[*]See Appendix 2 of Ref. 65 for the exact definitions of $\chi$ and d, and for the origin of the various factors of 2.

and

$$\chi_{eff} = 2d_{eff} \qquad (113)$$

where $d_{eff}$ is the effective nonlinear coefficient and $\overset{=}{\chi}$ is a third-rank tensor.

The value of the effective nonlinear coefficient depends on whether Type I or Type II phase matching is employed; it depends on the direction of propagation within the crystal for which phase matching is obtained, and on the nonzero components of the nonlinear susceptibility tensor. For uniaxial crystals, the effective nonlinear coefficient is given in Table 2 for those crystal classes lacking a center of symmetry.* The angles $\theta$ and $\varphi$ appearing in Table 2 and defined in Fig. 39 correspond to the direction of propagation for a collinear interaction. The values for $d_{eff}$ in Column I, labeled OOE refer to an interaction involving a single extraordinary ray and hence apply either to Type I phase matching in a negative uniaxial crystal (extraordinary pump) or to Type II phase matching in a positive uniaxial crystal (extraordinary signal *or* idler). The double refraction angle $\rho$ is that value corresponding to the single extraordinary ray. Column II, labeled OOE, gives the values of the effective nonlinear coefficient for an interaction involving two extraordinary rays, either Type I phase matching in positive uniaxial crystals or Type II phase matching in negative crystals. The double refraction angles $\rho$ and $\rho'$ refer to the two extraordinary rays, whether pump, signal, or idler. It is to be emphasized that the effective nonlinear susceptibility is *twice* the value given in the table.

In biaxial crystals, the effective nonlinear susceptibility can be found in a straightforward manner (as described above) once the phase-matching direction and the polarizations of the waves have been established. For cubic crystals, phase matching by birefringence compensation is not possible, although an effective susceptibility can be defined.

The magnitudes of the nonzero nonlinear coefficients for many nonlinear materials are given in the articles by Beckmann and Kurtz [72], Kurtz [126], and Singh [71]. The values for some important materials are given below. There is, however, one rule regarding the magnitudes of a nonlinear coefficient that generally applies to most materials. Originally formulated by Miller [132] and known as Miller's rule, it states that the nonlinear coefficient d of a given material is proportional to the product of the linear susceptibilities at the three frequencies involved times a constant $\delta$, known as the Miller delta, i.e.,

$$d = (\epsilon_0)\chi^{(1)}(\omega_p)\chi^{(1)}(\omega_s)\chi^{(1)}(\omega_i) \cdot \delta \qquad (mks) \qquad (114)$$

---

*The results presented in this table are generalized from the work of Midwinter and Warner [34] to include double refraction; the results do not assume coefficients equal to zero by the Kleinman symmetry condition.

**Table 2**

Effective Nonlinear Coefficients for Parametric Interactions in Uniaxial Crystals

| Class | (OOE) $d_{\text{eff}}$ | (OEE) $d_{\text{eff}}$ |
|---|---|---|
| $\bar{6}2m$ | $-d_{22}\sin 3\varphi \cos(\theta+\rho)$ | $d_{22}\cos 3\varphi \cos(\theta+\rho)\cos(\theta+\rho')$ |
| $6\ mm$ | $d_{15}\sin(\theta+\rho)$ | $0$ |
| $622$ | $0$ | $d_{14}^*\sin(\theta+\rho)\cos(\theta+\rho')$ |
| $\bar{6}$ | $(d_{11}\cos 3\varphi - d_{22}\sin 3\varphi)\cos(\theta+\rho)$ | $(d_{11}\sin 3\varphi + d_{22}\cos 3\varphi)\cos(\theta+\rho)\cos(\theta+\rho')$ |
| $6$ | $d_{15}\sin(\theta+\rho)$ | $d_{14}^*\sin(\theta+\rho)\cos(\theta+\rho')$ |
| $3m$ | $d_{15}\sin(\theta+\rho) - d_{22}\sin 3\varphi \cos(\theta+\rho)$ | $d_{22}\cos 3\varphi \cos(\theta+\rho)\cos(\theta+\rho')$ |
| $32$ | $d_{11}\cos 3\varphi \cos(\theta+\rho)$ | $d_{11}\sin 3\varphi \cos(\theta+\rho)\cos(\theta+\rho') + d_{14}^*\sin(\theta+\rho)\cos(\theta+\rho')$ |
| $3$ | $d_{15}\sin(\theta+\rho) + (d_{11}\cos 3\varphi - d_{22}\sin 3\varphi)\cos(\theta+\rho)$ | $(d_{11}\sin 3\varphi + d_{22}\cos 3\varphi)\cos(\theta+\rho)\cos(\theta+\rho') + d_{14}^*\sin(\theta+\rho)\cos(\theta+\rho')$ |
| $\bar{4}2m$ | $-d_{14}\sin 2\varphi \sin(\theta+\rho)$ | $d_{14}\cos 2\varphi \sin(2\theta+\rho+\rho')$ |
| $4\ mm$ | $d_{15}\sin(\theta+\rho)$ | $0$ |
| $422$ | $0$ | $d_{14}^*\sin(\theta+\rho)\cos(\theta+\rho')$ |
| $\bar{4}$ | $-(d_{15}\cos 2\varphi + d_{14}\sin 2\varphi)\sin(\theta+\rho)$ | $(d_{14}\cos 2\varphi - d_{15}\sin 2\varphi)\sin(2\theta+\rho+\rho')$ |
| $4$ | $d_{15}\sin(\theta+\rho)$ | $d_{14}^*\sin(\theta+\rho)\cos(\theta+\rho')$ |

Note: Terms indicated by an asterisk are zero when the Kleinman symmetry condition is assumed.

The permittivity of free space $\epsilon_0$ does not appear in cgs units. Since $\chi^{(1)} =$ $(n^2-1)/4\pi(\text{cgs})$, $(n^2-1)$ (mks), the nonlinear coefficient is roughly proportional to $(n^2-1)^3$. Whereas the d coefficients for different materials differ by many orders of magnitude, the Miller $\delta$ is relatively more constant for most materials, having a value (mks) $(3 \pm 2) \times 10^{-2}$ $(\text{m}^2/\text{coulomb})$. Thus it is a general rule that materials with large indices of refraction will be more nonlinear. For a thorough discussion of nonlinear optical and electrooptical phenomena, see the articles by Wemple and DiDomenico [127], and Ducuing and Flytzanis [128].

## 2. Phase Matching

As pointed out in previous sections, achievement of phase matching is imperative in any situation where nontrivial gains are to be obtained. In all oscillators constructed to date, crystalline birefringence has been used to overcome the effects of dispersion, and it appears to be the most useful method for achieving phase matching. A discussion of phase matching has been given in Section II. Some further comments here directly relate to material properties.

Whether a given material can or cannot be phase-matched depends on the values of its indices of refraction as functions of wavelength, and the wavelengths of the radiation fields for which phase matching is desired. For uniaxial crystals, the locus of phase matching directions lies on a cone centered about the optic axis of the crystal, Fig. 39. For biaxial crystals, there are several loci

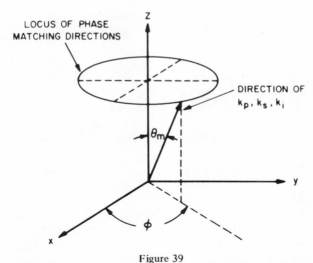

**Figure 39**
Locus of matching directions in a uniaxial crystal. The symbol $\theta_m$ designates the phase matching angle measured from the optic axis, $\varphi$ is the angle from the x axis.

possible, depending on the magnitudes of the differences between the three principal indices [35]. Determining the locus of phase-matched direction is straightforward even if mathematically involved.

It is important to note that all phase-matching directions are not equivalent relative to the magnitude of the effective nonlinear susceptibility. For example, in crystal class $\overline{4}2m$ and an interaction involving two ordinary waves and one extraordinary wave, $\chi_{eff} = -2d_{14} \sin\theta \sin 2\varphi$. In this case it is desirable to propagate at $\theta = \theta_m$ with $\varphi = 45°$, $135°$, etc. It can be seen from Table 2 that for other crystal classes, for a given phase matching angle $\theta_m$, the angle $\Phi$ is extremely important in determining $\chi_{eff}$ and an optimum $\Phi$ generally exists.

Several general observations regarding phase matching can be formulated. First of all, Type I, or parallel, phase matching requires approximately one-half as much birefringence as Type II, or orthogonal, phase matching does. Since most materials have a small birefringence, if they are phase-matchable at all it will generally be for a Type I interaction. It is also generally true that the closer an oscillator operates to degeneracy, the greater the birefringence required to achieve phase matching. Secondly, it is desirable from the point of view of threshold considerations to operate with the minimum double refraction angle. In uniaxial crystals, this implies propagating perpendicular to the optic axis, $\theta_m = 90°$. Referring to Table 2 shows that $\chi_{eff} = 0$ for interactions involving only one ordinary ray at $\theta = 90°$. Thus, noncritical phase matching (B = 0) requires an interaction involving two ordinary rays (OOE). For negative uniaxial crystals this corresponds to Type I phase matching; for positive uniaxial crystals, this corresponds to Type II phase matching. Hence it is more likely that noncritical phase matching can be achieved in negative uniaxial crystals, since less birefringence is required for Type I interactions.

## 3. Crystal Quality

The quality of a given nonlinear crystal largely determines its performance. Desirable physical properties include availability in large size, ability to take a good polish, durability, and resistance to humidity. Many materials now used do not satisfy all of these criteria.

Two of the most important optical properties are that a material have low optical losses at all the frequencies involved and that it be homogeneous and of high optical quality. Low losses are important for several reasons. First of all, any and all forms of loss (absorption or scattering) affect the threshold of an oscillator. Secondly, absorptive losses at signal, idler, or pump give rise to thermal distortions that can severely affect oscillator performance especially at high power levels [133, 134].

Crystalline inhomogeneity can affect the performance of an oscillator in at

least two ways. Inhomogeneities in the index of refraction in the transverse plane
result in beam distortion, which introduces losses due to mode coupling; these
losses effectively increase the threshold of the oscillator. A second effect of index
of refraction variations is a reduction in the gain resulting from nonuniform phase
matching conditions. The latter effect can result from index variations along the
direction of propagation [135, 136] and also transverse to it [137, 138]. As a general rule, less than one fringe of phase shift either along or transverse to the interaction region is required for the parametric interaction not to be degraded.
This in turn requires homogeneity of the indices to greater than $10^{-4}$. Inhomogeneities can be induced by strain or by compositional changes [139–141].
Byer et al. [142] have reported growth of $LiNbO_3$ with index variations $\approx 10^{-5}$
over crystals several cm in length by growing them from a congruently melting
composition [143]. Procedures for evaluating materials can be found in Refs.
135 and 142.

### 4. Optical Damage

All nonlinear as well as linear optical materials are damaged by sufficiently
high optical power densities. For a nonlinear material to be useful in oscillator
applications, it must not become damaged at power densities for which useful
oscillator performance is obtained. Optically induced damage may be of several
types, including both reversible and irreversible forms. Reversible damage, first
observed by Ashkin et al. [144] in $LiNbO_3$, results from illumination by visible
radiation and takes the form of a nonuniform index of refraction created by the
illumination. These induced refractive index inhomogeneities can be "erased"
either by ultraviolet illumination or by elevating the crystal temperature above
$160°C$. Recent findings suggest that this reversible form of damage may be
associated with $Fe^{2+}$, an impurity [145, 146]. Additional discussions of reversible optical damage are in Refs. 147–152.

Irreversible optical damage is here meant to imply actual physical damage
of the material. It may take the form of surface or volume damage and often
appears as filamentary tracks along the path of the beam resulting from self-
focusing. The subject of optical damage in materials is currently under intense
investigation and much work is reported in the literature. The reader is referred
to the references cited for details.

For a given material, the susceptibility to irreversible damage is usually
quoted as an optical power density or a threshold at which damage occurs,
although there are strong arguments that the optical damage process is proba-
bilistic [153, 154]. Values for damage thresholds that different researchers
quote often vary, with these differences related to crystal perfection and in
some cases experimental technique. Hence, thresholds for damage quoted here

are subject to revision. It is found that surface quality and cleanliness are important in determining surface damage characteristics and that inclusions and other imperfections strongly affect the powers at which volume damage occurs [154–156]. In addition, self-focusing of optical beams often increases the power density to the point that damage occurs [157, 158]. Self-focusing due to linear and nonlinear absorption processes has been found to be associated with the damage of at least one material, $Ba_2NaNb_5O_{15}$, limiting its use in pulsed oscillators [159]. Nonlinear absorption mechanisms as well as damage thresholds for some materials are found to depend on the wavelength of the radiation [160]. Recent studies strongly suggest that the intrinsic damage mechanism is avalanche breakdown within the material, caused by the peak optical electric field [153, 154, 161].

The subject of optical damage is of particular importance for optical parametric oscillators since the parametric gain and the occurrence of damage both depend on the optical power density. It is found that in some crystals damage occurs at power densities below which threshold occurs and in others at power densities only slightly in excess of threshold, limiting the useful gain. In such cases, operation of an oscillator is impossible or marginal. It has also been found that in addition to damage produced by the pump, damage can result from the high-power densities associated with the resonated wave(s), which can, for high Q cavities, exceed the pump power density [88]. Thus some materials that appear on paper to be good candidates for oscillators are found not to work because of problems of optical damage.

Further discussions of optical damage can be found in Refs. 162–168.

## B.  Some Useful Nonlinear Optical Materials

Some of the nonlinear materials used to construct devices and others that are potentially useful will now be described. Data concerned with physical constants such as index of refraction and nonlinear coefficients are believed to be reasonably accurate, although recent data have shown some earlier measurements to be in error. Crystal size and quality are apt to change and hence data presented herein must be interpreted as reflecting the state of the art at this writing.

The nonlinear coefficients given for a particular material will be expressed in mks units. To convert to cgs units, any particular coefficient is multiplied by $3 \times 10^4/(4\pi)$; i.e.,

$$d_{cgs} = \frac{3 \times 10^4}{4\pi} d_{mks} \qquad (115)$$

The values of most nonlinear coefficients are measured by optical second harmonic generation relative to standard materials. These are in turn converted to absolute values, using the value for ammonium dihydrogen phosphate (ADP) measured by Francois [169] and Bjorkholm and Siegman [170]. The standard value for ADP is taken to be

$$d_{36} \text{(mks)} = 0.575 \times 10^{-12} \text{ m/V} \pm 15\%$$

$(d_{36}\text{(cgs)} = 1.37 \times 10^{-9} \text{ esu})$ measured with a fundamental wavelength $\lambda_1 = 0.6328 \ \mu m$. Although some small frequency dependence of the nonlinear coefficients is to be expected, it is normally neglected. In light of the small frequency variation expected and the relatively large uncertainty in the measured value, this neglect seems well justified.

## 1. KDP, ADP

Potassium dihydrogen phosphate (KDP), $KH_2PO_4$, ammonium dihydrogen phosphate (ADP), $NH_4H_2PO_4$, and their deuterated forms have been the workhorses of nonlinear optics for many years and are still extremely useful. Along with the similar arsenates and salts of rubidium and cesium, they are grown from water solution. KDP and ADP and their isomorphs belong to point group $\overline{4}2m$ and are negative uniaxial. The effective transmission bands of KDP and ADP extend from around 2000 Å to approximately $1$–$1.2 \ \mu m$; the long wavelength absorption bands due to OH resonances can be extended further into the infrared, using the deuterated forms of these crystals. This is especially important when these materials are used in conjunction with the $1.06$-$\mu m$ radiation of Nd lasers. The transmission characteristics of the other isomorphs differ in their ultraviolet cutoffs. Because of the small dispersion in ADP and KDP and the relatively large birefringence ($\approx 0.05$), both Type I and Type II phase matching can be obtained.

ADP can be noncritically phase-matched for second harmonic generation from 5,320 Å to 2,660 Å by operating the crystal at a temperature of approximately $50°C$. This property is particularly useful for generating an ultraviolet pump by chain multiplication of the Nd laser output. This phase-matching property also permits the construction of a parametric generator capable of tuning the entire visible region of the spectrum [171]. Cesium dihydrogen arsenate has been found useful in noncritically phase-matching second harmonic generation from the fundamental of the Nd laser to 5,320 Å [172] and is thus potentially useful for an oscillator pumped at this wavelength covering the region around $1 \ \mu m$. Noncritical phase matching for a large range of wavelengths is possible using various isomorphs of KDP and ADP. Details can be found in Ref. 173.

KDP and ADP and their isomorphs can currently be obtained in large crystals of high optical quality, and can be polished to obtain a good surface finish. They are sensitive to water vapor and hence surfaces must be protected, usually by dielectric coatings or by quartz plates contacted to the crystal by index matching oil. Temperature tuning is possible using these materials, although an upper temperature limit near $100°C$ is set by decomposition of the materials.

Although the nonlinear coefficients of KDP and ADP are relatively small, their high optical quality, low absorption loss in the visible, resistance to optical damage, and large size make them very useful, especially in applications involving a pulsed pump source. Probably the most important use is for oscillators pumped in the ultraviolet covering the visible region of the spectrum [171]. These materials are among the most resistant to optical damage of the nonlinear optical materials; Bass [157] has reported a power density for volume damage in KDP of 2.7 GW/cm$^2$ at $\lambda = 1.064$ $\mu$m; Yarborough and Massey [171] report observing filamentary damage in ADP at a power level of 750 MW/cm$^2$ using radiation at $\lambda = 2,660$ Å; and Izrailenko et al. [174] report damage at 500 MW/cm$^2$ at $\lambda = 5,300$ Å. Dowley and Hodges [175, 176] report degradation of crystal quality in ADP due to sustained cw ultraviolet radiation (2,572 Å); and Wax et al. [177] detect some form of damage using a He-Ne laser.

The nonlinear coefficients and the fundamental wavelength at which they are measured are

ADP,    $d_{36} = 0.575 \times 10^{-12}$ m/V $\pm 15\%$   (0.6328 $\mu$m)

KDP,    $d_{36} = 0.47 \times 10^{-12}$ m/V $\pm 15\%$   (1.064 $\mu$m)

The value of $d_{36}$ for ADP is probably the most accurate measurement and is now accepted as the standard. Additional references to ADP and KDP and their isomorphs are in [178-181].

## 2. Lithium Iodate

Lithium iodate, LiIO$_3$, belongs to crystal class 6, and can be grown from water solution. It is available in cm-size crystals of high optical quality and takes a good polish. Surfaces can be protected from normal humidity by dielectric coatings. It has a useful nonlinear coefficient of $d_{31} = (5.6 \pm 0.3) \times 10^{-12}$ m/V [182], which is comparable to that of LiNbO$_3$ and roughly 10 times that of ADP. Recent measurements [130] indicate that $d_{14}$, which would be zero if the Kleinman symmetry condition held, has a value somewhere between 0.2 and $0.4 \times 10^{-12}$ m/V. This value is considerably smaller than $d_{31}$ and is of only marginal value.

Lithium iodate is negative uniaxial with an extremely large birefringence

($>$ 0.1). It is transmitting between $\approx$ 0.4 $\mu$m and 5 $\mu$m, and can be phase-matched for a Type I interaction using $d_{31}$ and for Type II using the smaller $d_{14}$ coefficient. It is reasonably resistant to optical damage, with a reported damage power level of 125 MW/cm$^2$ at $\lambda$ = 0.6943 $\mu$m [183], and 40 MW/cm$^2$ at $\lambda$ = 0.53 $\mu$m [174].

The primary disadvantage of this material is that its birefriengence is so large that double refraction effects limit the degree of focusing to a value considerably less than optimum. Its high optical quality and large nonlinear coefficient make it, however, a very useful material for nonlinear interactions in the visible. The temperature variation of the indices of refraction do not permit significant temperature tuning [184]; hence angle tuning is most useful. Several optical parametric oscillators have been reported using LiIO$_3$ [174, 183, 185, 186].

Additional references to the linear and nonlinear properties of LiIO$_3$ are in [187-189].

## 3.  Alpha-Iodic Acid

Alpha-iodic acid, $\alpha$-HIO$_3$ belongs to point group 222 and is negative biaxial [190]. Reported values for its nonlinear coefficients are $d_{14}$ = (7.3 $\pm$ 2.4) $\times$ 10$^{-12}$ m/V (1.064 $\mu$m) [190], and $d_{14}$ = (4.8 $\pm$ 0.9) $\times$ 10$^{-12}$ m/V (1.1526 $\mu$m) [191]. The material is grown from water solution, reportedly takes a good polish but surfaces must be protected to avoid deterioration. Izrailenko et al. [174] report construction of an oscillator using $\alpha$-HIO$_3$ and measure its damage threshold at 55 MW/cm$^2$ ($\lambda$ = 5300 Å).

## 4.  Lithium Niobate

Lithium niobate, LiNbO$_3$, one of the first "new" nonlinear materials to be studied, has become the workhorse material in constructing optical parametric oscillators. It belongs to point group 3m and is negative uniaxial. Its useful nonlinear coefficients are $d_{31}$ = $d_{15}$ = (5.2 $\pm$ 0.8) $\times$ 10$^{-12}$ m/V (1.1523 $\mu$m) [191] and $d_{22}$ = (3.1 $\pm$ 0.3) $\times$ 10$^{-12}$ m/V (1.0582 $\mu$m) [15]. It possesses sufficient birefringence to be phase-matched for Type I interactions but not for Type II interactions except possibly in the infrared. For pump wavelengths 0.45 $\mu$m and $\approx$ 0.7 $\mu$m, LiNbO$_3$ can be phase-matched at 90° to the optical axis, permitting optimal focusing conditions (B = 0). Because of the large variation of the indices of refraction with temperature [192-194], a LiNbO$_3$ optical parametric oscillator can be conveniently temperature-tuned. Crystals of LiNbO$_3$ of high optical quality can be grown in lengths exceeding 5 cm. The surfaces take a good optical polish and are not subject to degradation from environmental conditions such as humidity.

The primary drawback of $LiNbO_3$ as a nonlinear material is its susceptibility to refractive index variations induced by visible radiation [144]. These refractive index variations distort the optics of the crystal primarily for the extraordinary ray but are self-annealing for crystal temperatures greater than $160°C$-$200°C$. Wallace [195] has shown that by using various pump wavelengths and crystal temperatures greater than $160°C$, a parametric oscillator can be constructed to cover the wavelength range between $0.54\ \mu m$ and $3.65\ \mu m$. He also reports a bleaching of induced refractive index changes after several hours of illumination. From a practical point of view, this damage phenomenon has not limited the usefulness of the material for oscillator applications. Peterson et al. [145] have found a correlation between this damage phenomenon in $LiNbO_3$ and the impurity $Fe^{2+}$. Presumably high purity crystals will show damage effects to a lesser degree. Several theories regarding the mechanism for the induced refractive index effect have been given [149, 150]. Bass [158] has reported a threshold power density for catastrophic damage of $840\ MW/cm^2$ at $\lambda = 1.064\ \mu m$.

## 5.  Barium Sodium Niobate

Barium sodium niobate, $Ba_2NaNb_5O_{15}$, sometimes referred to as "bananas," belongs to point group mm2 and is negative biaxial. The degree of biaxiality of the crystal is small and for most purposes it behaves like crystals in point group 4 mm. The crystal is hard and takes a good polish. Crystals are available in lengths of 5 mm; longer crystals are scarce. Crystals of reasonably good quality can be grown, the primary problem being the presence of striae in the growth direction [196]. In spite of this problem, doubly resonant optical parametric oscillators have been constructed with thresholds as low as 3 mW [74].

Barium sodium niobate is negative biaxial with a birefringence $\approx 0.1$. For pump wavelengths between 0.45 and $0.6\ \mu m$, phase matching can be achieved along a principal dielectric axis without the effects of double refraction, permitting optimal focusing. The indices of refraction are temperature-dependent in such a way that temperature tuning of the oscillator is possible. In these respects, barium sodium niobate is similar to lithium niobate. Since the material goes through a structural transition from orthorhombic to tetragonal near $300°C$, operation of an oscillator must be exclusively above or below this temperature, as twinning occurs once a crystal has gone above $300°C$ and is returned to temperatures below this value [197]. Index of refraction data can be found in Ref. 197.

For materials transmitting in the visible portion of the spectrum, the useful nonlinear coefficients $d_{14}$ and $d_{15}$ of $Ba_2NaNb_5O_{15}$ are the largest. The values are $d_{15} = (14.6 \pm 0.7) \times 10^{-12}$ m/V and $d_{24} = (13.8 \pm 0.7) \times 10^{-12}$ m/V measured by second harmonic generation at $\lambda = 1.064 \, \mu m$ [197].

Barium sodium niobate does not display refractive index inhomogeneities induced by visible radiation at room temperature and above [198], in contrast to $LiNbO_3$ [144]. It does, however, suffer from irreversible surface and volume damage when irradiated by high peak powers at $0.532 \, \mu m$ [159], or a combination of radiation fields at 0.532 and $1.064 \, \mu m$ [199]. Recent studies of this damage indicate that it is associated with nonlinear absorption processes that result in thermal focusing of the beams. This nonlinear absorption has been qualitatively correlated with iron impurities [159].

Both pulsed and continuous doubly resonant oscillators have been constructed using barium sodium niobate [74, 100, 200, 201, 202]; the threshold of 3 mW for a continuously pumped DRO is the lowest reported to date [74]. The damage problem and lack of crystals of large size make it less desirable than $LiNbO_3$ for pulsed singly resonant oscillators. Its large nonlinear coefficient still makes it the most attractive material for continuously pumped oscillators pumped in the visible.

## 6. Proustite and Pyrargyrite

Proustite, $Ag_3AsS_3$, belongs to point group 3m and is negative uniaxial. It transmits from $0.63 \, \mu m$ to nearly 13 $\mu m$ with a slight absorption peak in the region of the $10.6$-$\mu m$ $CO_2$ laser line [203, 204]. Its useful nonlinear coefficients are $d_{31} = (15.1 \pm 2.2) \times 10^{-12}$ m/V and $d_{22} \approx d_{31}$. The magnitude of the birefringence is large, being $\approx 0.2$ over most of the transmission band. Index of refraction data can be found in Ref. 205.

Proustite is one of several interesting materials for applications in the infrared portion of the spectrum because of its large range of transparency. Ammann et al. [206] have reported the construction of an oscillator pumped at $1.064 \, \mu m$ using this material. They found that the material showed surface damage at power levels on the order of 450 $kW/cm^2$. Since the oscillator required a power density of this magnitude to reach threshold, its performance was judged marginal.

Hanna et al. [207] have obtained reliable operation of a proustite oscillator similar to that described by Ammann et al. by reducing the repetition rate of operation, by using a single-frequency pump source, and by using less than optimal focusing conditions to reduce the threshold pump intensity rather than the threshold pump power. They did, however, see damage at increased pump power densities. The dependence of the damage on repetition rate and power density is consistent with studies of damage on this material [160]. Hordvik et al. [117] report some degree of temperature-tuning of optical parametric fluorescence in this material. They find that heating the crystal to $T > 200°C$ produces on the surface a whitish film that cannot be removed by cleaning. It is thus probably too early to assess the ultimate capabilities of proustite.

Additional information on proustite can be found in Ref. 208.

Pyrargyrite, $Ag_3SbS_3$, belongs to crystal class 3m and is negative uniaxial. It is quite similar to proustite but with a slightly smaller band gap. Crystals that Gandrud et al. [204] studied were observed to have small black particles assumed to be metallic silver dispersed throughout the crystal. Pyrargyrite is transmitting roughly between 1 $\mu$m and 13 $\mu$m with a slight absorption peak to the long wavelength side of the 10.6-$\mu$m $CO_2$ line. Measured absorption coefficients at 10.6 $\mu$m are $\alpha^0$ (10.6 $\mu$m) = 0.34 ± 0.05 cm$^{-1}$ for the ordinary ray and $\alpha^e$(10.6 $\mu$m) = 0.08 ± 0.04 cm$^{-1}$ for the extraordinary ray [204]. The measured nonlinear coefficient is $d_{31}$ = (12.6 ± 4) $\times$ 10$^{-12}$ m/V and $d_{22}$ = (13.4 ± 4) $\times$ 10$^{-12}$ m/V. Gandrud and Boyd [209] find that intense 1.06-$\mu$m radiation causes a reversible increase in the absorption coefficients at both 1.06 and 10.6 $\mu$m. They also report reversible surface degradation. Further discussion of growth and optical properties is in [210, 211]. Studies of optical damage can be found in Ref. 160.

## 7. Tellurium

Tellurium, Te, belongs to crystal class 32 and possesses one of the largest nonlinear coefficients measured. The most recently reported value is $d_{11}$ = (920 ± 280) $\times$ 10$^{-12}$ m/V [211], but there has been a considerable range of values reported [212–214]. The material possesses a large birefringence and can be phase-matched. The transmission range of this material is between approximately 5 and 25 $\mu$m.

Considerable effort has been given to evaluating tellurium for nonlinear applications in the infrared. Although the material has many desirable properties, many undesirable properties have been found in these investigations. Gandrud and Abrams [215] found increased absorption of the 10.6-$\mu$m fundamental when generating the second harmonic at 5.3 $\mu$m; they attributed this to free carrier absorption. It was suggested that the carriers were generated by interband transitions due to multiphoton absorption of the 5.3- and 10.6-$\mu$m signals. Taynai et al. [216] report similar effects and further observe surface damage in the form of pits at a peak power density of 2–4 MW/cm$^2$ and melting at an average power density of 150 W/cm$^2$. Hanna et al. [160] find the occurrence of damage in tellurium strongly dependent on surface preparation, and they report a damage threshold greater than 30 MW/cm$^2$ at 10.6 $\mu$m for crystals that were either cleaved or etched to remove polishing damage. To date, useful devices have not been made with this material.

### 8. Cadmium Selenide

Cadmium selenide, CdSe, belongs to point group 6 mm and is positive uniaxial. It can be phase-matched for a Type II interaction only. When properly compensated [217, 218], it transmits from 0.9 to 25 $\mu$m. Crystals of good quality several cm long are available [19, 219]. The useful nonlinear coefficient $d_{31}$ = $27 \times 10^{-12}$ m/V ± 30% [219, 220]. Using a Nd:YAG laser pump at 1.833 $\mu$m, Herbst and Byer [219] have observed 35% gain for a signal at 10.6 $\mu$m, and measured a loss of 0.032 cm$^{-1}$ at this wavelength. Using this material, Herbst and Byer [88] and Davidov et al. [221] have also observed oscillation. They also report a damage threshold of 30 MW/cm$^2$. Although the overall tuning range for an oscillator pumped at 1.833 $\mu$m is limited to the range 10–14 $\mu$m, this material appears at present to have the best possibility of producing an oscillator covering the 1- to 10-$\mu$m range. Herbst and Byer [219] suggest that broader infrared coverage can be obtained by using another parametric oscillator to provide the pump.

### 9. Other Materials

There are, in addition to the above materials, several other interesting materials with potential device applications. Among these are the III-IV semiconductors that possess large nonlinear coefficients, e.g., $d_{14}$(GaAs) = 134 × $10^{-12}$ m/V [211]; they are cubic, however, and hence cannot be phase-matched in the usual manner. There is continuing interest in these materials for guided-wave interactions where phase matching can in principle be obtained (see Section II,B,4). The ternary analog of the II-VI and III-V semiconductors are currently receiving considerable attention since many possess sufficient birefringence to be phase-matchable. Some of these materials and their associated references are AgGaS$_2$ [222–226], AgGaSe$_2$ [227], ZnGeP$_2$ [220, 228], and CdGeAs$_2$ [226, 229]. Optical properties of many of these crystals can be found in Ref. 230. Computed tuning curves are found in Refs. 226 and 227. In addition to the above, some interest has been shown in cinnabar, HgS [160, 231–233]. More extensive listings of nonlinear optical materials are in Refs. 71, 72, 126.

## VII.   Experimental Results

Giordmaine and Miller [14, 99] operated the first optical parametric oscillator several years after the first proposals for such a device. Since this initial achievement, many oscillators have been constructed and studied. In early experiments, most work was performed on doubly resonant oscillators because of their lower threshold requirements. These experiments were concerned with achieving higher output power and efficiency, evaluating different methods for tuning, achieving wider tuning ranges, and investigating new nonlinear materials. Bjorkholm [234, 235] was the first to demonstrate a singly resonant oscillator and to point out many of its advantages. Many other workers have reported results on SRO's. Some effort has been placed on continuously pumped oscillators, which to date have only been operated in the doubly resonant mode. Although singly resonant, continuously pumped oscillators are in principle feasible, none has as yet been successfully operated. Because of a number of inherent advantages, these singly resonant oscillators are at present the subject of most of the current research.

In this section, optical parametric oscillator experiments are examined, with emphasis placed on those experiments that demonstrate important techniques or represent state of the art results. A summary of experimental results reported as of this writing is given in Tables 3, 4, and 5.*

## A.  Pump Sources

The majority of pulsed optical parametric oscillators have been pumped with Q-switched ruby or neodymium lasers or their harmonics. An oscillator pumped by the output of a dye laser (Expt. 28) and one pumped by a $CaF_2$:Dy laser at 2.36 $\mu$m (Expt. 31) are exceptions. The range of pump wavelengths thus extends from 0.266 $\mu$m to 2.36 $\mu$m. Some considerations have been given to using pulsed gas lasers as pumping sources. Also, mode-locked picosecond pump sources have been used to pump parametric generators (large, single-pass gains) to produce tunable picosecond sources (Expts. 33, 34).

Early experiments were performed with multimode pump sources (both longitudinal and transverse); results have improved when single mode lasers have been used. For operation of either an SRO or DRO, lowest-order transverse mode operation of the pump is highly desirable. As discussed in Section IV,C, it is important to have a single longitudinal mode pump when pumping a DRO, but as Young et al. [78] show, the SRO can tolerate a finite pump linewidth. In summary, to obtain high-quality reproducible oscillator performance, it is necessary to have a high-quality reproducible pump source.

---

*When reference is made to an experiment in this section, a number in parentheses refers to the experiment number found in the first column of Tables 3 and 4.

Table 3

Summary of Pulsed Optical Parametric Oscillator Experiments

| Experiment number | Pump | Material | Tuning method and range | Threshold, output power, and efficiency | Comments and references |
|---|---|---|---|---|---|
| 1 | 0.529 $\mu m$ (SHG of CaWO$_4$:Nd laser:Multimode) | LiNbO$_3$ $\ell = 0.53$ cm | Temperature $\lambda_s$:0.97–1.06 $\mu m$ $\lambda_i$:1.15–1.06 $\mu m$ | $P^{th}_s = 6.7$ kW $P_s = 15$ W $\eta^{ext} \approx 0.1\%$ (DRO) | First oscillator. Observed cluster effect. Rapid tuning near degeneracy [14, 99]. |
| 2 | 0.53 $\mu m$ (SHG of Nd laser:Multimode) | KDP $\ell = 3$ cm | Angle $\lambda_s$:0.957–1.06 $\mu m$ $\lambda_i$:1.178–1.06 $\mu m$ | $S^{th}_p = 10$ MW/cm$^2$ $P_s + P_i = 5$ kW $\eta^{ext} \approx 0.03\%$ (DRO) | Type II phase-matching [245]. |
| 3 | 0.53 $\mu m$ (SHG of CaWO$_4$Nd and Nd:Glass lasers) | LiNbO$_3$ $\ell = 0.614$ | Temperature $\lambda_s = 0.73$–0.832 $\mu m$ $\lambda_i$:1.93–1.4 $\mu m$ | $P_s + P_i = 1$ kW $\eta^{ext} \approx 1\%$ (DRO) | Visible operation [246]. |
| 4 | 0.53 $\mu m$ (SHG of CaWO$_4$:Nd laser) | LiNbO$_3$ (3) $\ell = 0.6$–0.9 cm | Angle $\lambda_s$:0.684–1.06 $\mu m$ $\lambda_i$:2.36–1.06 $\mu m$ | $P_s + P_i = 50$ W $\eta^{ext} \approx 0.1\%$ (DRO) | Large tuning range [247]. |
| 5 | 0.35 $\mu m$ (Third harmonic of Nd:Glass:Multimode) | KDP | Angle $\lambda_s$:0.53 $\mu m$ ± 5% $\lambda_i$:1.06 $\mu m$ ± 10% | (DRO) | Tuning obtained in visible [248]. |
| 6 | 0.53 $\mu m$ (SHG of Nd:Glass; Single mode) | KDP | Angle $\lambda_s$:0.96–1.06 $\mu m$ $\lambda_i$:1.18–1.06 $\mu m$ | $P^{th}_p = 2$–3 MW $\eta^{ext} \approx 3\%$ (DRO) | Generally improved performance using single mode pump [248]. |

Table 3 (Continued)

| Experiment number | Pump | Material | Tuning:method and range | Threshold, output power, and efficiency | Comments and references |
|---|---|---|---|---|---|
| 7 | 0.6943 $\mu$m (Ruby) | LiNbO$_3$ $\ell = 0.7$ cm | Angle $\lambda_s$:1.0–1.08 $\mu$m $\lambda_i$:2.27–1.95 $\mu$m Electrooptic 50 Å with E = 7.5 kV/cm | $P_s + P_i = 38$ kW $\eta^{ext}$ (DRO) | Electrooptic tuning [249]. |
| 8 | 0.53 $\mu$m (Nd:Glass) | KDP $\ell = 3.3$ cm | Temperature $\lambda_s$:1.01–1.06 $\mu$m $\lambda_i$:1.12–1.06 $\mu$m Electrooptic | $S_p^{th} \approx 18$–20 MW/cm$^2$ (DRO) | KDP cooled near Curie temperature to enhance electrooptic tuning [250]. |
| 9 | 0.6943 $\mu$m (Ruby:Single mode) | LiNbO$_3$ $\ell = 0.935$ cm | $\lambda_s = 1.04$ $\mu$m $\lambda_i = 2.08$ $\mu$m | $P_p^{th} = 65$ kW (DRO) $\eta_{sig}^{ext} = 22\%$ (DRO) $\eta_{sig}^{ext} = 6\%$ (SRO) | High efficiency DRO. First operation of an SRO. Pump depletion [234]. |
| 10 | 0.53 $\mu$m (SHG of Nd:Glass) Single mode | LiNbO$_3$ $\ell = 0.8$ cm | $\lambda_s = 0.96$ $\mu$m $\lambda_i = 1.18$ $\mu$m | $P_p^{th} = 5$ kW $\eta_{total}^{ext} = 36\%$ (DRO) | High efficiency, pump depletion [251]. |
| 11 | 0.532 $\mu$m (SHG of Nd:YAG Multifrequency) | BaNaNb$_5$O$_{15}$ $\ell = 0.5$ cm | Temperature $\lambda_s$:0.948–1.056 $\mu$m $\lambda_i$:1.214–1.072 $\mu$m | $P_p^{th} = 13$ W $P_s + P_i = 0.1$ W $\eta^{ext} \approx 10^{-3}$ (DRO) | Low threshold. Broad linewidth. Efficiency below value expected [200]. |

| | | | | | |
|---|---|---|---|---|---|
| 12 | 0.53 μm | ADP | | for $S_p^{inc} = 70$ MW/cm$^2$ $P_s + P_i = 100$ kW $\eta^{ext} \approx 1\%$ for 10 p-sec pulse | Used multipass, traveling-wave, nonresonant interaction. Also reported results using uncoated mirror stacks [252]. |
| 13 | 0.6943 μm (Ruby:Single frequency) | LiNbO$_3$ $\ell = 0.935$ cm | $\lambda_s$:0.98–1.04 μm $\lambda_i$:2.38–2.08 μm | $P_s = 250$ kW $\eta_{sig}^{ext} = 28\%$ (SRO) | Compared spectral properties of DRO and SRO [235]. |
| 14 | 0.6943 μm (Single transverse mode) | LiNbO$_3$ $\ell = 1.4$ cm | Temperature, Angle $\lambda_s$:1.05–1.20 μm $\lambda_i$:2.05–1.64 μm | $P_{sig} = 340$ kW $\eta_{sig}^{ext} = 45\%$ (SRO) | Noncollinear geometry. Tuned by varying angle of pump beam to cavity axis [36]. |
| 15 | 1.064 μm (YAG:Nd:Repetitively Q-switched: Several longitudinal modes) | LiNbO$_3$ $\ell = 0.35$ cm | Temperature $\lambda_s$:1.95–2.13 μm $\lambda_i$:2.35–2.13 μm | $P_p^{th} = 25$W (peak) $P_s + P_i \approx 17$ mW (ave) $= 170$ W (peak) $\eta^{ext} = 8.5\%$ (DRO) | Repetitively pulsed at high repetition rate [73]. |
| 16 | 0.6943 (Ruby:Single frequency) | LiNbO$_3$ $\ell = 0.935$ cm | $\lambda_s = 1.064$ μm $\lambda_i = 2.00$ μm | $P_s = 100$ kW $\eta^{ext} \approx 3\%$ (Resonant mode) | Used radiation injection [94]. |
| 17 | 0.6943 (Ruby:Single frequency) | LiNbO$_3$ $\ell = 1$ cm | $\lambda_s = 1.015$ μm $\lambda_i = 2.22$ μm | Etalon reduced output power by a factor of 4 | Used etalon to obtain single-longitudinal mode operation [96]. |
| 18 | 1.064 μm (YAG:Nd, repetitively Q-switched) | LiNbO$_3$ $\ell = 0.4$ cm | Temperature $\lambda_s,\lambda_i \approx 2.13$ μm | $P_s + P_i = 350$ mW (ave) | Internal oscillation, high peak power, high efficiency, repetitively pulsed [253]. |

Table 3 (Continued)

| Experiment number | Pump | Material | Tuning: method and range | Threshold, output power, and efficiency | Comments and references |
|---|---|---|---|---|---|
| 19 | 0.53 μm (SHG of Nd:) | KDP | | $P_p^{th} \approx 3-5$ MW $\eta^{ext} \approx 7\%$ (energy) | Obtained narrow linewidth by using two crystals with phase shifting medium between [254]. |
| 20 | 1.064 μm (Nd:YAG: Repetitively Q-switched; Several longitudinal modes) | $Ag_3AsS_3$ $\ell = 0.38$ cm | Temperature $\lambda_s, \lambda_i \approx 2.13$ μm | $S_p^{th} \approx 450$ kW/cm² output power small | DRO. Sporadic operation. Damage to crystal at 450 kW/cm² [206]. |
| 21 | 0.6943 μm (Ruby: Single transverse mode) | $LiIO_3$ $\ell = 0.8$ cm | Angle $\lambda_s$: 0.84–0.96 μm $\lambda_i$: 4.0–2.5 μm | $S^{th} \approx 60$ MW/cm² $\eta_{res}^{ext} \approx 1\%$ | SRO. Damage to crystal at 125 MW/cm² [183]. |
| 22 | 0.473 μm 0.526 μm, 0.561 μm, 0.659 μm (SHG of Nd:YAG; Repetitively Q-switched $TEM_{00}$) | $LiNbO_3$ $\ell = 5$ cm | Temperature 0.55 μm < λ < 3.65 μm | $P_p^{th}$: 200–600 W $\eta^{ext} \approx 46\%$ | SRO. Stable operation, high efficiency, broad tuning range [195]. |
| 23 | 0.53 μm (SHG of Nd:Glass; Single mode) | $LiIO_3$ $\ell = 1.6$ cm | Angle $\lambda_s$: 0.68–1.06 μm $\lambda_i$: 2.4–1.06 μm | $S_p^{th} = 10$ MW/cm² $\eta^{ext} = 8\%$ | SRO Tuning limited by idler absorption. Damage at 40–50 MW/cm² [174]. |
| | | $\alpha$-$HIO_3$ $\ell = 2.5$ cm | 0.96 μm < λ < 1.2 μm | | Filamentary damage at 55 MW/cm² [174]. |

| | Pump | Crystal | Tuning / Range | Power | Comments |
|---|---|---|---|---|---|
| 24 | 0.266 μm (Fourth harmonic of Nd:YAG, TEM$_{00}$) | ADP $\ell$ = 5 cm | Temperature, Angle 0.42 μm$<\lambda<$0.73 μm | $P_s + P_i$ = 10 W (ave) 100 kW (peak) $\eta^{ext} \approx 25\%$ | High gain, single pass— no mirrors. Tuned full visible spectrum [171]. |
| 25 | 0.6943 (Ruby, TEM$_{00}$) | LiIO$_3$ 0.85 cm | Angle 1.1 μm$<\lambda<$1.9 μm Sum frequency generation 0.425 μm$<\lambda<$0.51 μm | $P^{th}$ = 200 kW $S_s^{th}$ = 5 MW/cm$^2$ $P_s^{ext} \approx$ 50 kW $P_{sum} \approx$ 10 kW | DRO. Mixed output of oscillator with pump to generate sum frequency [185]. |
| 26 | 0.532 μm (SHG of Nd:YAG) | LiNbO$_3$ $\ell$ = 5 cm | | $P_p^{th}$ = 2 kW | Obtained linewidth of 0.001 cm$^{-1}$ [97]. |
| 27 | 0.266 μm (Fourth harmonic of Nd:YAG, TEM$_{00}$) | ADP | Temperature ($\Delta T$ = 17°C) 0.458 μm$<\lambda<$0.638 μm | | SRO. Tuned most of visible [255]. |
| 28 | 0.56 μm to 0.62 μm (Tunable dye laser pumped at 0.532 μm) | LiNbO$_3$ $\ell$ = 5 cm | Vary $\lambda_p$ and temperature 0.72 μm$<\lambda<$2.6 μm | $\eta$ = 5% from 0.532 μm to tunable output | SRO. Rapid tuning by changing pump frequency [256]. |
| 29 | 1.064 μm (Nd:YAG) | LiIO$_3$ | Angle 1.95 μm$<\lambda<$2.34 μm (DRO) 3.8 μm$<\lambda<$4.2 μm (SRO) | $P + P_i$ = 13 kW (peak) 20 mW (average) at 80 pps (DRO) | SRO and DRO. Intracavity oscillator [186]. |
| 30 | 1.833 μm (Nd:YAG) | CdSe $\ell$ = 2.1 cm | Angle (a) $\lambda_s$ = 2.2 μm (b) 9.8 μm$<\lambda<$10.4 μm | $P_p^{th}$ = 550 W (SRO) 40% Pump | SRO. Crystal damage limits operation to two times threshold. Reflected pump beam to reduce threshold [88]. |

Table 3 (Continued)

| Experiment number | Pump | Material | Tuning:method and range | Threshold, output power, and efficiency | Comments and references |
|---|---|---|---|---|---|
| 31 | 2.36 $\mu$m (Dy$^{2+}$:CaF$_2$) | CdSe $\ell$ = 2.5 cm | $\lambda_s$ = 3.37 $\mu$m $\lambda_i$ = 7.86 $\mu$m | $S_p^{th}$ = 3 MW/cm$^2$ $P_s + P_i \approx$ 5 kW (peak) | Mirror damage limited operation near threshold [221]. |
| 32 | 1.065 $\mu$m (Nd:CaWO$_4$ Single frequency TEM$_{00}$) | Ag$_3$AsS$_3$ | Angle 1.82 $\mu$m $< \lambda <$ 2.56 $\mu$m | $S_p^{th} <$ 8.5 MW/cm$^2$ $P_s + P_i \approx$ 1 kW (peak) | DRO. Single-frequency pump and lower repetition rate reduced damage problems [207]. |
| 33 | 0.531 $\mu$m (second harmonic of mode-locked Nd:Glass laser) | Ba$_2$NaNb$_5$O$_{15}$ $\ell$ = 0.5 cm | Temperature 0.96 $\mu$m $< \lambda <$ 1.16 $\mu$m | $S_p^{th} \approx$ 200 MW/cm$^2$ $P_s + P_i \approx$ 300 W (peak) | Single pass. Tunable p-sec pulses [257]. |
| 34 | 0.53 $\mu$m (second harmonic of mode-locked Nd:Glass laser) | KDP $\ell$ = 6 cm | Angle 0.78 $\mu$m $< \lambda <$ 1.65 $\mu$m | $S_p^{th} \approx$ 500 MW/cm$^2$ $\eta^{ext} \approx$ 1% | Single pass. Tunable p-sec pulses. Observed self-focusing and self-phase modulation of pump [258]. |

Summary of Continuous Optical Parametric Oscillator Experiments

| Experiment number | Pump | Material | Tuning: method and range | Threshold, output power, and efficiency | Comments and references |
|---|---|---|---|---|---|
| 35 | $0.532\ \mu m$ (SHG of YAG:Nd; Multifrequency) | $BaNaNb_5O_{15}$ $\ell = 0.5$ cm | Temperature $\lambda_s$:0.98–1.06 $\mu m$ $\lambda_i$:1.16–1.06 $\mu m$ | $P_p^{th} = 45$ mW $P_s + P_i = 3$ mW $\eta^{ext} \approx 1\%$ (DRO) | Spiking output, broad linewidth [201]. |
| 36 | $0.5145\ \mu m$ (Argon:Multi-longitudinal mode) | $LiNbO_3$ $\ell = 1.65$ cm | Temperature $\lambda_s$:0.68–0.705 $\mu m$ $\lambda_i$:2.11–1.90 $\mu m$ | $P_p^{th} = 410$ mW $P_s = 1.5$ mW $\eta^{ext} \approx 0.1\%$ (DRO) | Used full multifrequency power of pump. Spiking output [76]. |
| 37 | $0.5145\ \mu m$ (Argon:Single frequency) | $LiNbO_3$ $\ell = 3.4$ cm | $\lambda_s$:0.66–0.7 $\mu m$ $\lambda_i$:2.32–1.94 $\mu m$ | $P_p^{th} = 150$ mW $\eta^{int} = 60\%$ (DRO) | Ring-cavity configuration; more stable operation [86]. |
| 38 | $0.5145\ \mu m$ (Argon-Single frequency:Stabilized) | $Ba_2NaNb_5O_{15}$ $\ell = 0.5$ cm | $\lambda_s$:1.01 $\mu m$ $\lambda_i$:1.05 $\mu m$ | $P_p^{th} = 2.8$ mW $P_s + P_i = 50$ mW $\eta^{ext} = 50\%$ (DRO) | Nonspiking. Single-longitudinal mode operation [74]. |
| 39 | $0.5145\ \mu m$ (Argon) | $Ba_2NaNb_5O_{15}$ $\ell = 0.5$ cm | $\lambda_s$:1.01 $\mu m$ $\lambda_i$:1.05 $\mu m$ | $P_s + P_i = 3$ mW | Internal oscillation. Observed repetitively pulsing instability [81]. |
| 40 | $0.488\ \mu m$ (Argon) | $Ba_2NaNb_5O_{15}$ $\ell = 0.5$ cm | $\lambda_s$:0.64–0.66 $\mu m$ $\lambda_i$:2.25–2.0 $\mu m$ | $P_p^{th} = 200$ mW $\eta^{ext} \approx 1\%$ | DRO. Visible operation [202]. |
| 41 | $0.5145\ \mu m$ (Argon) | $Ba_2NaNb_5O_{15}$ $\ell = 0.5$ cm | | | DRO. Time-resolved study of spectral behavior. Observed simultaneous oscillation on multiple clusters [100]. |

Table 5

Summary of Optical Parametric Oscillator Mixing Experiments

| Experiment number | Frequencies mixed | Material | Wavelength range | Comments and references |
|---|---|---|---|---|
| 42 | Generated second harmonic of signal and idler and sum of signal and pump. $\lambda_p = 0.659\ \mu m$ (SHG of Nd:YAG) | LiIO$_3$ | $0.448\ \mu m < \lambda < 0.61\ \mu m$ | Mixing crystal inside optical parametric cavity. 10% conversion of pump to sum frequency output [255]. |
| 43 | (a) Rhodamine 6G dye laser (SHG) (b) Sodium fluorescein dye laser + 0.493 $\mu m$ | ADP | $0.261\ \mu m < \lambda < 0.315\ \mu m$ | Mixing crystal inside dye laser cavity. 600-W peak and 10–30 mW average power [259]. |
| 44 | 0.694 $\mu m$ + dye laser | LiNbO$_3$ | $3\ \mu m < \lambda < 4\ \mu m$ | Mixing crystal outside dye laser cavity. 6-kW peak power [260]. |
| 45 | 0.694 $\mu m$ + dye laser | LiIO$_3$ | $4.1\ \mu m < \lambda < 5.2\ \mu m$ | Mixing crystal inside dye laser cavity. 100-W peak power [261]. |
| 46 | 0.694 + dye laser | Ag$_3$AsS$_3$ $\ell = 0.5$ cm | $10.1\ \mu m < \lambda < 12.7\ \mu m$ | Mixing crystal outside dye laser cavity 0.1-W peak power limited by damage [262]. |

Another consideration important for pulsed oscillators is the time required for the signal and idler fields to grow from their spontaneous level to their final values. For efficient energy conversion to be obtained, it is desirable that the risetime of the oscillator be as small a fraction of the pump-pulse duration as possible. In Fig. 40, the growth of signal and idler and the depletion of the transmitted pump are shown, clearly displaying the finite risetime. The risetime is controlled by the excess gain per pass through the nonlinear crystal and the length of the oscillator cavity. Growth of between 100 dB and 140 dB for the resonant wave is needed to produce pump depletion. The oscillator risetime can be reduced by minimizing the oscillator-cavity length and by increasing the pump-power density, but crystal damage sets an upper limit to the pump-power density that can effectively be used. Under certain circumstances, it may thus be desirable to use pump pulses of longer duration than the typical 20-30 nsec Q-switched pulse. Murray and Harris [236] have discussed a technique for lengthening the pulse duration of a Q-switched laser while preserving its energy content by intracavity optical second harmonic generation. In this case, the second harmonic is used to pump the oscillator. Young et al. [237] have experimentally demonstrated pulse lengthening by this technique. An analysis of the risetime of pulsed parametric oscillators, with the time dependence of the pump explicitly taken into account has been made by Pearson et al. [238].

Continuous optical parametric oscillators, listed in Table 4, have been pumped in the blue-green region of the spectrum with the argon-ion laser as well as the second harmonic of the Nd:YAG laser (Expt. 35). The argon-ion laser has received the most use since it is a readily available device, delivers high power, and can be made to operate in a single longitudinal mode. The latter property is particularly important since all continuous oscillators constructed to date have been doubly resonant in operation. The doubled Nd:YAG laser can deliver high average powers [239], but to date has not been operated in a single longitudinal mode. No continuously pumped oscillator using a pump wavelength longer than $0.532 \ \mu m$ has been reported. This fact is primarily due to the higher threshold requirements for infrared oscillators and the thermal problems associated with the high average power densities involved.

## B.  Materials

Experimental oscillators have been constructed using KDP, ADP, $LiNbO_3$, $\alpha$-$HIO_3$, $Ba_2NaNb_5O_{15}$, CdSe, $LiIO_3$, and $Ag_3AsS_3$ as the nonlinear element. KDP and especially ADP are most useful for oscillators pumped in the ultraviolet and in applications where high peak powers are involved. Because of their relatively small nonlinear coefficients and their absorption bands in the near infrared,

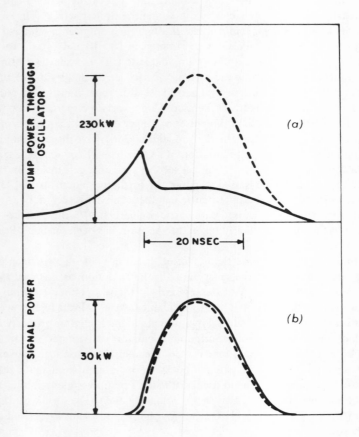

**Figure 40**
Waveforms of the transmitted pump and the external signal power for a pulsed DRO. In (a), the dashed line shows the shape of the pump pulse when no parametric oscillations are present, and the solid line shows the pump depletion when oscillation occurs. In (b) the signal power is shown as the solid curve, and the dashed curve shows the difference between the two curves in (a) [234].

they are not as useful as $LiNbO_3$ and $LiIO_3$ for oscillators pumped in the visible. They have also been found to be extremely useful in generating pumps by harmonic generation. Lithium niobate, $LiNbO_3$, is the material most used in optical parametric oscillators, and it has produced the most impressive experimental results reported to date. Its large nonlinear coefficient, ability to be noncritically phase-matched, availability in large, high-quality crystals, and relatively high resistance to damage when operated at a sufficiently high temperature are characteristics primarily responsible for its usefulness. Lithium iodate, $LiIO_3$, is also available in high optical quality and possesses a large nonlinear coefficient. Its inability to be noncritically phase-matched is the greatest drawback to this material. Several experiments using $LiIO_3$ have been reported (Expts. 21, 23, 25, 29). Although an oscillator using $\alpha$-$HIO_3$ has been reported (Expt. 23), there does not appear to be much current interest in this material.

Barium sodium niobate, $Ba_2NaNb_5O_{15}$, has the largest nonlinear coefficient of any material useful in the visible and near infrared regions of the spectrum, and it can be noncritically phase-matched for many applications. The relatively low susceptibility to optically induced irreversible damage limits its usefulness for high-power-pulsed applications. It is still, however, the best material for low-power, continuously pumped oscillators. Recent correlation of the damage phenomena with impurities [159] suggests that the damage problem may be overcome and the usefulness of this material thereby increased. Initial results reported using proustite, $Ag_3AsS_3$ (Expt. 20), were found to be inferior to those obtained with $LiNbO_3$ in a similar configuration (Expt. 15); the problem, at least in part, is due to surface damage induced by the 1.06-$\mu$m pump radiation. More recently, improved performance has been obtained (Expt. 32). Work on this material is being pursued because of the large transparency region extending to 13 $\mu$m. Successful operation of CdSe oscillators holds further promise for oscillators operating in the infrared (Expts. 30, 31).

As noted in Section VI, numerous other materials are being investigated, especially for infrared applications. It is very likely that some of these materials will be useful in making oscillators and may prove to be superior to the materials from which oscillators have been so far constructed.

### C. Tuning

The essential feature of the optical parametric oscillator is its tunability. Several methods for tuning oscillators have been investigated, including temperature tuning, angle tuning, electric field tuning, tuning by varying the pump frequency, and a form of angle tuning applicable for noncollinear interactions.

Temperature tuning, when it can be obtained, tends to be slow but has the advantage that cavity alignment is not affected, as it may be when rotation of the crystal is used. Angle tuning may be achieved more rapidly than by varying temperature but may require readjustment of the cavity especially when curved mirrors are used. In most cases, the amount of angie tuning available is limited by the finite aperture of the crystal.

Electrooptic tuning is achieved by applying electric fields to the nonlinear crystal, thereby varying the indices of refraction via the electrooptic effect and producing a change in the frequencies for which phase matching is achieved. In principle, tuning can be extremely rapid but the usefulness of this method is limited by the small degree of tuning attainable. For example, in Expt. 7, 50 Å of tuning was obtained with an applied electric field of 7.5 kV/cm in $LiNbO_3$ and in Expt. 8 it was necessary to cool the KDP crystal to a temperature near its Curie temperature (123 K) to obtain any effective electrooptic tuning. For fine tuning or rapid scanning over small frequency ranges, electrooptic tuning could prove useful.

Falk and Murray (Expt. 14) have considered another potentially fast method of tuning. They use an SRO employing a noncollinear interaction, as shown in Fig. 41. The pump enters the nonlinear crystal at an angle to the resonator axis and the nonresonant signal wave also makes an angle with respect to the resonant idler. Tunability can be achieved by temperature tuning, by rotating the crystal,

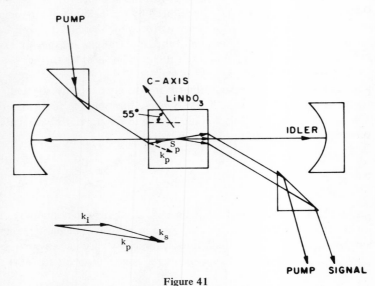

**Figure 41**
Schematic of the noncollinear singly resonant oscillator [36].

or by varying the angle the pump makes with the resonator axis. The latter effect can be used to produce extremely rapid tuning if the direction of the pump is varied, for example, by electrooptic or acoustooptic beam deflectors.

Wallace (Expt. 28) has reported rapid tuning of an optical parametric oscillator pumped by a dye laser. In these experiments, a rapidly tunable dye laser operating between 5,600 and 6,200 Å was used to pump an oscillator whose output wavelength was made to tune from 7,200 Å to 2.6 μm. Although this method was less efficient than the directly pumped oscillator, it achieved much more rapid tuning.

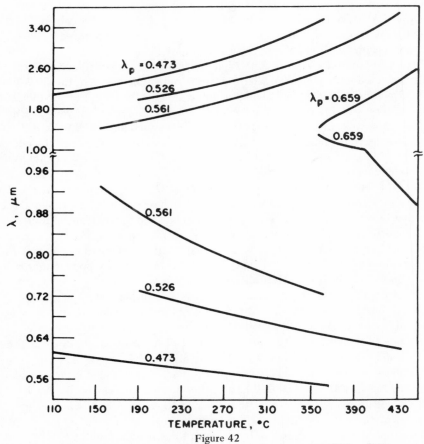

Figure 42

Tuning curves as a function of temperature for a singly resonant oscillator. Pump wavelengths are shown on the figure. Note the scale change near 1 μm [195].

Three experiments in particular demonstrate the range of tuning that can be obtained by optical parametric oscillators. In the first experiment, reported by Wallace (Expt. 22), the second harmonics of several of the lines of a repetitively Q-switched Nd:YAG laser were used to pump a singly resonant oscillator using crystals of $LiNbO_3$ up to 5 cm long. Tuning was achieved by using temperature tuning together with different pump wavelengths. The results are shown in Fig. 42. Tuning was achieved from 0.55 $\mu$m to 3.65 $\mu$m, representing nearly three octaves of tuning capability. As discussed below, the output power and overall performance were also good.

Yarborough and Massey (Expt. 24) have reported a second, very interesting example of the tunability of optical parametric oscillators. With a flash-lamp-pumped Nd:YAG laser, they generated the fourth harmonic of the Nd output at 0.266 $\mu$m using two cascaded second harmonic generators; they used this to pump an ADP crystal 5 cm long. In their experiment, they used no mirrors, relying on the extremely high gain (100-dB single-pass gain) produced by the pump, together with some small feedback from the uncoated crystal faces to obtain oscillation. By varying the crystal temperature between 50 and 105°C, they achieved tuning of the oscillator over the full visible region of the spectrum. The experimentally observed oscillator tuning curve is shown in Fig. 43. In addition to temperature tuning of the oscillator, rotation of the crystal was used, as shown in Fig. 44. In this case, the interaction was noncollinear and the signal and idler beams left the crystal as distinct beams, one on either side of the pump.

Campillo and Tang (Expt. 25) have suggested another interesting possibility for extending the tuning range of optical parametric oscillators. They have constructed a DRO pumped by a ruby laser, using $LiIO_3$. The tuning characteristics of the oscillator itself are shown in Fig. 25. They have extended the tuning range further by externally mixing the transmitted pump and the oscillator output in a second $LiIO_3$ crystal to produce the sum frequency. In doing so, they have produced sum frequency output over the frequency range extending from 0.51 $\mu$m to 0.42 $\mu$m, as shown in Fig. 45. They achieved sum frequency powers approaching 10 kW, indicating the practicality of this scheme.

Wallace (Expt. 42) has reported similar results by incorporating a crystal of $LiIO_3$ inside the optical parametric oscillator cavity to generate either the second harmonic of the signal or idler or the sum of the pump and signal frequencies. In this case, tuning from 4,475 to 6,100 Å was obtained. Bey and Tang [240] and Giallorenzi and Reilly [241] have discussed the theory of coupled parametric oscillation and up-conversion. In a related experiment using a tunable dye laser and crystals of ADP and KDP within the dye laser cavity, Wallace has generated tunable ultraviolet radiation from 2,610 Å to 3,150 Å, with average powers of 10 to 30 mW (Expt. 43). Up-conversion achieved either by harmonic generation of a tunable source or by mixing a tunable source with a fixed frequency seems to be a practical method of extending the range of tunability, especially into the ultraviolet.

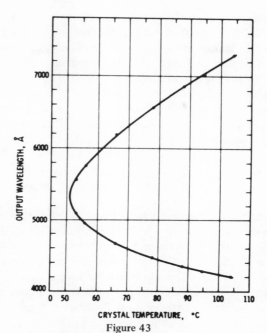

Figure 43

Tuning curve as a function of temperature for a high-gain parametric generator pumped at 2660 Å [171].

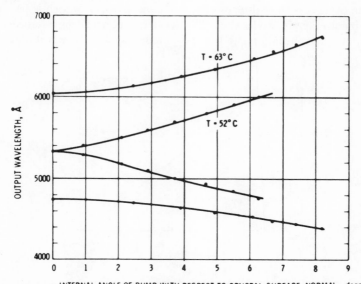

Figure 44

Tuning curve as a function of angle for T = 52°C and T = 63°C [171].

Tunability in the infrared can be achieved by mixing a tunable source and a fixed frequency (e.g., the pump) or two tunable frequencies to form their difference frequency. This technique may have some advantages over direct parametric oscillation in the infrared since the mixing does not involve a threshold, and poorer quality crystals can be used with satisfactory results. Crystal damage at the high-power densities corresponding to high conversion efficiencies remains a problem. Several experiments have been reported in which a tunable dye laser and its pump have been mixed to generate a difference frequency in the infrared (Expts. 44–46).

## D.   Linewidth and Frequency Control

As discussed in Section IV,B, the accuracy with which the SRO tunes is expected to be superior to the accuracy of the DRO. In particular, the need for the signal and idler in the DRO to be resonant gives rise to an erratic nature of the tuning (see Section IV,B,2). The earliest observations by Giordmaine and Miller (Expt. 1) showed that the DRO could oscillate on several separate groups of several modes each. They referred to the groups as clusters and the spacing between separate groups as the cluster spacing. Bjorkholm (Expt. 13) has studied a pulsed oscillator operated both as an SRO and as a DRO, and he has compared the output spectra. His results are shown in Fig. 46. The spectra shown in (a), (b), and (c) are for operation as a DRO and correspond to increasing pump power in going from (a) to (c). The existence of several clusters is clearly seen, especially at high pump power levels. Weller et al. (Expt. 41) have obtained time-resolved spectral outputs of a continuous DRO showing mode hopping and the cluster

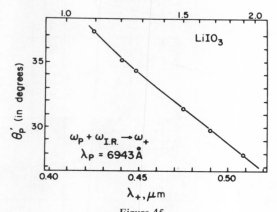

**Figure 45**
Tuning curve for the sum frequency output produced by mixing the pump with the output of a doubly resonant oscillator [185].

effect. For a discussion of this effect, refer to Fig. 30 and the associated text. In comparison, the spectral output of the same oscillator operating as an SRO is shown in Fig. 46(d). Here only a single group of modes is oscillating. The spectral width of a given group appears broader than in (a)-(c), but this effect is attributed to the transient operation of the oscillator.

More recent experimental results have shown that when an SRO reaches steady state, the linewidth of the resonant wave is of the order of 1 cm$^{-1}$ or less, and the nonresonant wave has a linewidth approaching that of the pump (see Fig. 9). Thus an SRO pumped by a narrow-linewidth pump can be expected to produce narrow-linewidth signal and idler.

As discussed in Section IV,B,1, several techniques have been proposed and explored for producing extremely narrow spectral outputs. Kreuzer showed that an intracavity etalon could be used to narrow the spectrum of the SRO to a single longitudinal mode (Fig. 28). Using a three-mirror cavity similar to that discussed by Smith [98], Pinard and Young (Expt. 26) have obtained linewidths less than 10$^{-3}$ cm$^{-1}$, with the ultimate linewidth determined by mechanical vibrations. This value is comparable to linewidths achievable with dye lasers. For a discussion of single-frequency lasers, the reader is referred to the chapter by P. W. Smith that appears in this volume.

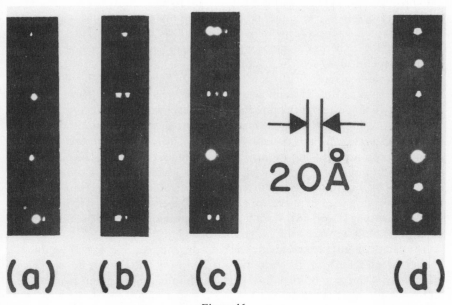

**Figure 46**
(a), (b), (c) Spectral output of a doubly resonant oscillator. (d) Spectral output of an singly resonant oscillator [235].

Narrow linewidth operation of the DRO has been achieved (Expt. 38); this was discussed in Section IV,B,2. These results show that a high degree of pump frequency and cavity length control is required if narrow linewidth and output frequency control is desired. Under most experimental conditions, narrow-linewidth, reproducible operation will be achieved with the SRO; accordingly, most emphasis is being placed on this form of oscillator.

## E. Threshold, Output Power, and Efficiency

For pulsed oscillators, a low threshold power is not a particularly important consideration since most Q-switched lasers generate more than enough pump power to achieve threshold. As a result, most but not all pulsed oscillators have used nonoptimum, flat-mirror geometries. Threshold powers are typically of the order of 10 kW for a flat-mirror DRO using $LiNbO_3$, and of the order of several MW, using KDP. With a curved-mirror geometry, pulsed thresholds of 13 W and 25 W respectively have been reported for doubly resonant oscillators, when $Ba_2NaNb_5O_{15}$ (Expt. 11) and $LiNbO_3$ (Expt. 15) have been used.

Thresholds for the SRO are typically an order of magnitude higher than thresholds for the DRO. For an SRO, with centimeter length $LiNbO_3$ and a flat-mirror geometry, reported thresholds range from 25 kW to 150 kW. Using $LiNbO_3$ crystals up to 5 cm long and a nearly optimum, curved-mirror geometry, Wallace (Expt. 22) reports thresholds between 200 W and 600 W. This value is sufficiently low to permit pumping with the second harmonic of a continuously pumped, repetitively Q-switched Nd:YAG laser.

To get thresholds sufficiently low that they can be attained with continuous lasers, one must take care to optimize the parametric interaction. This requires using cavity configurations that produce small beam waists, and also requires optimum focusing of the pumping radiation into the cavity. Perhaps the most useful configuration for this purpose is the nearly hemispherical resonator. This resonator possesses the features that the beam radius, or spot size, is conveniently adjustable by varying the mirror spacing and that it is as stable as a confocal resonator [242]. With this type of resonator configuration, cw thresholds as low as 3 mW have been observed for a DRO using a crystal of $Ba_2NaNb_5O_{15}$ that is 5 mm long (Expt. 38). More typically, continuously pumped DRO thresholds of 100–200 mW are observed (Expts. 36, 37, 40).

The values of output power and efficiency depend to a large extent on the pump power level used. Efficiencies reported for early DRO's were poor—typically 1% or below. This may be attributed to the use of multimode pump sources. More recently, power conversion efficiencies approaching 50% have been reported for a pulsed SRO (Expt. 22) and for a cw DRO (Expt. 38). For example, Wallace (Expt. 22) reports achieving average output powers of 70–105 mW and an average power conversion efficiency as high as 46%, using as a pump the second harmonic of a Nd:YAG laser at 0.532 $\mu$m, repetitively Q-switched at 1 kHz.

Peak powers as high as 340 kW have been reported for a pulsed SRO (Expt. 14). The nonresonant parametric generator on which Yarborough and Massey (Expt. 24) reported has produced up to 10 mW of average power, 100 kW peak power, and 25% external conversion efficiency over portions of the visible spectrum.

The highest efficiency reported to date was achieved using an intracavity optical parametric oscillator, as Ammann et al. (Expt. 18) have described. By placing the oscillator crystal within the cavity of a Nd:YAG laser, they could take advantage of the higher power densities available. The laser was continuously pumped and repetitively Q-switched and produced an average tunable output of 350 mW at a wavelength near 2.13 $\mu$m; this represented 75% conversion of the available 1.064-$\mu$m power. In recent experiments, 1.8 W of average power has been achieved using this system [243].

The highest output power for a cw oscillator is nearly 50 mW, corresponding to an efficiency of approximately 50% (Expt. 38). In many cases, thermal blooming in the nonlinear crystals limits the efficiencies achieved.

One interesting aspect of the operation of pulsed optical parametric oscillators involves the anomalous limiting of the transmitted pump power. For doubly resonant oscillators, limiting of the transmitted pump occurs at levels in excess of the threshold value, in contrast with the theory of Section III,A,1. For singly resonant oscillators, the transmitted pump does not pass through zero (implying complete conversion) but shows a limiting behavior similar to that expected for the doubly resonant oscillator. Bjorkholm [244] has attributed these departures from theory to the fact that oscillators are usually pumped by gaussian beams whereas the theories apply to plane waves. By modifying the plane wave theory to account for a gaussian pump, Bjorkholm obtains good agreement with theory. Details can be found in Ref. 244.

A more detailed discussion of experimental results is in the references cited in Tables 3, 4, and 5. Further improvements can be expected particularly in techniques for obtaining narrow-linewidth operation, which is essential for high-resolution spectroscopy, and in the extent of coverage of wavelength regions by oscillators. Although there is as yet little reported use of the optical parametric oscillator, many experiments are contemplated and new and exciting applications can be expected for the near future.

## VIII.  Related Parametric Effects

In previous sections attention has been paid to the optical parametric oscillator, which is but one of several devices based on the interaction of electromag-

296 R. G. Smith

netic waves in nonlinear media. In this section a brief discussion, with references, is given of some of the other devices using nonlinear parametric interactions.

## A. Backward Wave Oscillator

In the oscillators described in the previous sections, the energy flow of the pump signal and idler, when interacting in the nonlinear medium, were assumed to be in the same direction. An interaction of this type is called a forward-wave interaction. It is possible for one of the waves to propagate in a direction opposite to that of the other two; this is referred to as a backward-wave interaction. If the pump and the signal propagate in the +z direction and the idler propagates in the -z direction, the Tien-Suhl relations become

$$\omega_p = \omega_s + \omega_i \tag{116}$$

$$k_p = k_s - k_i \tag{117}$$

If these relations are satisfied in some material possessing a nonzero $\chi^{(2)}$, then the oppositely traveling signal and idler can experience gain. When this gain is sufficient, oscillation can result, and this type of oscillator is referred to as a backward-wave oscillator, or BWO. References are Harris [263], Hsu and Tittel [22], Meadors [264], Kroll [9], Tien [31], Aslaksen [265]. Since feedback is provided locally, the BWO does not require mirrors. The BWO is especially attractive for producing oscillations in the infrared. To date, difficulties in finding nonlinear materials of good optical quality that are transmitting in the infrared and which satisfy Eqs. (116) and (117) have not permitted experimental demonstration of a BWO.

## B. Stimulated Polariton Scattering

Parametric interactions of the type discussed in this chapter have been limited to waves that are totally electromagnetic in character. Raman scattering, on the other hand, involves the interaction of two or more electromagnetic waves and one or more modes that are nonelectromagnetic in character. A polariton is an excitation of a crystal that is partly electromagnetic and partly mechanical and derives from vibrational modes that are infrared-active. Parametric interactions involving polaritons are thus not totally electromagnetic and have not been included in this chapter; they are usually considered under Raman scattering. There are, however, several characteristics of polariton scattering similar to parametric effects discussed here.

Both Raman and polariton scattering may be either stimulated or spontaneous. In most types of Raman scattering, the scattered frequency (signal) is insensitive to the angle between the incident light (pump) and the scattered light (signal). There is thus no convenient method for tuning stimulated Raman scattering. On the other hand, the dispersion relation for the polariton results in a dependence of the frequency of the scattered radiation on the angle between the incident and the scattered light. Stimulated polariton scattering is thus tunable just as the parametric oscillation is. Further, the polariton, since it is partly electromagnetic radiates coherently at the idler, again a characteristic of an optical parametric oscillator.

Several experiments on stimulated polariton scattering have been performed, all using $LiNbO_3$ as the nonlinear material [266-270]. The degree of tunability observed was in general small in these experiments ($\approx 100$ cm$^{-1}$); in the experiment of Yarborough et al. [268], however, a considerable amount of far infrared radiation was observed.

## C.  Infrared Up-Conversion

In this chapter, attention has been paid to the parametric interaction in which gain is achieved (i.e., $\omega_p = \omega_s + \omega_i$) and in particular to the case of large gains where oscillation is possible. It is also possible to mix two waves to form their sum or difference frequency. A special case of this mixing is optical second harmonic, or sum-frequency generation. Another case involves the mixing of a high-frequency visible, or near-infrared, wave with another wave in the infrared to produce a sum- or difference-frequency wave. As discussed in Section VII, such a mixing process, when one or both frequencies is tunable, provides a means for generating tunable ultraviolet (sum-frequency) or tunable infrared (difference-frequency) sources.

Another application involves mixing a visible or near-visible pump with an infrared signal to form the sum- or difference-frequency that is in the visible or near-visible where improved detectors are available. Up-conversion has been considered for infrared radiation conveying either temporal or spatial information. Detailed discussions can be found in Refs. 271 through 279.

# List of Symbols

| | |
|---|---|
| A | Area |
| $\underline{A}$, $\underline{B}$, $\underline{C}$ | Coefficients in the expression for the tuning curve of the oscillator |
| b | Confocal parameter; dispersive constant |
| $b_p$, $b_s$, $b_i$ | Confocal parameter of pump, signal, and idler respectively |
| B | Parameter characterizing the degree of beam walk off due to double refraction |
| c | Speed of light in vacuum |
| DRO | Doubly resonant oscillator |
| d | Second-order dispersive constant; nonlinear coefficient |
| $d_{eff}$ | Effective nonlinear coefficient |
| $\underline{E}_p$, $\underline{E}_s$, $\underline{E}_i$ | Electric field vector of pump, signal, and idler respectively |
| $\underline{\mathscr{E}}_p$, $\underline{\mathscr{E}}_s$, $\underline{\mathscr{E}}_i$ | Slowly varying, complex vector Fourier amplitude of pump, signal, and idler electric fields respectively |
| $\mathscr{E}_p$, $\mathscr{E}_s$, $\mathscr{E}_i$ | Slowly varying complex scalar amplitude of pump, signal, and idler electric fields respectively |
| $\mathscr{E}_k$, $\mathscr{E}_\ell$ | kth, $\ell$th Cartesian components of total electric field |
| $\hat{e}_p$, $\hat{e}_s$, $\hat{e}_i$ | Unit vector along the direction of the pump, signal, and idler electric fields respectively |
| $f(\delta, \zeta_1, \zeta_2, \ldots)$ | A function relating the degeneracy parameter to independent variables |
| $g = \dfrac{k_s k_p}{2 k_i}$ | Factor appearing in the expression for the angular dependence of frequency of spontaneous emission |
| $G_s$, $G_i$ | Gain of the injected signal and idler waves respectively |
| $\bar{h}_m(\xi, B)$ | Parameter determining the threshold of parametric oscillators using gaussian beams |
| $\bar{h}_m(B)$ | Maximum value of $\bar{h}_m(\xi, B)$ for a given B |
| $\hbar$ | Planck's constant $\div 2\pi$ |
| $\underline{k}_p$, $\underline{k}_s$, $\underline{k}_i$ | Vector propagation constant of pump, signal and idler respectively |
| $k_p$, $k_s$, $k_i$ | Magnitude of propagation constant of pump, signal, and idler respectively |
| $k_0$ | Propagation constant of signal and idler waves at degeneracy |
| K | Parameter in expression for gain constant; defined by Eq. (10) |
| $\ell$ | Length of nonlinear crystal |
| $L_s$, $L_i$ | Round-trip cavity loss (power) at signal and idler respectively (excluding transmission losses) |
| $L_r$ | Round-trip cavity loss at the resonant wave of an SRO |
| $n_p$, $n_s$, $n_i$ | Refractive index of pump, signal, and idler respectively |
| $n_o$, $n_e$ | Ordinary and extraordinary index of refraction respectively of a uniaxial crystal |
| $n_{extr}$ | Refractive index of extraordinary ray propagating in a uniaxial crystal at an angle $\theta$ to the optic axis |

| | |
|---|---|
| $n_0$ | Index of refraction of signal and idler waves at degeneracy |
| $n_3'$ | Index of refraction of a pump wave required to satisfy phase matching |
| $P_p^{inc}, P_p^r, P_p^{tr}$ | Incident, reflected, and transmitted pump power |
| $P_p^{th}$ | Threshold pump power |
| $P_s, P_i$ | Total power generated at signal and idler respectively |
| $P_s^{ext}, P_i^{ext}$ | Signal and idler powers coupled out of oscillator cavity |
| $\underline{\mathcal{P}}$ | Total polarization of the medium including linear and nonlinear contributions |
| $\underline{\mathcal{P}}_{linear}$ | Linear polarization of the medium |
| $\underline{\mathcal{P}}^{NL}$ | Nonlinear polarization of the medium |
| $\mathcal{P}_j^{NL}$ | Cartesian component of the nonlinear polarization |
| $r$ | Ratio of mirror transmission to cavity loss; radial coordinate (gaussian beams) |
| $r^2$ | Ratio of incident idler and signal power densities normalized to their frequency ratio |
| $r_p^2$ | Power reflection coefficient of mirror at pump frequency |
| $S_p, S_s, S_i$ | Power density at pump, signal, and idler respectively |
| $S_{po}, S_{so}$ | Power density at beam center of gaussian pump and signal beams respectively |
| $S_0$ | Power density of incident signal |
| SRO | Singly resonant oscillator |
| $t$ | Time |
| $T_s, T_i$ | Transmission of mirror at signal and idler respectively |
| $T_r$ | Mirror transmission for the resonant wave of an SRO |
| $w_p, w_s, w_i$ | Beam radius of gaussian beam at pump, signal, and idler respectively |
| $w_{op}, w_{os}, w_{oi}$ | Minimum beam radius of gaussian beam at pump, signal, and idler respectively |
| $x, y, z$ | Cartesian coordinates |
| $Z_0$ | Impedance of free space $\approx 377$ ohms |
| $\alpha_s, \alpha_i$ | Total round-trip power loss at signal and idler respectively |
| $\beta$ | Parameter used in characterizing the operation of an SRO |
| $\Gamma_0$ | Gain constant for parametric interaction |
| $\Gamma$ | Reduced gain constant |
| $\delta$ | Degeneracy parameter–a measure of deviation of signal and idler frequencies from degeneracy; Miller's delta |
| $\delta\mathcal{E}_s, \delta\mathcal{E}_i$ | Incremental change in amplitude of signal and idler fields respectively |
| $\delta\ell$ | Incremental change in cavity length |
| $\delta w_p, \delta\nu_p$ | Incremental change in pump frequency |
| $\Delta k = k_p - k_s - k_i$ | Momentum mismatch between pump, signal, and idler |
| $\Delta n = n_o - n_e$ | Difference between ordinary and extraordinary refraction indices in a uniaxial crystal |
| $\Delta\omega$ | Bandwidth = intrinsic linewidth of spontaneous parametric emission |

| | |
|---|---|
| $\Delta\omega'$ | Intermode spacing of cavity |
| $\Delta\omega'_s, \Delta\omega'_i$ | Intermode spacing of cavity at signal and idler respectively |
| $\Delta\omega_{cl}$ | Cluster spacing |
| $\epsilon_0$ | Permittivity of free space |
| $\zeta_1, \zeta_2$ | Independent variables controlling the tuning of the oscillator |
| $\eta^{int}$ | Internal conversion efficiency |
| $\eta^{ext}$ | External conversion efficiency |
| $\eta^{ext}_{res}$ | External efficiency of the resonant wave of an SRO |
| $\eta^{ext}_{nonres}$ | External efficiency of the nonresonant wave of an SRO |
| $\theta$ | Angle between the direction of propagation of a wave and the optic axis of a uniaxial crystal |
| $\theta_m$ | Phase matching angle |
| $\theta_s$ | Angle between signal and pump waves (spontaneous emission) |
| $\lambda_p, \lambda_s, \lambda_i$ | Wavelength of pump, signal, and idler respectively |
| $\mu_0$ | Permeability of free space |
| $\nu_p, \nu_s, \nu_i$ | Frequency of pump, signal, and idler respectively (Hertz) |
| $\xi = \ell/b$ | Parameter determining the degree of focusing of a gaussian beam |
| $\rho$ | Double refraction angle |
| $\varphi_p, \varphi_s, \varphi_i$ | Initial phase of pump, signal, and idler field respectively; phase of the same fields on reflection from a mirror |
| $\varphi = \varphi_p - \varphi_s - \varphi_i$ | Phase difference between incident pump, signal, and idler fields; phase difference between the three waves upon reflection from a mirror; angle in Fig. 39. |
| $\varphi_{opt}$ | Phase difference between pump, signal, and idler giving optimum gain |
| $\Phi$ | Ratio of incident pump power to threshold pump power |
| $\Phi_0$ | Ratio of incident pump power to threshold pump power with $T_s = T_i = 0$ |
| $\chi_{eff}$ | Effective nonlinear susceptibility |
| $\chi^{(2)}_{jk\ell}$ | Tensor characterizing the second-order nonlinear response of the medium |
| $\omega_p, \omega_s, \omega_i$ | Angular frequency of pump, signal, and idler respectively |
| $\omega_{so}, \omega_{io}$ | Signal and idler frequencies that satisfy momentum conservation |
| $\omega_{sn}, \omega_{im}$ | Specific resonant frequency of cavity at signal and idler respectively |
| $\omega_s(\theta_s)$ | Frequency of signal at an angle $\theta_s$ to the direction of pump beam (spontaneous parametric emission) |
| $\omega_s(0)$ | Frequency of signal in direction of pump wave (spontaneous parametric emission) |

# References

1. T. H. Maiman, *Nature* **187**, 493 (1960).
2. H. Kressel, in *Lasers: A Series of Advances,* Vol. 3 (A. K. Levine and A. J. DeMaria, eds.) Marcel Dekker, New York, 1971.
3. M. Bass, T. F. Deutsch, and M. J. Weber, in *Lasers: A Series of Advances,* Vol. 3 (A. K. Levine and A. J. DeMaria, eds.), Marcel Dekker, New York, 1971.
4. P. Lallemand, in *The Raman Effect* (A. Anderson, ed.), Marcel Dekker, New York, 1971.
5. C. K. N. Patel and E. D. Shaw, *Phys. Rev.,* **B3**, 1279 (1971).
6. A. Mooradian, S. R. J. Brueck, and F. A. Blum, *Appl. Phys. Letters,* **17**, 481 (1970).
7. J. A. Giordmaine and D. A. Kleinman, U.S. Patent 3,234,475, issued February 8, 1966, Filed (December 11, 1961).
8. R. H. Kingston, *Proc. IRE* **50**, 472 (1962).
9. N. M. Kroll, *Phys. Rev.,* **127**, 1207 (1962); reprinted *Proc. IEEE,* **51**, 110 (1963).
10. S. A. Akhmanov and R. V. Khokhlov, *Soviet Phys. JETP,* **16**, 252 (1963).
11. P. A. Franken, A. E. Hill, C. W. Peters, and G. Weinreich, *Phys. Rev. Letters,* **7**, 118 (1961).
12. J. A. Giordmaine, *Phys. Rev. Letters* **8**, 19 (1962).
13. P. D. Maker, R. W. Terhune, M. Nisenoff, and C. M. Savage, *Phys. Rev. Letters* **8**, 21 (1962).
14. J. A. Giordmaine and R. C. Miller, *Phys. Rev. Letters,* **14**, 973 (1965).
15. G. D. Boyd, R. C. Miller, K. Nassau, W. L. Bond, and A. Savage, *Appl. Phys. Letters,* **5**, 234 (1964).
16. S. E. Harris, *Proc. IEEE,* **57**, 2096 (1969).
17. J. A. Giordmaine, "Parametric Optics," in *Quantum Optics,* course 42, Proceedings of the International School of Physics, "Enrico Fermi," Academic Press, New York, 1969, pp. 493-520.
18. S. A. Akhmanov and R. V. Khokhlov, *Soviet Phys. Uspekhi,* **9**, 210 (1966).
19. R. L. Byer, *Treatise in Quantum Electronics* (H. Rabin and C. L. Tang, eds.), Academic Press, New York, 1973.
20. J. E. Bjorkholm, Proceedings of the Conference on Short Laser Pulses and Coherent Interactions, Chunia, Crete, Greece, July 13-26, 1969, to be published.
21. A Yariv, *IEEE J. Quantum Electron.,* **QE-2**, 30 (1966).
22. H. Hsu and F. K. Tittel, in *Lasers and Applications* (W. S. C. Chang ed.), Engineering Experiment Station, Ohio State University, Columbus, 1963.
23. W. H. Louisell, *Coupled Mode and Parametric Electronics,* Wiley, New York, 1960.
24. A. Yariv and W. H. Louisell, *IEEE J. Quantum Electron.,* **QE-2**, 418 (1966).
25. J. A. Armstrong, N. Bloembergen, J. Ducuing, and P. S. Pershan, *Phys. Rev.,* **127**, 1918 (1962).
26. J. M. Yarborough and E. O. Ammann, *Appl. Phys. Letters,* **18**, 145 (1971).
27. R. A. Andrews, H. Rabin, and C. L. Tang, *Phys. Rev. Letters,* **25**, 605 (1970).
28. E. O. Ammann, J. M. Yarborough, and J. Falk, *J. Appl. Phys.,* **42**, 5618 (1971).
29. D. A. Kleinman, *Phys. Rev.,* **126**, 1977 (1962).
30. R. G. Smith, *J. Appl. Phys.,* **41**, 4121 (1970).
31. P. K. Tien, *J. Appl. Phys.,* **29**, 1347 (1958).
32. P. K. Tien and H. Suhl, *Proc. IRE,* **46**, 700 (1958).
33. M. Born and E. Wolf, *Principles of Optics,* 4th ed., Pergamon Press, Oxford, 1970.
34. J. E. Midwinter and J. Warner, *British J. Appl. Phys.,* **16**, 1135 (1965).
35. M. V. Hobden, *J. Appl. Phys.,* **38**, 4365 (1967).
36. J. Falk and J. E. Murray, *Appl. Phys. Letters,* **14**, 245 (1969).
37. G. D. Boyd and C. K. N. Patel, *Appl. Phys. Letters,* **8**, 313 (1966).
38. D. B. Anderson, R. R. August, and W. A. McDowell, *IEEE J. Quantum Electron.,* **QE-2**, lxiv (1966).

39. G. E. Smith, *IEEE J. Quantum Electron.*, **QE-4**, 288 (1968).
40. D. B. Anderson and J. D. McMullen, *IEEE J. Quantum Electron.*, **QE-5**, 354 (1969).
41. Y. Suematsu, *Japan. J. Appl. Phys.*, **9**, 798 (1970).
42. A. Ashkin, G. D. Boyd, and D. A. Kleinman, *Appl. Phys. Letters*, **6**, 179 (1965).
43. D. B. Anderson and J. T. Boyd, *Appl. Phys. Letters*, **19**, 266 (1971).
44. E. M. Conwell, *IEEE J. Quantum Electron.*, **QE-9**, 867 (1973).
45. J. T. Boyd, *IEEE J. Quantum Electron.*, **QE-8**, 788 (1972).
46. F. W. Dabby, A. Kestenbaum, and U. C. Paek, *Opt. Commun.*, **6**, 125 (1972).
47. S. Somekh and A. Yariv, *Appl. Phys. Letters*, **21**, 140 (1972).
48. K. Sakuda and A. Yariv, *Opt. Commun.*, **8**, 1 (1973).
49. C. L. Tang and P. P. Bey, *IEEE J. Quantum Electron.*, **QE-9**, 17 (1973).
50. S. Somekh and A. Yariv, *Opt. Commun.*, **6**, 301 (1972).
51. N. Van Tran and C. K. N. Patel, *Phys. Rev. Letters*, **22**, 463 (1969).
52. P. P. Bey, J. F. Giuliani, and H. Rabin, *Phys. Rev. Letters*, **19**, 819 (1967).
53. R. K. Chang and L. K. Galbraith, *Phys. Rev.*, **171**, 993 (1968).
54. J. Jerphagnon, *Ann. Télécommun.*, **23**, 203 (1968).
55. W. B. Gandrud, *IEEE J. Quantum Electron.*, **QE-7**, 132 (1971).
56. J. J. Wynne and N. Bloembergen, *Phys. Rev.*, **188**, 1211 (1969).
57. H. Kogelnik, in *Lasers: A Series of Advances* (A. K. Levine, ed.), Vol. 1, Marcel Dekker, New York, 1966.
58. S. A. Akhmanov, A. I. Kovrigin, A. S. Piskarskas, V. V. Fadeev, and R. V. Khokhlov, *JETP Letters (transl)*, **2**, 191 (1965).
59. S. A. Akhmanov, A. G. Ershov, V. V. Fadeev, R. V. Khokhlov, O. N. Chunaev, and E. M. Shvom, *JETP Letters (transl.)*, **2**, 285 (1965).
60. C. K. N. Patel, *Appl. Phys. Letters*, **9**, 332 (1966).
61. M. J. Colles and R. C. Smith, *Appl. Phys. Letters*, **10**, 309 (1967).
62. C. C. Wang and G. W. Racette, *Appl. Phys. Letters*, **6**, 169 (1965).
63. G. D. Boyd and A. Ashkin, *Phys. Rev.*, **146**, 187 (1966).
64. R. H. Kingston and A. L. McWhorter, *Proc. IEEE*, **53**, 4 (1965).
65. G. D. Boyd and D. A. Kleinman, *J. Appl. Phys.*, **39**, 3597 (1968).
66. E. O. Ammann and P. C. Montgomery, *J. Appl. Phys.*, **41**, 5270 (1970).
67. G. D. Boyd and F. R. Nash, *J. Appl. Phys.*, **42**, 2815 (1971).
68. R. Asby, *Phys. Rev.*, **B2**, 4273 (1970).
69. E. W. Aslaksen, *J. Opt. Soc. Am.*, **61**, 320 (1971).
70. D. J. Kuizenga, *Appl. Phys. Letters*, **21**, 570 (1972).
71. S. Singh in *Handbook of Lasers* (R. Presley, ed.), Chemical Rubber Publishing, Cleveland, 1971.
72. R. Bechmann, and S. K. Kurtz in Landolf-Börnstein, Group 3, Vol. 2, (Springer-Verlag, Berlin).
73. E. O. Ammann, M. K. Oshman, J. D. Foster, and J. M. Yarborough, *Appl. Phys. Letters*, **15**, 131 (1969).
74. R. G. Smith, *IEEE J. Quantum Electron.*, **QE-9**, 530 (1973).
75. S. E. Harris, *IEEE J. Quantum Electron.*, **QE-2**, 701 (1966).
76. R. L. Byer, M. K. Oshman, J. F. Young, and S. E. Harris, *Appl. Phys. Letters*, **13**, 109 (1968).
77. S. E. Harris, *IEEE J. Quantum Electron.*, **QE-3**, 205 (1967).
78. J. F. Young, R. B. Miles, S. E. Harris, and R. W. Wallace, *J. Appl. Phys.*, **42**, 497 (1971).
79. A. Ashkin, G. D. Boyd, and J. M. Dziedzic, *Phys. Rev. Letters*, **11**, 14 (1963).
80. R. Asby, *J. Opto-Electron.*, **1**, 165 (1969).
81. R. G. Smith and J. V. Parker, *J. Appl. Phys.*, **41**, 340 (1970).
82. R. G. Smith, unpublished results.
83. J. E. Bjorkholm, *IEEE J. Quantum Electron.*, **QE-5**, 293 (1969).
84. J. M. Manley and H. E. Rowe, *Proc. IRE*, **47**, 2115 (1959).
85. A. E. Siegman, *Appl. Opt.*, **1**, 739 (1962).
86. R. L. Byer, A. Kovrigin, and J. F. Young, *Appl. Phys. Letters*, **15**, 136 (1969).
87. J. E. Bjorkholm, A. Ashkin, and R. G. Smith, *IEEE J. Quantum Electron.*, **QE-6**, 797 (1970).

88. R. L. Herbst and R. L. Byer, *Appl. Phys. Letters,* **21**, 189 (1972).
89. L. B. Kreuzer, in Proceedings on the Joint Conference on Lasers and Optoelectronics, Univ. of Southampton IERE, London, 53 (1969).
90. M. K. Oshman and S. E. Harris, *IEEE J. Quantum Electron.,* **QE-4**, 491 (1968).
91. J. Falk, J. M. Yarborough, and E. O. Ammann, *IEEE J. Quantum Electron.,* **QE-7**, 359 (1971).
92. R. L. Byer and S. E. Harris, *Phys. Rev.,* **168**, 1064 (1968).
93. A. I. Kovrigin and R. L. Byer, *IEEE J. Quantum Electron.,* **QE-5**, 384 (1969).
94. J. E. Bjorkholm and H. G. Danielmeyer, *Appl. Phys. Letters,* **15**, 171 (1969).
95. S. E. Harris, *Appl. Phys. Letters,* **14**, 335 (1969).
96. L. B. Kreuzer, *Appl. Phys. Letters,* **15**, 263 (1969).
97. J. Pinard and J. F. Young, *Opti. Commun.,* **4**, 425 (1972).
98. P. W. Smith, Chapter 2 of this volume.
99. J. A. Giordmaine and R. C. Miller, in *Physics of Quantum Electronics* (P. L. Kelley, B. Lax, and P. E. Tannenwald), eds., McGraw-Hill, New York, 1966, pp. 31-42.
100. J. F. Weller, T. G. Giallorenzi and R. A. Andrews *J. Appl. Phys.,* **43**, 4560 (1972).
101. J. Falk, *IEEE J. Quantum Electron.,* **QE-7**, 230 (1971).
102. R. G. Smith, J. G. Skinner, J. E. Geusic, and W. G. Nilsen, *Appl. Phys. Letters,* **12**, 97 (1968).
103. M. W. Dowley, *J. Opto-Electron.,* **1**, 179 (1969).
104. D. A. Kleinman, *Phys. Rev.,* **174**, 1027 (1968).
105. W. H. Louisell, A. Yariv, and A. E. Siegman, *Phys. Rev.,* **124**, 1646 (1961).
106. J. P. Gordon, W. H. Louisell, and L. R. Walker, *Phys. Rev.,* **129**, 481 (1963).
107. W. G. Wagner and R. W. Hellwarth, *Phys. Rev.,* **133**, A915 (1964).
108. S. E. Harris, M. K. Oshman, and R. L. Byer, *Phys. Rev. Letters,* **18**, 732 (1967).
109. D. Magde and H. Mahr, *Phys. Rev. Letters,* **18**, 905 (1967).
110. D. Magde, R. Scarlet, and H. Mahr, *Phys. Rev.,* **171**, 383 (1968).
111. D. N. Klyshko, *JETP Letters (trans.),* **6**, 23 (1967).
112. T. G. Giallorenzi and C. L. Tang, *Phys. Rev.,* **166**, 225 (1968).
113. T. G. Giallorenzi and C. L. Tang, *Appl. Phys. Letters,* **12**, 376 (1968).
114. J. P. Budin, B. Godard, and J. Ducuing, *IEEE J. Quantum Electron.,* **QE-4**, 831 (1968).
115. T. G. Giallorenzi and C. L. Tang, *Phys. Rev.,* **184**, 352 (1969).
116. A. J. Campillo and C. L. Tang, *Appl. Phys. Letters,* **16**, 242 (1970).
117. A. Hordvik, H. R. Schlossberg, and C. M. Stickley, *Appl. Phys. Letters,* **18**, 448 (1971).
118. D. L. Weinberg, *Appl. Phys. Letters,* **14**, 32 (1969).
119. J. G. Meadors, W. T. Kavage, and E. K. Damon, *Appl. Phys. Letters,* **14**, 360 (1969).
120. D. L. Weinberg, *J. Appl. Phys.,* **41**, 4239 (1970).
121. F. Davidson, J. Klebba, C. Lawrence and F. Tittel, *Appl. Phys. Letters,* **17**, 117 (1970).
122. J. S. Kruger and T. J. Gleason, *J. Appl. Phys.,* **41**, 3903 (1970).
123. D. N. Klyshko and D. P. Krindach, *Opt. and Spectr.,* **26**, 532 (1969).
124. D. N. Klyshko, A. N. Penin, and B. F. Polkovnikov, *Soviet Phys. JETP Letters,* **11**, 5 (1970).
125. J. E. Pearson, A. Yariv, and U. Ganiel, *Appl. Opt.,* **12**, 1165 (1973).
126. S. K. Kurtz, in *Laser Handbook* (F. T. Arecchi and E. O. Schulz DuBois, eds.), North-Holland, Amsterdam, 1972.
127. S. H. Wemple and M. DiDomenico, Jr., in *Applied Solid State Science,* Vol. 3 (R. Wolfe, ed.), Academic Press, New York, 1972.
128. J. Ducuing and C. Flytzanis, in *Optical Properties of Solids* (F. Abeles, ed.), North-Holland, Amsterdam, 1970.
129. J. F. Nye, *Physical Properties of Crystals,* Oxford Univ. Press, New York, 1957.
130. M. Okada and S. Ieire, *Phys. Letters,* **34A**, 63 (1971).
131. S. Singh, W. A. Bonner, and L. G. van Uitert, *Phys. Letters,* **38A**, 407 (1972).
132. R. C. Miller, *Appl. Phys. Letters,* **5**, 17 (1964).
133. F. W. Dabby and J. R. Whinnery, *Appl. Phys. Letters,* **13**, 284 (1968).
134. R. L. Carman, A. Mooradian, P. L. Kelley, and A. Tafts, *Appl. Phys. Letters,* **14**, 136 (1969).

135. F. R. Nash, G. D. Boyd, M. Sargent III, and P. M. Bridenbaugh, *J. Appl. Phys.,* **41**, 2564 (1970).
136. R. G. Smith, *J. Appl. Phys.,* **41**, 3014 (1970).
137. J. E. Midwinter, *Appl. Phys. Letters,* **11**, 128 (1967).
138. H. Tsuya, Y. Fujino, and K. Sugibuchi, *J. Appl. Phys.,* **41**, 2557 (1970).
139. H. Fay, W. J. Alford, and H. M. Dess, *Appl. Phys. Letters,* **12**, 89 (1968).
140. J. G. Bergman, A. Ashkin, A. A. Ballman, J. M. Dziedzic, H. J. Levinstein, and R. G. Smith, *Appl. Phys. Letters,* **12**, 92 (1968).
141. J. E. Midwinter, *J. Appl. Phys.,* **39**, 3033 (1968).
142. R. L. Byer, J. F. Young, and R. S. Feigelson, *J. Appl. Phys.,* **41**, 2320 (1970).
143. P. M. Bridenbaugh, J. R. Carruthers, J. M. Dziedzic, and F. R. Nash, *Appl. Phys. Letters,* **17**, 104 (1970).
144. A. Ashkin, G. D. Boyd, J. M. Dziedzic, R. G. Smith, A. A. Ballman, H. J. Levinstein, and K. Nassau, *Appl. Phys. Letters,* **9**, 72 (1966).
145. G. E. Peterson, A. M. Glass, and T. J. Negran, *Appl. Phys. Letters,* **19**, 130 (1971).
146. J. J. Amodei, D. L. Staebler, and A. W. Stephens, *Appl. Phys. Letters,* **18**, 507 (1971).
147. H. J. Levinstein, A. A. Ballman, R. T. Denton, A. Ashkin, and J. M. Dziedzic, *J. Appl. Phys.,* **38**, 3101 (1967).
148. R. G. Smith, D. B. Fraser, R. T. Denton, and T. C. Rich, *J. Appl. Phys.,* **39**, 4600 (1968).
149. F. S. Chen, *J. Appl. Phys.,* **40**, 3389 (1969).
150. W. D. Johnston, Jr., *J. Appl. Phys.,* **41**, 3279 (1970).
151. J. J. Amodei and D. L. Staebler, *Appl. Phys. Letters,* **18**, 540 (1971).
152. J. J. Amodei, *Appl. Phys. Letters,* **18**, 22 (1971).
153. M. Bass and H. H. Barrett, *IEEE J. Quantum Electron.,* **QE-8**, 338 (1972).
154. M. Bass and D. W. Fradin, *IEEE J. Quantum Electron.,* **QE-9**, 890 (1973).
155. N. Bloembergen, *Appl. Opt.,* **12**, 661 (1973).
156. C. R. Guiliano, *Appl. Phys. Letters,* **21**, 39 (1972).
157. M. Bass in NBS Special Publication # 341, December 1970.
158. M. Bass, *IEEE J. Quantum Electron.,* **QE-7**, 350 (1971).
159. D. P. Schinke and R. G. Smith, unpublished results.
160. D. C. Hanna, B. Luther-Davies, H. N. Rutt, R. C. Smith, and C. R. Stanley, *IEEE J. Quantum Electron.,* **QE-8**, 317 (1972).
161. D. W. Fradin, E. Yablonovitch, and M. Bass, *Appl. Opt.,* **12**, 700 (1973); *Pro-Proceedings 1972 ASTM-NBS Symp. Laser Damage,* Boulder, Colorado, June 1972.
162. A. J. Glass and A. H. Guenther, Eds., *Damage in Laser Materials,* NBS Special Publication 341, U.S. Government Printing Office, Washington, D.C., 1970.
163. A. J. Glass and A. H. Guenther, eds., *Damage in Laser Materials,* NBS, Special Publication 356, U.S. Government Printing Office, Washington, D.C., 1971.
164. A. J. Glass and A. H. Guenther, eds., *Laser Induced Damage in Optical Materials,* NBS Special Publication, U.S. Government Printing Office, Washington, D.C., 1972 to be published.
165. A. J. Glass and A. H. Guenther, *Appl. Opt.,* **12**, 637 (1973); and other articles in the same issue.
166. G. M. Sverev, E. A. Levchuk, E. K. Maldutis, and V. A. Pashkov, *Soviet Phys. Solid State (transl),* **11**, 865 (1969).
167. G. M. Sverev, E. A. Levchuk, and E. K. Maldutis, *Soviet Phys. JETP (transl),* **30**, 400 (1970).
168. G. M. Sverev, E. A. Levchuk, and E. K. Maldutis, *Soviet Phys. JETP (trans.),* **31**, 794 (1970).
169. G. E. Francois, *Phys. Rev.,* **143**, 597 (1966).
170. J. E. Bjorkholm and A. E. Siegman, *Phys. Rev.,* **154**, 851 (1966).
171. J. M. Yarborough and G. A. Massey, *Appl. Phys. Letters,* **18**, 438 (1971).
172. T. A. Rabson, H. J. Ruiz, P. L. Shah, and F. K. Tittel, *Appl. Phys. Letters,* **20**, 282 (1972).
173. R. S. Ahdav and R. W. Wallace, *IEEE J. Quantum Electron,* **QE-9**, 855 (1973).

174. A. I. Izrailenko, A. I. Kovrigin and P. V. Nikles, *JETP Letters (trans.)* **12**, 331 (1970).
175. M. W. Dowley, *Appl. Phys. Letters*, **13**, 395 (1968).
176. M. W. Dowley and E. B. Hodges, *IEEE J. Quantum Electron.*, **QE-4**, 552 (1968).
177. S. I. Wax, M. Chodorow, and H. E. Puthoff, *Appl. Phys. Letters*, **16**, 157 (1970).
178. V. S. Suvorov, A. S. Sonin, and I. S. Rez, Soviet Phys. JETP (trans.) **26**, 33 (1968).
179. F. Zernike, *J. Opt. Soc. Am.*, **54**, 1215 (1964).
180. R. A. Phillips, *J. Opt. Soc. Am.*, **56**, 629 (1966).
181. J. E. Pearson, G. A. Evans, and A. Yariv, *Opt. Commun.*, **4**, 366 (1972).
182. J. Jerphagnon, *Appl. Phys. Letters*, **16**, 298 (1970).
183. L. S. Goldberg, *Appl. Phys. Letters*, **17**, 489 (1970).
184. F. R. Nash, J. G. Bergman, G. D. Boyd, and E. H. Turner, *J. Appl. Phys.*, **40**, 5201 (1969).
185. A. J. Campillo and C. L. Tang, *Appl. Phys. Letters*, **19**, 36 (1971).
186. L. S. Goldberg, *IEEE J. Quantum Electron.*, (abstract), **QE-8**, 573 (1972).
187. G. Nath and S. Haussühl, *Appl. Phys. Letters*, **14**, 154 (1969).
188. G. Nath and S. H. Haussühl, *Phys. Letters*, **29A**, 91 (1969).
189. U. Deserno and G. Nath, *Phys. Letters*, **30A**, 483 (1969).
190. S. K. Kurtz, T. T. Perry, and J. G. Bergman, Jr., *Appl. Phys. Letters*, **12**, 186 (1968).
191. J. E. Bjorkholm, *IEEE J. Quantum Electron.*, **QE-4**, 970 (1968); Errata, **QE-5**, 260 (1969).
192. R. C. Miller, G. D. Boyd, and A. Savage, *Appl. Phys. Letters*, **6**, 77 (1965).
193. G. D. Boyd, W. L. Bond, and H. L. Carter, *J. Appl. Phys.*, **38**, 4090 (1967).
194. M. V. Hobden and J. Warner, *Phys. Letters*, **22**, 243 (1966).
195. R. W. Wallace, *Appl. Phys. Letters*, **17**, 497 (1970).
196. L. G. van Uitert, J. J. Rubin and W. A. Bonner, *IEEE J. Quantum Electron.*, **QE-4**, 622 (1968).
197. S. Singh, D. A. Draegert, and J. E. Geusic, *Phys. Rev.*, **B2**, 2709 (1970).
198. J. E. Geusic, H. J. Levinstein, J. J. Rubin, S. Singh, and L. G. van Uitert, *Appl. Phys. Letters*, **11**, 269 (1967); Errata, *Appl. Phys. Letters*, **12**, 224 (1968).
199. R. B. Chesler, M. A. Karr and J. E. Geusic, *Proc. IEEE*, **58**, 1899 (1970).
200. R. G. Smith, J. E. Geusic, H. J. Levinstein, S. Singh, and L. G. van Uitert, *J. Appl. Phys.*, **39**, 4030 (1968).
201. R. G. Smith, J. E. Geusic, H. J. Levinstein, J. J. Rubin, S. Singh, and L. G. van Uitert, *Appl. Phys. Letters*, **12**, 308 (1968).
202. C. Lawrence and F. Tittel, *J. Appl. Phys.*, **42**, 2137 (1971).
203. K. F. Hulme, O. Jones, P. H. Davies, and M. V. Hobden, *Appl. Phys. Letters*, **10**, 133 (1967).
204. W. B. Gandrud, G. D Boyd, J. H. McFee, and F. H. Wehmeier, *Appl. Phys. Letters*, **16**, 59 (1970).
205. M. V. Hobden, *J. Opto-Electron*, **1**, 159 (1969).
206. E. O. Ammann and J. M. Yarborough, *Appl. Phys. Letters*, **17**, 233 (1970).
207. D. C. Hanna, B. Luther-Davies, H. N. Rutt, and R. C. Smith, *Appl. Phys. Letters*, **20**, 34 (1972).
208. D. M. Boggett and A. F. Gibson, *Phys. Letters*, **28A**, 33 (1968).
209. W. B. Gandrud and G. D. Boyd, *Opt. Commun.*, **1**, 187 (1969).
210. J. D. Feichtner, R. Johannes, and G. W. Roland, *Appl. Opt.*, **9**, 1716 (1970).
211. J. H. McFee, G. D. Boyd, and P. H. Schmidt, *Appl. Phys. Letters*, **17**, 57 (1970).
212. C. K. N. Patel, *Phys. Rev. Letters*, **15**, 1027 (1965).
213. N. Van Tran, *L'Onde Electrique*, **48**, 965 (1967).
214. J. Jerphagnon, M. Sourbe, and E. Balifol, *Compt. Rend.*, **263**, 1067 (1966).
215. W. B. Gandrud and R. L. Abrams, *Appl. Phys. Letters*, **17**, 302 (1970).
216. J. D. Taynai, R. Targ and W. B. Tiffany, *IEEE J. Quantum Electron.*, **QE-7**, 412 (1971).
217. R. A. Bermeister, Ph.D. dissertation, Material Science, Stanford University, 1965.
218. Ming-Pan Hung, N. Ohashi, and K. Igaki, *Japan J. Appl. Phys.*, **8**, 652 (1969).
219. R. L. Herbst and R. L. Byer, *Appl. Phys. Letters*, **19**, 527 (1971).
220. G. D. Boyd, E. Buehler, and F. G. Storz, *Appl. Phys. Letters*, **18**, 301 (1971).

221. A. A. Davidov, L. A. Kulevskii, A. M. Prokorov, A. D. Savel'ev, and V. V. Smirnov, JETP Letters (trans.) 15, 513 (1972).

222. M. V. Hobden, *Acta. Crys.*, **A24**, 676 (1968).

223. V. M. Cound, P. H. Davies, K. F. Hulme, and D. Robertson, *J. Phys.*, **C3**, L83 (1970).

224. D. S. Chemla, P. J. Kupecek, D. S. Robertson, and R. C. Smith, *Opt. Commun.*, **3**, 29 (1971).

225. G. D. Boyd, H. Kasper, and J. H. McFee, *IEEE J. Quantum Electron.*, **QE-7**, 563 (1971).

226. G. D. Boyd, E. Beuhler, F. G. Storz, and J. H. Wernick, *IEEE J. Quantum Electron.*, **QE-8**, 419 (1972).

227. G.D. Boyd, H. M. Kasper, J. H. McFee, and F. G. Storz, *IEEE J. Quantum Electron.*, **QE-8**, 900 (1972).

228. G. D. Boyd, W. B. Gandrud and E. Buehler, *Appl. Phys. Letters*, **18**, 446 (1971).

229. R. L. Byer, H. Kildal, and R. S. Feigelson, *Appl. Phys. Letters*, **19**, 237 (1971).

230. G. C. Bahr and R. C. Smith, *Phys. Stat. Solidi*, **13**, 157 (1972).

231. J. Jerphagnon, E. Betifol, G. Tsoucaris, and M. Sourbe, *Compt. Rend.*, Series B, **265**, 495 (1967).

232. W. L. Bond, G. D. Boyd, and H. L. Carter, *J. Appl. Phys.*, **38**, 4090 (1967).

233. G. D. Boyd, T. J. Bridges, and E. G. Burkhardt, *IEEE J. Quantum Electron.*, **QE-4**, 515 (1968).

234. J. E. Bjorkholm, *Appl. Phys. Letters*, **13**, 53 (1968).

235. J. E. Bjorkholm, *Appl. Phys. Letters*, **13**, 399 (1968).

236. J. E. Murray and S. E. Harris, *J. Appl. Phys.*, **41**, 609 (1970).

237. J. F. Young, J. E. Murray, R. B. Miles, and S. E. Harris, *Appl. Phys. Letters*, **18**, 129 (1971).

238. J. E. Pearson, U. Ganiel, and A. Yariv, *IEEE J. Quantum Electron.*, **QE-8**, 433 (1972).

239. J. E. Geusic, H. J. Levinstein, S. Singh, R. G. Smith, and L. G. van Uitert, *Appl. Phys. Letters*, **12**, 306 (1968).

240. P. P. Bey and C. L. Tang, *IEEE J. Quantum Electron.*, **QE-8**, 361 (1972).

241. T. G. Giallorenzi and M. H. Reilly, *IEEE J. Quantum Electron.*, **QE-8**, 302 (1972).

242. G. D. Boyd, in *Proceedings of the Third International Quantum Electronics Conference* (P. Grivet and N. Bloembergen, eds.), Columbia Univ. Press, New York, 1964, p. 1173 ff.

243. E. O. Ammann, private communication.

244. J. E. Bjorkholm, *IEEE J. Quantum Electron.*, **QE-7**, 109 (1971).

245. S. A. Akhmanov, A. I. Kovrigin, V. A. Kolosov, A. S. Piskarskas, V. V. Fadeev, and R. V. Khokhlov, *JETP Letters (trans.)* **3**, 241 (1966).

246. J. A. Giordmaine and R. C. Miller, *Appl. Phys. Letters*, **9**, 298 (1966).

247. R. C. Miller and W. A. Nordland, *Appl. Phys. Letters*, **10**, 53 (1967).

248. S. A. Akhmanov, O. N. Chunaev, V. V. Fadeev, R. V. Khokhlov, D. N. Klyshko, A. I. Kovrigin, and A. S. Piskarskas, *Modern Optics*, vol. 17, Polytechnic Press, New York, pp. 343-346.

249. L. B. Kreuzer, *Appl. Phys. Letters*, **10**, 336 (1967).

250. G. V. Krivoshchekov, S. V. Kruglov, S. I. Marennikov, and Yu. N. Polivanov, *JETP Letters (trans.)* 7, 63 (1968).

251. L. B. Kreuzer, *Appl. Phys. Letters*, **13**, 57 (1968).

252. A. G. Akmanov, S. A. Akhmanov, R. V. Khokhlov, A. I. Kovrigin, A. S. Piskarskas, and A. P. Svkhorukov, *IEEE J. Quantum Electron.*, **QE-4**, 828 (1968).

253. E. O. Ammann, J. M. Yarborough, M. K. Oshman, and P. C. Montgomery, *Appl. Phys. Letters*, **16**, 309 (1970).

254. Yu. N. Belyaev, A. M. Kiselev, and G. I. Friedman *JETP Letters (trans.)* 9, 263 (1969).

255. R. W. Wallace, *IEEE J. Quantum Electron.*, (abstract), **QE-7**, 307 (1971).

256. R. W. Wallace, *IEEE J. Quantum Electron.*, **QE-8**, 819 (1972).

257. T. A. Rabson, H. J. Ruiz, P. L. Shah, and F. K. Tittel, *Appl. Phys. Letters*, **21**, 129 (1972).

258. K. P. Burneika, M. V. Ignatavichus, V. I. Kabelka, A. S. Piskarskas, and A. Yu. Stabinis, JETP Letters (trans.) *16*, 257 (1972).

259. R. W. Wallace, *Opt. Commun.*, **4**, 316 (1971).
260. C. F. Dewey, Jr., and L. O. Hocker, *Appl. Phys. Letters*, **18**, 58 (1971).
261. D. W. Meltzer and L. S. Goldberg, *Opt. Commun.*, **5**, 209 (1972).
262. D. C. Hanna, R. C. Smith, and C. R. Stanley, *Opt. Commun.*, **4**, 300 (1971).
263. S. E. Harris, *Appl. Phys. Letters*, **9**, 114 (1966).
264. J. G. Meadors, *J. Appl. Phys.*, **40**, 2510 (1969).
265. E. W. Aslaksen, *IEEE J. Quantum Electron.*, **QE-6**, 612 (1970); *Opt. Commun.*, **2**, 169 (1970).
266. S. K. Kurtz and J. A. Giordmaine, *Phys. Rev. Letters*, **22**, 192 (1969).
267. J. Gelbwachs, R. H. Pantell, H. E. Puthoff, and J. M. Yarborough, *Appl. Phys. Letters*, **14**, 258 (1969).
268. J. M. Yarborough, S. S. Sussman, H. E. Puthoff, R. H. Pantell, and B. C. Johnson, *Appl. Phys. Letters*, **15**, 102 (1969).
269. B. C. Johnson, H. E. Puthoff, I. SooHoo, and S. S. Sussman, *Appl. Phys. Letters*, **18**, 181 (1971).
270. S. S. Sussman, B. C. Johnson, J. M. Yarborough, H. E. Puthoff, R. H. Pantell, and J. SooHoo, Polytechnic Institute of Brooklyn, Microwave Research Institute Symposium XX.
271. R. A. Andrews, *IEEE J. Quantum Electron.*, **QE-6**, 68 (1970).
272. A. H. Firester, *J. Appl. Phys.*, **40**, 4842, 4849 (1969); **41**, 703 (1970); *Appl. Opt.*, **9**, 2266 (1970).
273. W. B. Gandrud and G. D. Boyd, *Opt. Commun.*, **1**, 187 (1969).
274. D. A. Kleinman and G. D. Boyd, *J. Appl. Phys.*, **40**, 546 (1969).
275. J. E. Midwinter, *Appl. Phys. Letters*, **12**, 68 (1968); **14**, 29 (1969).
276. G. D. Boyd, W. B. Gandrud, and E. Buehler, *Appl. Phys. Letters*, **18**, 446 (1971).
277. J. Warner, *Appl. Phys. Letters*, **12**, 222 (1968); **13**, 360 (1968).
278. Y. Klinger and F. R. Arams, *Proc. IEEE*, **57**, 1797 (1969).
279. J. Falk and J. M. Yarborough, *Appl. Phys. Letters*, **19**, 68 (1971).

# Author Index

Numbers in brackets are reference numbers and indicate that an author's work is referred to although his name is not cited in the text. Underlined numbers show the page on which the complete reference is listed.

## A

Aagard, R. L., 31[146], 70
Abrams, R. L., 129[39], 163[143], 167 [143], 168[39], 183, 186, 274 [215], 305
Abrosimov, G. V., 112[196], 119
Adams, S. L., 168[158], 186
Ahdav, R. S., 269[173], 304
Ahmed, S. A., 159[121], 185
Akhmanov, S. A., 190, 192[18], 204[58, 59], 205[58, 59] 242[245], 277[245, 248], 279[252], 297[245, 248, 252], 301, 302, 306
Akmanov, A. G., 279[252], 297[252], 306
Alford, W. J., 267[139], 304
Alkemade, C. Th. J., 112[202], 119, 175 [179], 187
Allen, L., 130[46], 183.
Allen, R. B., 18[72, 73, 75], 32[72, 73], 33[75], 68
Alting, H., 139[74], 140[74], 184
Alves, R. V., 3[16], 67
Ammann, E. O., 18[91], 45[91], 46[91], 69, 193[26, 28], 207[66], 210[66], 211[66], 212[66], 213[66], 216[73], 237[91], 273[206], 279[73, 253], 280 [206], 295[243], 297[243, 253], 301, 302, 303, 305, 306
Amodei, J. J., 267[146, 151, 152], 304
Ananev, Yu. A., 94[51], 116
Anderson, D. B., 200[38, 40, 43], 301, 302
Andrews, R. A., 193[27], 253[100], 273 [100], 283[100], 297[271], 301, 303, 307
Andringa, K., 3[18], 18[88], 45[88], 47 [88], 67, 69
Arams, F. R., 297[278], 307
Arecchi, F. T., 124[24], 144[78], 159[24], 182, 184

Armstrong, J. A., 192[25], 194[25], 195 [25], 200[25], 201[25], 301
Arnold, D. H., 94[64], 116
Arrathoon, R., 94[50], 116, 122[20], 123 [21], 125[21], 126[31], 131[31], 132 [20], 135[21], 152[21], 153[21, 31, 99], 154[21], 156[21], 157[20, 31], 160[20], 162[20], 163[20, 21, 31], 164[31], 167[31], 168[31, 160], 173 [170], 178[21, 203], 179[203], 182, 184, 186, 187
Asami, S., 144, 184
Asawa, C. K., 2[8], 67
Asby, R., 207[68], 216, 218[80], 302
Ashkin, A., 200[42], 204[63], 207[63], 218[79], 229[87], 236[87], 253[63], 267[140, 144, 147], 272[144], 273 [144], 302, 304
Aslaksen, E. W., 207[69], 296[265], 297 [265] 302, 307
Assousa, G. E., 164[146], 186
August, R. R., 200[38], 301

## B

Bagdasarov, Kh. S., 3[17], 67
Bahr, G. C., 275[230], 297[230] 306
Baird, K. M., 98[73], 116, 172[164], 173 [164], 186
Baker, J. A., 93[37], 115
Bakeyev, A. A., 99[85], 116
Baldwin, G. D., 18[69, 101], 31[69], 45 [101], 68, 69
Balifol, E., 274[214], 305
Ballman, A. A., 5[34], 67, 267[140, 144 147], 272[144], 273[144], 304
Balmer, P., 9[140], 10[140], 11[140], 12 [140], 14[140], 15[140], 18[140], 20 [140], 22[140], 27[140], 70
Barber, H. P., 101[119], 104[119], 117
Barger, R. L., 110[182, 183], 113[183], 118
Barker, W. B., 106[153], 118
Barnes, F. S., 18[64], 30[64], 68
Barrett, H. H., 267[153], 268[153], 304
Barro, J. M., 18[68], 30[68], 31[68], 32 [68], 36[68], 68
Bashkin, S., 163[139], 164[139], 185
Basil, I. T., 18[69], 31[69], 68

309

## H

# Subject Index

## A

Absolute stability, 63
Absorption, 6, 10
ADP, *see* Ammonium dihydrogen phosphate
Afterglows, 160-163
  flowing, 161-162
  time resolved, 160-161
Alpha-iodic acid, 271, 287
Ammonium dihydrogen phosphate (ADP), 215, 257, 269-271, 287, 290
Amplification factor, 40, 42
Amplitude modulation, 47
Atom-atom inelastic collisions, 121-124, 132-135
Atomic excitation processes, 121-124
Atomic parameters, 159-171
  collisional, 159-168
  radiative, 164-171
Axial modes, *see* Modes in laser resonators

## B

"Bananas," *see* Barium sodium niobate
Barium sodium niobate, 46, 204, 215-216, 248, 251, 268, 272-273, 287
Beam intensity, 38
Biaxial crystals, 263
Blanc's law, 140
Branching ratios in Nd:YAG, 11

## C

Cadmium germanium arsenide, 275
Cadmium selenide, 275
Cathode destruction, He-Ne, 172
Cat's eye resonator, *see* Laser resonators
Cavity losses, 37
Chirp, 47
Cinnabar, 275
Cluster spacing, 248, 250, 292
Codoping, 4
Cold cavity lifetime, 36
Collinear phase matching, 255
Collision processes, 121-137, 143-157, 163-168
  basic mechanisms, 121-124
  cross sections, *see* Cross sections

line broadening, 164-165
Penning, 124, 160-161
rate integrals, 132-135
second kind, 122-123
spectroscopic limitations, 127-130
spin exchange, 121-123, 131-132, 154
two-body inelastic, 144-145
Controlled pulsing, 41
Cross relaxation, 18, 21, *see also* Line broadening
Cross sections, 121-124, 132-138, 157, 159-168
  atom-atom, 121-124, 132-135, 157, 159-168
  electron-atom, 121-124, 132-138, 157, 159-168
  empirical, 123, 135, 153
  in $Nd^{3+}$, 12, 26
  Thompson, 136-137
Crystal
  growth of YAG, 3
  quality, 266
Crystalline phases in Nd:YAG, 4

## D

Damping constant, 39
Degeneracy parameter, 238
Degenerate frequency, 238
Degradation of Nd:YAG, 23
Detailed balance, 121-124
Detuning, 48, 52
Diffraction loss, *see* Modes in laser resonators
Diffusion, 137-141, 159-163
  ambipolar, 137-141
  constant and length in Nd:YAG, 23
  metastable, 159-163
Dispersion in YAG, 5, 37, 49
Dispersive constant, 239
Distributed feedback, 92
Distribution coefficient, 4
Doppler broadening, *see* Line broadening
Doppler shift, 41
Double refraction angle, 208, 263
Double refraction parameter, 208

325